FRESHWATER ISSUES

A Reference Handbook

Other Titles in ABC-CLIO's
CONTEMPORARY
WORLD ISSUES
Series

Books in the Contemporary World Issues series address vital issues in today's society such as genetic engineering, pollution, and biodiversity. Written by professional writers, scholars, and nonacademic experts, these books are authoritative, clearly written, up-to-date, and objective. They provide a good starting point for research by high school and college students, scholars, and general readers as well as by legislators, businesspeople, activists, and others.

Each book, carefully organized and easy to use, contains an overview of the subject, a detailed chronology, biographical sketches, facts and data and/or documents and other primary-source material, a directory of organizations and agencies, annotated lists of print and nonprint resources, a glossary, and an index.

Readers of books in the Contemporary World Issues series will find the information they need in order to have a better understanding of the social, political, environmental, and economic issues facing the world today.

FRESHWATER ISSUES

A Reference Handbook

Zachary A. Smith and Grenetta Thomassey

CONTEMPORARY WORLD ISSUES

A B C  C L I O

Santa Barbara, California
Denver, Colorado
Oxford, England

Library of Congress Cataloging-in-Publication Data

Smith, Zachary A. (Zachary Alden), 1953–
    Freshwater issues : a reference handbook / by Zachary A. Smith and Grenetta Thomassey.
    p. cm. -- (Contemporary world issues)
Includes index.
 ISBN 1-57607-649-0 (hardcover : alk. paper); 1-57607-650-4 (eBook)
    1. Fresh water. 2. Water-supply. I. Title: Fresh water issues. II. Thomassey, Grenetta. III. Title. IV. Series.

TD345.S65 2003
333.91—dc21

                         2002156738

06 05 04 03 02 01   10 9 8 7 6 5 4 3 2 1

This book is also available on the World Wide Web as an e-book. Visit abc-clio.com for details.

ABC-CLIO, Inc.
130 Cremona Drive, P.O. Box 1911
Santa Barbara, California 93116-1911

This book is printed on acid-free paper ∞.
Manufactured in the United States of America

For Lelia—Thanks for everything, Mom
For Bull—The first of many books for you, Dad, with love
and gratitude for your support and encouragement

Contents

Preface

This book is devoted to freshwater management and to many of the challenges and potential solutions that exist on the topic. The first two chapters provide the reader with basic information about freshwater. Chapter 1 covers essential information about our water supply, the pressures of the demand for water, and the technology and infrastructure involved in water-development systems. The chapter begins with information on ecosystems, the hydrologic cycle, types of freshwater supplies, and watersheds. It includes answers to such questions as Where does water come from? How much do we have? How much do we need or demand? The chapter concludes with an overview of U.S. water standards and pollution issues.

Chapter 2 explains water rights, the challenges of water allocation, and the kind of problems that arise when water systems are developed and then managed for society. It includes the foundations of basic U.S. water law and also covers economic concerns. The chapter ends with a discussion of the various interests involved in water-policy decisions, including the water industry, private and public interests, and environmental actors. This information provides the reader with a background that makes the subsequent historical information about water management easier to understand and appreciate.

The historical information is presented in Chapters 3 and 4. Chapter 3 begins with a short discussion of the government framework in which water-policy decisions are made. It then presents a narrative of important moments in the history of water management. This is followed by a pair of lists in Chapter 4. The first gives brief synopses of important federal policy decisions, and the second does the same for state, local, or international policies that hold historical significance.

Chapters 5 through 7 provide useful reference materials on the topic of freshwater. Chapter 5 is devoted to facts and data, including statistics, reports, tables, and so on that will give the reader a quick reference for important information. Chapter 6 is a directory of organizations, associations, and government and international agencies related to water matters. Finally, Chapter 7 presents selected print and nonprint resources on freshwater, including lists of films, videos, software, Internet sites, and other electronic and print reference works. A glossary of terms is provided at the end of the book.

The authors sincerely hope you will find this volume useful and informative.

Acknowledgments

The authors are grateful to several people. Lu Kramer, thank you very much for your diligent, excellent work and for literally going out of your way to offer support in times of need. Charlene Wingo, your generous contribution of time and effort is deeply appreciated; your work was extremely useful. Aubrey Fink, your hard work and time was very valuable; thank you so much for your willingness to help.

1

Water Supply, Demand, and Development

Water Management

Water, land, and air are essential to life on planet Earth. These form the atmosphere, continents, and oceans and provide the environment that supports life on the surface of the planet. Water holds a special place and function in this arrangement. At the start of the twenty-first century, water—part of an intricate balance in nature—has long since become something we must manage carefully.

This book is intended as a reference for anyone interested in the use and management of freshwater resources. In the first two chapters, we provide very basic information about freshwater: What it is, where it comes from, how much we have, and how much we need or demand. These chapters also explain water rights, the challenges of water allocation, and the kind of problems that arise when water is managed for society. This basic information provides the reader with a background that makes the historical information about water management easier to understand and appreciate.

This chapter includes two parts. The first part, "The Freshwater Supply," describes the water supply system. We will discuss basic hydrology and the quality standards used for U.S. water supplies. In the second part, "Demand and Development," we address the demand for freshwater in the United States and compare this demand to that of the rest of the world. Also, we discuss the development of water technology and infrastructure that has become so crucial to the management of this important resource.

The Freshwater Supply

Basic Hydrology

Ecosystems

To understand basic hydrology, it is helpful to first have an understanding of ecosystems. An ecosystem is a grouping of plants, animals, and nonliving things that interact within a specific or defined environmental area that has been identified by humans for study, conservation, protection, and management purposes. The earth itself is a large ecosystem, often referred to as the ecosphere or biosphere.[1]

However, ecosystems are not isolated units, independent of external environments. Rather, an ecosystem is "open" in that it is connected to and interacts with other ecosystems on the planet. The sun is the common source of energy for all ecosystems, and it is also the only source of interaction between the earth and external systems. With the exception of this energy from the sun, the resources the planet started with are the same resources that exist today. The only qualification to that statement is that these resources are constantly changing form. They are dynamic, not static.[2] One of the most important components of change in our ecosystem environment is the hydrologic cycle.

The Hydrologic Cycle

Hydrology is the study of how water moves through and is naturally stored in the hydrologic cycle, also referred to as the water cycle. The hydrologic cycle is a "closed" system because no new significant amounts of water enter the cycle.[3] Earth has all the water it will ever have.

The freshwater cycle ecosystem is a natural distillation and pumping mechanism, constantly operating with neither a beginning nor an end. Heat energy from the sun and the force of gravity keep water moving through the cycle, in which the oceans are

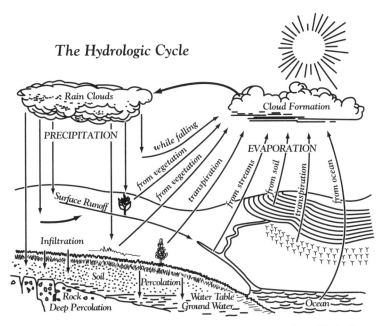

Figure 1.1 The Hydrologic Cycle. *Source:* Department of Agriculture, *Yearbook of Agriculture* (Washington, DC: Government Printing Office, 1955).

the major source of water and the atmosphere provides the delivery system back to the land. The cycle results in water concentrations at various places on the planet: in lakes, rivers, wetlands, oceans, soil penetration, and groundwater. These concentrations provide us with many types of aquatic ecosystems.[4]

The hydrologic cycle is often represented as a simple, basic operation, such as is illustrated in Figure 1.1. The key elements of the cycle are evaporation, condensation, and precipitation. Evaporation from surface water sources, damp soil, and transpiration from plants all provide moisture to the atmosphere. This moisture is transformed into a gaseous state and stored in the atmosphere as water vapor. These processes are collectively known as evapotranspiration, a term that encompasses all types of evaporation from earth or water surfaces into the atmosphere.

Water vapor in the atmosphere condenses back into a liquid state to form clouds and drops of water. When these drops are large enough, or when they are driven by wind or air currents, they fall to earth as precipitation. This precipitation can happen in a variety of forms: rain, snow, freezing rain, hail, or fog drip. The intensity, type, amount, and frequency of precipitation depends on a variety of factors, including geography, climate, and season of the year.

This basic representation of the water cycle is useful for a general understanding of where our water comes from and where it goes. However, it can also be a source of misconceptions. The illustration in Figure 1.1 is based on two assumptions: (1) The hydrologic cycle is a closed system. (2) The illustration represents reality. The first assumption is acceptable when considering the entire hydrologic environment. However, the second assumption is problematic because the diagram represents all the processes and storage locations in one illustration, which implies that all the processes represented are uniform or occur simultaneously. Although such models can be useful, they do not accurately represent the complex variability of the hydrologic cycle or the magnitude of its components.[5]

Types of Freshwater Supplies

There are two types of freshwater supplies: surface water sources and groundwater sources. Surface water sources are supplies of water on the ground, which take two patterns. The first is diffused surface waters, or waters moving over the surface of the earth that are not part of any defined stream channel. Examples of this include precipitation runoff and standing water in swamps, marshes, and wetlands. The second is streams, or watercourses, which have a special legal definition. That is, a surface stream "must be a body of water that flows, usually in a channel having a bed and sides or banks. The flow may be either constant or intermittent."[6]

Water in the ground is also divided into two categories. The first is subterranean streams, which must meet the same definition as surface streams. Second is percolating water, which passes through the ground beneath the earth without passing through definite channels. Percolating water may provide underground storage that can be collected using wells, tunnels, or drainage galleries, or it may flow naturally to the earth's surface via seeps or springs.[7]

This percolating water is found from a few feet to hundreds of feet beneath the surface of the earth. It moves through rocks that are cracked or broken and in the spaces between gravel and sand. When these spaces become saturated with water, the water becomes groundwater. If there is enough of it to supply a spring or a well, this saturated zone of groundwater is called an aquifer.[8]

An aquifer is "one or more geologic formations containing sufficient saturated porous and permeable material to transmit water at a rate sufficient to feed a spring or for economic extraction by a well. It is the combination of two Latin words, aqua or water, and ferre, to bring; literally, it means something that brings water."[9]

Additional water that seeps into existing aquifers is called recharge. An aquifer can be recharged from surface sources, such as streams fed by mountain runoff when snowpack melts in the spring. However, the recharge also occurs from runoff from the irrigation of crops or turf, such as lawns or golf courses. It also can come from stormwater runoff and the discharge of treated sewage in municipal areas. Because of this, recharge can be a source of trouble for aquifers. If recharge is insufficient—when more water is taken from aquifers by pumping than is recharged—a condition called overdraft occurs. Overdrafting of aquifers can also lead to serious consequences, including a drop in the water table. Even though the groundwater supply in any given area may be considered large, it took thousands of years to accumulate. If a dramatic influx of population and groundwater pumping occurs in these areas, overdraft can become a serious problem leading to things such as lower water yields from wells, the drying up of streams and rivers, and a degradation in the water quality.[10]

We also use water from saline sources. In the United States, the total amount of water withdrawn in 1995 included the following approximate quantities: 66 percent from fresh surface water, 19 percent from groundwater aquifers, and 15 percent from saline surface water (mainly as an industrial coolant). Data published in 2001 show that the total amount of water withdrawn globally from surface and groundwater sources has increased nine times from the amount used in 1900.[11]

Watersheds

Watersheds are dynamic and changeable areas of landscape. The boundaries of a watershed correspond with natural features of the land upon which water collects in a channel from snowmelt, direct precipitation, or other storage. The water then flows to a common outlet, such as a stream, river, wetland, lake, ocean, or, occasionally, an underground passage providing flow to a groundwater reservoir.[12]

Watersheds rarely correspond to political boundaries. This sometimes creates management problems. Hence, attempts have been made to adjust political boundaries to correspond with the boundaries of a watershed. More often, collaborative efforts are used to coordinate the management of a particular watershed.[13] Additional information on watershed groups and alliances can be found in Chapter 6.

Freshwater Resource Bases

Global Water Supply Figures

Data on global water supplies show that enormous quantities of water are available on the planet. However, the water available to sustain human use in populated regions of the earth is much less than the total water in the hydrosphere. The future global availability of freshwater is projected to be very close to the potential human need for water, based on historical usage figures.[14] This means that any surplus in the global freshwater supply is steadily disappearing. With so much water in the hydrosphere, why is so much of it inaccessible for human use?

The oceans contain about 97 percent of global water. The remaining 3 percent of the water is freshwater, but more than half of that is unavailable for human uses because it is locked in glaciers or permanent snowfields. Therefore, surface water and groundwater aquifers are the main resources we have for freshwater access. However, these freshwater sources make up less than 1.5 percent of the total global water supply, and, as Ralph Wurbs has noted, considering the rate of "population growth, rapid industrial development, and continuing expansion of irrigated agriculture," the demand for limited freshwater resources will dramatically increase.[15]

In the global water budget, precipitation on land is more than adequate for human and environmental needs. It is the *availability* of water—when and where it is needed—that is the problem. The existing supply of freshwater would support our present and projected population, but the water and the people are distributed unevenly across the globe.[16] (Statistics and specific data measurements for all the topics addressed in this section appear in Chapter 5 of this book.)

Challenges to the Water Supply

According to a recent report by the Central Intelligence Agency (CIA), "by 2015 nearly half the world's population—more than 3 billion people—will live in countries that are 'water-stressed'—have less than 1,700 cubic meters of water per capita per year—mostly in Africa, the Middle East, South Asia, and northern China."[17] Barbara Rose Johnson and John M. Donahue point out that many people who currently face water shortages live in degraded watersheds. These places experience water scarcity that has resulted from various causes including deforestation, which increases erosion and runoff and results in microclimatic changes. Also, global climate change is becoming increasingly cited as the reason for particularly unpredictable and violent weather, which influences the hydrosphere and precipitation distribution and totals.[18]

The CIA report explains that in the developing world, 80 percent of water usage goes toward irrigated agriculture. This is unsustainable because by 2015, a number of developing countries will not be able to maintain these levels of irrigated agriculture. Competing demands for water will arise from increased population, urbanization, and pollution, among other things. However, this is not just a problem for the lesser-developed nations. In March 2001, the Economic Research Service (ERS) of the U.S. Department of Agriculture (USDA) reported that 80 percent of the U.S. consumptive water use (and more than 90 percent in many western states) is devoted to agriculture.[19] Again, because of competing demands, this level is unsustainable.

Still, agriculture must continue to produce food for the nations of the world, and problems will continue to arise. For example, the CIA report states that a major problem in many of the world's important grain-growing regions will be the over-pumping of groundwater. To better understand why, it is important to realize that about 1,000 tons of water is needed to produce a ton of grain. Because of this heavy use in grain-producing areas in northern China, the water table is falling at a rate of five feet per year. For the same reason, water tables throughout India are falling by an average of three to ten feet per year.[20] Clearly, it is extremely important that water resources be managed effectively by government and private sectors throughout the world.[21]

As noted above, projections for global water supplies also suggest there will also be challenges for the future of U.S. freshwater availability. Although this will not be as severe as in many parts of the less-developed world, the United States also faces serious water quantity shortages on a regional basis—primarily in parts of the West and Southwest.

Standards for U.S. Water Supplies

Brief Overview of Quality Standards

Water policy in the United States is very fragmented and decentralized, with at least twenty-seven federal agencies being involved in some capacity. In addition, states and tribal governments, pursuant to Environmental Protection Agency (EPA) guidelines, are responsible for developing water quality standards for the protection of drinking water. Even though the U.S. Congress has periodically passed federal water-pollution control acts since 1912 (see Chapter 3), the role of the federal government is not paramount. The design and implementation of water-pollution control programs is left to state and local governments.[22]

Setting standards for U.S. drinking water quality can be problematic. For example, the difficulty of carrying out risk analyses and scientific uncertainty make it hard to determine what are safe exposures to chemicals. Whatever standards are set rely upon the strength and effectiveness of any water-pollution legislation that is passed and on the ability to purify water well enough to meet those standards.[23]

There has generally been an improvement in water quality over the past twenty-five years in the United States, but challenges remain. The potential causes for harm to a body of water are as varied as human activity itself. According to the EPA, the 1994 national water quality inventory showed that "nearly 40 percent of surveyed waters in the United States remain too polluted for fishing, swimming, and other uses."[24]

Pollution Issues

Water pollution is generally divided into two categories: point source pollution and non–point source pollution. The first type, point source pollution, is pollution that originates from a specific location, such as a sewer, pipe, or ditch. These pollution outlets typically come from sewage treatment plants, landfills, factories, hazardous waste sites, and leakage from storage tanks containing gasoline or other toxic materials. The 1972 Clean Water Act established standards for the treatment of municipal wastewater. Today, however, many municipal wastewater-treatment plants do not meet these standards. These offenders continue to discharge into freshwater sources wastewater that has only received primary treatment (the lowest level of treatment), violating Clean Water Act requirements.[25]

Non–point sources of pollution are more difficult to address. Unlike point source pollution, for which Clean Water Act standards have been set, non–point source pollution has very few controls, and the controls that are in place tend to be ineffectual. Common non–point sources of water pollution are irrigation runoff containing salts and pesticide residue, runoff from animal feedlots, salts from salting roads in the winter, and storm runoff from urban streets. Non–point sources of pollution can be very difficult to solve, since it is harder to detect them or to collect data about them. Even though Congress has directed the states—particularly the coastal states—to address these issues, most have not done so.

Groundwater pollution comes from many sources, including hazardous waste sites, irrigation runoff, salts from winter roads, landfills, and wastewater disposal. All of these sources of pollution are increasing, and that fact—along with the lack of legislation to confront the problems they cause—makes groundwater pollution an issue that will probably persist for some time.

Potential Health Effects of Water Pollution

The chemicals and wastes found in our drinking water have numerous effects on health, causing problems that range from cancer to infant death. And these problems stem from chemical threats that we can identify. Regulations and laws have been written to protect water quality and human health, but more is needed. Federal water quality standards fall short when it comes to the majority of chemicals found in water sources. These are chemicals whose health effects we know nothing about. (See Chapter 3 for U.S. laws regulating pollution.)

Demand and Development

Demand for Water in the United States

U.S. water demands are rising. As noted in the prior sections, what is often referred to as a water supply problem is actually a problem of water distribution. Sometimes the demand for water does not coincide with the place water is located. In other cases, the water is there, but it is not available for all demands because of legal restrictions. Distribution, regulatory decisions, and attitudes toward conservation can be limited or expanded by political protection of existing uses.[26]

General Uses

As Ralph Wurbs puts it, water uses are "generally classified as either consumptive or in-stream." Consumptive use refers to water that is withdrawn from a resource but not returned to that body of water. An example of consumptive use is agricultural irrigation when there are no return flows to the water resource. Instream uses of water may take water out of a stream, lake, river, or aquifer, but it is then returned to the resource in some manner. Instream uses "include such activities as navigation and hydroelectric power generation."[27]

He further notes that the largest proportion of instream water use in the United States goes to cooling at thermoelectric power plants. However, after the water circulates through the cooling system, most of it is returned to the source from where it was taken. Thus, the amount of consumptive use is low, and this is a good example of an instream use.[28] It should be noted that the water is usually much warmer when it is returned to the source after being used this way. This warmer temperature has the potential to adversely affect the ecosystem involved, which may be a cause for concern. In terms of consumptive use, though, the totals are low when compared to other uses, such as agricultural irrigation.

Agricultural irrigation is responsible for more consumptive use than any other sector of water demand. However, Wurbs notes that irrigation is vital for many reasons: "It increases the area of land that can be productively farmed, raises crop yields, stabilizes productivity, enhances farm income and employment, helps alleviate poverty, and contributes to regional development. But after irrigation, typical return flows range from virtually nil to about half the water withdrawn." Additionally, agricultural irrigation systems are notorious for waste from seepage and evaporation. "In recent years, given the depletion of groundwater reserves and competition from cities, the use of water for irrigation has leveled off and even decreased in regions of the United States and elsewhere."[29]

Demand Problems

It is common for people in the United States and other developed nations to use more water than they really need. For example, water-inefficient landscaping and plumbing are prolific, despite the fact that other options exist. Many cities waste much of their water through undetected pipeline leaks in aging water-distribution systems. There are short-term solutions, such as water rationing, to such water crises as drought. And long-term solutions include water-efficient toilets, improved irrigation equipment, and landscaping tailored to the natural ecosystem In addition, some cities mandate conservation in new construction or provide incentives for water conservation in the home. In other areas, educational campaigns have been designed to curb water use. Another important long-term solution is water-pricing incentives that encourage conservation and the use of improved technology. That is sometimes a difficult strategy to implement because it usually requires raising water rates—never a popular option.[30]

International Comparisons

Compared to global use levels, water use in the United States is staggering. The human body needs to consume less than two quarts of water a day to stay alive. However, Americans use an average of close to ninety gallons of water a day per person for domestic and personal uses. Added to this is industrial demand, making water the most heavily used natural resource in the United States. Manufacturing and energy production use a total of 140 billion gallons of water every day, or about 600 additional gallons per person. Added to this is agricultural use: The water needed to produce an average day's food for a family of four is about 3,200 gallons. When personal, industrial, energy, and agricultural uses are added together, the average American uses approximately 1,500 gallons of water per day.[31] This amounts to 547,500 gallons per person annually.

To put these use levels into perspective, consider the following. If some predictions hold, the water-stressed nations will only have 130,000 gallons per person per year by 2025—only 24 percent of the water used by U.S. residents today.[32] Currently, many nations face water shortages from swelling populations, mismanagement of natural resources, and unequal distribution. In other nations, people die of thirst. According to the U.S. Agency for International Development (USAID), more than one-third of the world's population currently face chronic water shortages. The report goes on to project that by 2025, similar shortages will affect between 2.4 and 3.2 billion people.[33]

Uncertainties in Water-Resource Bases

Water industry professionals use a concept known as "safe yield" to describe the sustainability of a source of water. A water system is operating "within safe yield" if the demand for water is less than the amount a water system can always deliver, even in the driest years. Safe yield is what all water supply systems strive for, but increasing demand makes this less and less possible, nationwide and around the globe.[34]

Global population growth and excessive water consumption by affluent nations make equitable distribution a growing problem. As this trend continues, the average amount of freshwater available to each person decreases. If nations and governments do not address these problems, global water scarcity is inevitable.

Development of Water Supplies: Technology and Infrastructure

As noted earlier, problems associated with water pollution are largely dealt with at state and local levels. In the 1970s, the federal government turned its attention to water quality as the "remaining unsolved water problem." Prior to that, federal attention was mainly focused on development and reclamation projects, including the construction of dams, levees, and canals to control water for human needs.[35]

Water Supply Systems

To manage water for human use, various water supply systems have been constructed in the United States. These systems provide drinking water, agricultural irrigation, waterways for navigation and commerce, flood control, and hydroelectricity. They have required major construction projects to dredge harbors and lakes, to build dams, levees, and storage or containment facilities, and generally to harness wild rivers.

The conventional approach to water management that guided the construction of these water supply systems includes four basic steps outlined by Rogers: First, a water source is located and protected. Second, the water is transported from the source to the user. In this step, water storage may be provided at the source end, the user end, or both ends of the transportation system. Third, the water is distributed to users. Finally, any wastewater that results must be disposed of in some manner.[36]

Precipitation and population have generally governed the construction of dams and other water-development facilities. If the technology of water supply systems had not been used extensively in the United States for the first half of the twentieth century, most of the arid West would never have been able to support the large population centers of such cities as Phoenix, Tucson, Las Vegas, or the entire southern California region. In addition, agricultural production in the West would be completely different. Most of California's precipitation occurs in the northern third of the state. However, due to sophisticated development projects, California's Central Valley is one of the world's most productive agricultural regions. The Central Valley and State Water Projects make this possible, despite the fact that this area has very minimal precipitation during the summer growing season.[37]

The Future of Water Infrastructure

At the start of the twenty-first century, development and reclamation projects are not as aggressively pursued as they once were. Daniel Beard, former head of the U.S. Bureau of Reclamation, proclaimed in 1994, "The dam-building era in the United States is now over." He offers several reasons for this. First, the best sites have already been used, and the most economical projects have already been undertaken. Also, public funds for construction are limited, and the regulatory regime is increasingly challenging. Finally, there is greater competition for water.[38]

Beard adds that if the dam-building era is over, something must replace it. He suggests several ways to improve water-policy directions, including pricing water at its real value, considering the environmental impact of large-scale water projects, and giving serious consideration to conservation and improved efficiency. These are "soft solutions"—solutions that stress non-structural policy approaches to balance the needs of competing users.[39] In Chapter 2 we explore these allocation and management problems in detail.

Notes

1. Zachary A. Smith, *The Environmental Policy Paradox*, 2nd ed. (Englewood Cliffs, NJ: Prentice Hall, 1995), 1.

2. Robert W. Adler notes in his article "Addressing Barriers to

Watershed Protection" that an ecosystem approach to environmental management or protection, in general, focuses on the overall health of entire ecosystems (*Environmental Law* 25, no. 4 [Fall 1995]: 973). Such an approach addresses multiple sources of actual or potential harm. This is in contrast to a focus on individual species or individual sources of harm, which was the traditional approach to natural resource protection and management until the last two decades of the twentieth century.

3. Peter E. Black, *Watershed Hydrology* (Chelsea, MI: Ann Arbor Press, 1996), 1–2.

4. Peter Rogers, *America's Water: Federal Roles and Responsibilities* (Cambridge: MIT Press, 1996), 25.

5. Rogers, *America's Water,* 26. Black, *Watershed Hydrology,* 3, 4.

6. Richard A. Wehmhoefer, "Water in the Southwest," in *Water and the Future of the Southwest,* ed. Zachary A. Smith (Albuquerque: University of New Mexico Press, 1989), 20.

7. Ibid.

8. This information is based on descriptions from the University of Arizona Water Resources Research Center, located in the College of Agriculture (online; available: http://ag.arizona.edu/AZWATER/ main. html; http://ag.arizona.edu/AZWATER/ALT/azmap/ground. html; accessed November 30, 2002), 1.

9. University of Arizona Water Resources Research Center (online; available: http://ag.arizona.edu/AZWATER/glossary/aquifer.html; http://ag.arizona.edu/AZWATER/reference/gloss.html; accessed November 30, 2002; link from alphabetical listing under the letter "A"), 1.

10. University of Arizona Water Resources Research Center (online; available: http://ag.arizona.edu/AZWATER/main.html; http://ag.arizona.edu/AZWATER/ALT/azmap/ground.html; accessed November 30, 2002), 1.

11. Ralph A. Wurbs, "Managing Our Precious Liquid Asset," *World and I,* 15, no. 10 (October 2000): 133; Peter H. Gleick, "Making Every Drop Count," *Scientific American,* February 2001, 42.

12. Black, *Watershed Hydrology,* 13.

13. The U.S. Environmental Protection Agency (EPA) website addresses approaches to watershed management in great detail. The EPA notes that "watersheds are defined by natural hydrology, they represent the most logical basis for managing water resources. The resource becomes the focal point, and managers are able to gain a more complete understanding of overall conditions in an area and the stressors which affect those conditions." In 1991, senior EPA managers placed a high priority on developing and supporting comprehensive state and tribal watershed approach strategies because it makes sense

environmentally, financially, socially, and administratively. EPA Office of Water, EPA800-F-96-001 (February 1996), "Why Watersheds?" in Environmental Protection Agency Website (online; available: http://www.epa.gov/OWOW/watershed/why.html; accessed March 25, 2001), 1.

14. Rogers, *America's Water,* 28.

15. Wurbs, "Managing Our Precious Liquid Asset," 132.

16. Ibid.; Barbara Rose Johnson and John M. Donahue, "Introduction," in *Water, Culture, and Power: Local Struggles in a Global Context,* ed. John M. Donahue and Barbara Rose Johnson (Washington, DC: Island Press, 1998), 1–2.

17. CIA, "Global Trends 2015" (online; available: http://www. cia. gov/cia/publications/globaltrends2015/index.html#link8b; accessed February 21, 2001). According to the website, the report was prepared under the direction of the National Intelligence Council (NIC), working with a range of nongovernmental institutions and experts. Numerous specialists from academia and the private sector contributed to the study. The website notes that many of the judgments in this report derive from efforts to distill the diverse views expressed.

18. Johnson and Donahue, "Introduction," 1–2.

19. CIA, "Global Trends 2015," 1; Economic Research Service of the U.S. Department of Agriculture Website (online; available: http://www. ers.usda.gov/Briefing/wateruse; accessed November 30, 2002), 1.

20. CIA, "Global Trends 2015," 1.

21. According to Wurbs, in addition to supplying water for human use, water-resource development and management entities will face many challenges across the globe. For example, he notes that demand will increase for things like flood-damage reduction, drainage solutions, erosion control, water quality improvements and maintenance, and environmental protection ("Managing Our Precious Liquid Asset," 132).

22. In 1998, the EPA announced the Water Quality Criteria and Standards Plan, developed by the EPA Office of Science and Technology in the Office of Water, for working together with states and tribes to enhance and improve water quality criteria and standards across the nation. The plan describes six program initiatives that the EPA will take over the next decade, and it will guide the EPA and the states and tribes in the development and implementation of criteria and standards. It provides a basis for enhancements to the total maximum daily load (TMDL) program, national pollutant discharge elimination system (NPDES) permitting, non–point source pollution control, wetlands protection, and other water resources management efforts. The EPA website provides a fact sheet and the final version of the plan (online; available:

http://www.epa.gov/waterscience/criteria, link to the Draft Standards and Criteria Strategy; accessed February 21, 2001).

23. Smith, *The Environmental Policy Paradox,* 110.

24. EPA Office of Watersheds, Oceans, and Wetlands, "Watershed Approach Framework," on Environmental Protection Agency Website (online; available: http://www.epa.gov/OWOW/watershed/framework. html; accessed June 25, 2001), 1–2.

25. Smith, *The Environmental Policy Paradox,* 106–110.

26. Ibid., 118.

27. Wurbs, "Managing Our Precious Liquid Asset," 132–133.

28. Ibid., 118.

29. Ibid., 133–137.

30. Ibid., 133; Grenetta Thomassey Fink and Zachary Smith, "Arizona Government and Politics," in *Uniting a Diverse Arizona: Background Report Prepared by Northern Arizona University,* ed. Kathryn Cruz Uribe, Margot Nason, and Frances Julia Riemer (Flagstaff: Seventy-Fifth Arizona Town Hall, October 31–November 3, 1999), 93.

31. William Ashworth, *Nor Any Drop to Drink* (New York: Summit Books, 1982), 19–20.

32. Gleick, "Making Every Drop Count," 42.

33. "When the Well Runs Dry: Population Pressures Threaten Global Water Supply" (online; available: http://www.populationcon-nection.org/Reports_Publications/Reports/report18.html; accessed November 30, 2002), 1. See also USAID, "Population and the Environment: A Delicate Balance" (online; available:http://www.usaid.gov/pop_health/pop/publications/docs/popenv.pdf; accessed November 30, 2002), 1.

34. Ashworth, *Nor Any Drop to Drink,* 17–18.

35. Rogers, *America's Water,* 72.

36. Ibid., 105.

37. Wurbs, "Managing Our Precious Liquid Asset," 135.

38. Daniel P. Beard, "Water Policy for the Next Generation," *World Rivers Review* 11, no. 3 (July 1996): 1–2; quotation at 1.

39. Ibid., 2–3.

2

Water Rights, Allocation Challenges, and Management Problems

This chapter is devoted to water rights, the challenges of water allocation, and the kind of problems that arise when water is managed for society. The first part, "Water Rights," describes water as a natural resource and discusses how being a resource—that is, something that can be priced, owned, bought, and sold—relates to the question of rights. It also describes the foundation for U.S. water law. The second part, "Water Allocation Challenges," is devoted to allocation of water. It examines economic and social concerns, including ownership and pricing. Finally, the third part, "Water-Management Problems," discusses the water industry, environmental interests, and alternative approaches to water-management problems.

Does water belong to everyone? If not, who owns it? Since water is so vital to human existence, is it logical and ethical to assign ownership to water? If so, under what circumstances is ownership valid, and how does this ownership ensure that all humans have access to necessary water supplies? In the following sections, these questions and others will be explored.

Water Rights

Water as a Natural Resource

Before we address water rights, we must first discuss water as a natural resource. Natural resources have been defined as "natu-

17

rally occurring resources and systems that are useful to humans, or could be under plausible technological, economic, and social considerations."[1] The point of this definition is that natural resources are only resources if they are useful to people and if their existence or possession is valuable to humans in some way. In the case of water, the concept of value includes economic, cultural, health, and ethical problems associated with the use and distribution of the resource, as well as recreational, aesthetic, and spiritual values.[2]

Natural resources are divided into two categories. The first is nonrenewable resources, also known as stock resources. These are resources that we have in stock for our use, but once the supply is gone, it is gone for good. An example of a nonrenewable resource is oil. The second category is renewable resources, also called flow resources. These are resources that can be restocked or recovered again in some way, over time.[3] At this point in the evolution of our solar system, sunshine is a good example of a renewable resource for the planet.

In addition, renewable and nonrenewable resources are further broken down into three other types. The first type comprises those resources that can be easily held as private property, such as land. The second type comprises "common-pool resources," that is, resources that are used by and belong to everyone, such as the air we breathe. The final type comprises "fugitive resources," that is, resources that elude the idea of simple ownership. Examples of this type are fish and wildlife populations that move across privately owned land or flowing rivers that move through private property. These categories of natural resource designation have evolved over time, with the growth of human population and the development of modern technology and lifestyles. However, because society has become more complicated, the distinction between renewable or nonrenewable resources is not always easy to determine.[4]

It is important to make these distinctions and to define categories for water and other natural resources. Resources become less abundant as the world is further developed for human use, and these categories clarify who has the right to use them. There is often stiff competition for water, and the categories help form a foundation upon which laws can be made. The rule of law is extremely important because so many types of needs must be recognized. The absence of clearly defined rights and rules of liability can create a dangerous situation; lives have been lost over water disputes.[5]

U.S. Water Law—The Foundation of Rights

Water law in the United States can differ widely in various areas, but it has historically been established with the underlying notion that there are substantial public rights to the resource. This means that everyone—the public—should have adequate rights and access. However, water law may initially develop from one set of historical circumstances, but then be changed to accommodate different modern circumstances. The idea is that the success of any law should be evaluated in terms of what society needs from that law. When private water rights are in question, administrative systems are often established in an effort to regulate and enforce these rights, based on the broad public interest. As a result, U.S. water law has developed into roughly three systems—riparian rights, prior appropriation, and hybrid states—but these systems sometimes overlap.[6] Each of these will now be explained in detail, followed by an explanation of one other special system in the United States known as reserved rights.

Development of the Humid East: Riparian Rights

Landowners with property bordering a waterway are considered riparians. The location of their land has special advantages because it has access to the water. In the eastern United States, water is plentiful, and laws regarding water developed historically from what is known as the riparian rights doctrine. Some scholars attribute the origin of riparian rights to English common law. Others believe it is the product of the civil law that evolved as the East developed. Either way, it has taken on a uniquely American flavor. Historically, most jurisdictions in the eastern United States adopted a "natural flow" rule that gave riparians the right to have water flow past their land in undiminished quantity or quality. This is the basis for riparian rights. Prior to the eighteenth century, navigation and fishing rights were at the core of most formal water disputes. With the emergence of the Industrial Revolution, however, water-driven mills provided a need for uniform laws that would apply to the increasing number and type of disputes involving access to the natural flow of streams in the growing eastern United States.[7]

Eventually, the natural flow rule ran into problems on the question of access by others to the natural flow of the water, both before and after it left the riparian's land. Therefore, from some of the earliest cases on the issue, the courts tempered the doctrine with "reasonable use" principles—that is, riparians must use water in a way that is "reasonable" in relation to all other users. If there is not enough water to satisfy the needs of all riparians in a water system, then all must reduce their use in proportion to their rights, which is sometimes based on the amount of land owned. If other owners want the right to use water on nonriparian land, they may do so if they pay for any harm caused to the riparians.[8]

As put simply, by Wehmhoefer, the riparian rights doctrine states that if your property touches a stream, you are entitled to the full flow of the stream. However, you must make reasonable use of it. Therefore, whatever you use the water for, you need to return the stream to its natural channel before it leaves your land. Finally, your use must be reasonable to the corresponding rights of owners lying below you on the stream.[9]

To some extent, riparian rights still apply in twenty-nine states. They also apply in some of the states with hybrid water rights systems, which we describe below. Getches points out that in all states, riparian landowners have special rights to use waters adjoining their property. However, laws have largely modified riparian rights in most jurisdictions that follow the doctrine. For example, today the laws usually require riparians to obtain permits from a state agency to use the water. In addition, if the water is navigable, certain uses by the general public must also be tolerated by riparians.[10]

Challenges of the Arid West: Prior Appropriation

The U.S. West has not ignored the doctrine of riparian rights, but it is definitely not the prevailing law in that region. The 100th meridian passes through the United States and runs from the Dakotas to Texas. It is also known as the north-south dry line: Rainfall on the western side is insufficient to grow crops. The appropriation doctrine, also called the doctrine of prior appropriation, provides a framework for the body of water law that evolved in the nineteenth century in the western United States to meet the challenges of developing this arid region. The roots of prior appropriation are found in the customs of miners on federal public lands at that time. Prior appropriation became the law in the courts because it was already the law of miners and farmers.[11]

Mining uses water, whether it is done by hand, panning for gold, or by mechanical hydraulic mining operations. From the start, water was necessary to individual miners. As the practice became more industrial, it eventually required large amounts of water. Miners developed their own water law before any federal or state legislature made any declarations on the topic, just as they had done with mining laws. The key was a simple rule used for the capture of water: "First in time, first in right."

This rule of priority, rooted in time, was directly opposed to the foundations of the riparian rights doctrine. As Charles Wilkinson explains, the sharing of water or the tempering of the right to use water (by applying reasonable use considerations) made no sense to the miners. What did make sense was for a miner (or eventually a mining company) to divert an entire stream to provide for his operations. Otherwise, miners could not rely on the stability of any claim, for no claim could be stable if the water needed to operate it could not also be claimed.[12]

Another mining rule, due diligence, required miners to actively work a claim. If a mine was not actively worked, the right to the claim was considered abandoned. This concept also applied to the water needed to work a claim. Water users had the right to keep using the water, and it was a vested property right—the same as the right to mine hardrock minerals in a claim. In addition, once the initial appropriation of water had been made, the right could be leased or sold as private property from the time it was first put to use. First in time, first in right.[13]

In time, this principle of prior appropriation was extended to define the water rights of farmers and other water users in the West. Whereas most jurisdictions that use the principle of prior appropriation consider water to be a public resource, owned by no one, the right to use water is granted on the application of water to a "beneficial use." Granting water rights is based on when a person applies a quantity of water to a beneficial use—farming, mining, and so on—and those rights continue as long as the beneficial use is maintained.[14] Eventually, state laws defined preferred water rights and even subsidized them, with the help of the federal government. Water was declared to be public, but most western water was captured for private profit. A prevailing attitude in the West became "The right to divert . . . shall never be denied."[15]

In summary, prior appropriation rests on the following key points: (1) Ownership of riparian lands does not identify the right to appropriate water. (2) The first in time is first in right. (3) Right is lost by not using, or abandoning, the right to use the water. (4) Beneficial use of water is the foundation, measurement tool, and limit of the appropriative right.[16]

In nine states—Alaska, Arizona, Colorado, Idaho, Montana, Nevada, New Mexico, Utah, and Wyoming—appropriation law is exclusive, that is, all water law is based on the principle of prior appropriation.[17] For example, in Arizona, the water code declares that all water of the state from all sources of supply is subject to prior appropriation.

Hybrid State Systems

As noted earlier, U.S. water law has developed into roughly three systems. This section is devoted to the so-called hybrid water rights systems used in many states. An immediate clarification is required. The use of the word "hybrid" does not limit the potential combination of systems to just riparian rights and prior appropriation, which are discussed above. For example, Hawaii and Louisiana have hybrid water rights systems. However, Hawaii's system combines recent, modern statutes with laws from the ancient Hawaiian Kingdom. Louisiana's water law is rooted in the French Civil Code.[18]

In ten other states, a different hybrid system does combine riparian rights and prior appropriation. These systems coexist in California, Kansas, Mississippi, Nebraska, North Dakota, Oklahoma, Oregon, South Dakota, Texas, and Washington. These states are also categorized as using the "California doctrine" because that was the first state to fully develop a hybrid system.[19]

Other states were originally riparian but later adopted prior appropriation. Historically, substantial riparian rights had already been established in those states when prior appropriation laws were passed. However, it was found that neither system was entirely satisfactory for states on the West Coast, nor for central states that lie between higher elevations and lower land and that have more rainfall east of the dry line. Today, in most such states, appropriation is the basis of new water rights, but California, Nebraska, and Oklahoma still allow riparians to originate new uses with water rights that take precedence over those of prior appropriators, under certain circumstances.[20]

Another hybrid system, pueblo water rights, is found in a few places in the Southwest. In New Mexico and California, the courts have occasionally decided in favor of the application of pueblo water rights. Arizona, Texas, and Colorado have also used this system. As Getches explains it, the system is based on claims tracing back to land grants and principles applied in the region before it became part of the United States. The rights descend from mandates, either by the Spanish Crown or by the Mexican government, declaring that municipalities could use all the naturally occurring water needed for residents within their boundaries. Water could also be shared with neighboring pueblos. In 1848, the territories in question were ceded to the United States in the Treaty of Guadalupe Hidalgo. This treaty confirmed traditional property rights, including pueblo water rights, which extend to both surface flows and groundwater.[21]

Pueblo water rights have been crucial to the expansion of some California cities. Modern legal decisions have held that the use of water is not required to keep a municipal pueblo right alive. In other words, successor cities could displace long-established uses, including in cases where the water had not been used historically. Therefore, Los Angeles was able to claim pueblo water rights to meet growing needs from increasing population, because it was a successor to a pueblo right.[22]

Reserved Rights

One final water rights system should be addressed because it has special implications for many states. This is the system of reserved rights, which traces its roots to an attempt to protect Indian reservations. Tribes were isolated and confined to reservations for two key reasons: to facilitate the settlement of the United States generally and the West in particular, and to convert Native Americans to farmers. In 1908, tribal water priorities were established in a Supreme Court case, *Winters v. United States,* in which the Supreme Court enunciated what has come to be known as the *Winters* Doctrine. The Court ruled in favor of tribal water rights, reasoning that tribes had possessed sovereignty and real property rights in their territories long before treaties were established with the United States. Following this logic, it was established that tribes therefore "reserved"—or retained—the rights to use their land and water. Tribes had command of all the beneficial use of land and water, whether this use was applied to hunting, grazing, agriculture, or the arts of developing their own brand of civilization. These Indian rights were considered superior to any laws of any state.[23]

Unfortunately, problems still exist on the question of reserved rights. Tribes often have not used or claimed their rights, and later settlers on some land, especially in the West, subsequently claimed and used them. As a result, many water rights in the West can sometimes be uncertain. Examples of this occur in

Arizona, where Indian water right claims more than exceed the entire flow of the Colorado River. The reserved rights doctrine was created to assure that Indian lands had water.[24] The doctrine also applies to public lands set aside for other "reservations" designated by the federal government. These federal reservations include national parks, Bureau of Land Management properties, and other federal lands.

Water Allocation Challenges

In the first part of this chapter, we established a foundation for water rights in the idea of water as a natural resource, and we have described the fundamental framework for U.S. water law. We now turn to a discussion of challenges to water allocation and management problems that spring from this foundation and framework.

Economic and Social Concerns

It is not possible to address the subject of water allocation and water politics without also examining the economic and social concerns that are intertwined with the formation of water policy. Economic and social concerns are related to the question of rights and laws because they result in the ultimate stage of water-policy creation: the political process.[25] The subsequent creation of policy has an impact upon society, and for this reason, it is important to understand some of these issues involved in water allocation.

Some have argued that economic needs have shaped water policy in the western United States more than any other factor, including the aridity of the region. Water allocation challenges exist in every region of the United States, and economic concerns are given considerable weight when policy decisions are made nationwide. In addition, if market failures do not respond to economic or financial approaches, political imperatives emerge as society's search for answers to economic questions. The following sections will describe a few neoclassical economic concepts that have an impact on water allocation policy, and they will also examine some economic and social aspects to the ownership and pricing of water.[26]

Neoclassical Economic Concepts

The dominant approach to economics in society at the start of the twenty-first century is said to be neoclassical. Neoclassical economics assume that society faces unlimited wants and demands from individuals but that these wants are constrained by limited resources. Scarcity is the reason that the management of society's resources is so important in economics: Resources are scarce, and society has less to offer than people want to have.[27]

Scarcity is a key factor in water allocation decisions. Resource depletion, and especially water depletion, can cause the disintegration of societies and entire civilizations. That, scholars theorize, is what happened to the Mayans on the ancient Yucatan Peninsula in Mexico and to the Hohokam in Arizona. However, resource depletion is not always the cause of economic instability. Rather, it is a symptom of economic and social instability. In the modern world, instability in society increases uncertainty and may lead to economic disruptions, including recession or even economic depression. The result can often accelerate resource depletion.[28]

Neoclassical economic theory also notes that the main problems faced by any economy are lack of growth, unemployment, and inflation. The prevailing neoclassical economic paradigm argues that individual behavior supports the common good and that unregulated markets can work to solve problems affecting the common good, as they arise. The paradigm simultaneously argues that markets provide for the common good and effectively replace the need for an emphasis upon communities.

However, critical scholars argue that communities are necessary at different geographical scales to define the social good, adapt the social order, and manage environmental systems. These arguments have led to challenges to the dominant paradigm of neoclassical economic approaches to water allocation.

For example, ecological economics (EE) addresses the question of scale. The question is, "How large can an economy become before it begins to harm the ecosystem that . . . sustains it?"[29] EE asserts that economic markets cannot provide an answer to this problem because they offer no method for deciding or defining a desirable scale of growth. Rather, the dominant paradigm is unlimited growth, and that assumes an unlimited scale. However, is that a prudent approach, since there is now evidence that economic growth can significantly affect the environment? Air and water pollution, toxic and hazardous wastes, species extinction, and loss of biomass are a few examples of negative impacts upon ecosystems due to economic growth and development. Therefore, as Peter Montague puts it, it might be possible for the economy to grow too large and exceed the capacity of ecosystems to thrive. If such a point is achieved, the market will have become "unsustainably large." The environment will no longer be able to absorb the waste, and further growth would "diminish the carrying capacity of the planet," that is, it would diminish its ability to sustain life.[30]

Another important element of neoclassical economic thought used for understanding water policy is the idea that the use of economic resources is focused on meeting two specific economic goals: efficiency and equity. A simple but useful way to think about efficiency and equity is to say that "efficiency refers to the size of the economic pie, and equity refers to how the pie is divided."[31]

Efficiency strives to achieve the maximum output of goods and services, using inputs or resources that cost the least. Efficiency is the underlying force driving globalization. As new democracies are created and regional trade agreements are made, the search for efficiency motivates the drive to eliminate barriers to trade, in order to make more products available in more markets at reasonable prices. Because water use is vital to these globalization efforts, the question of efficient water use is very important to allocation policy on both domestic and international levels.

Equity as an economic goal is more difficult to measure. What is fair? Whose notion of fairness is used? Neoclassical economics asserts that the answers to such questions must be established by society. However, the question then becomes, Whose notion of fairness rises to the top? Politics and power determine this, despite the neoclassical economic assumption that markets, left to their own devices, will reveal what society believes is fair and equitable. Social and political imperatives start with equity, and on the question of water allocation, they have traditionally held that "no group or individual in society should bear a disproportionate cost in obtaining the basic water required for survival." However, society also expects the government to prevent wasteful spending, so economic subsidies of any kind are subject to scrutiny and political pressure.[32]

Equity is an assumed component of public policy in the United States, but it is difficult to accomplish. Nearly everyone agrees that "fair" and "unfair" distributions exist in society. What is "fair" and how we should achieve it are the questions that bring economics into the political realm. However, it is generally recognized that markets cannot solve this problem. These questions must be answered by people who decide what is fair, usually politicians and bureaucrats. Public policy is subsequently designed to accomplish that fair distribution. Only based on their decisions and designs can the market then allocate resources efficiently.[33]

Unfortunately, even with both efficiency and fairness, an economy can still be large enough to damage the ecosystem simply because of its scale. Yet, as Montague states, economists and business and political leaders usually only acknowledge the problems of allocation and distribution. The problem of scale has not been acknowledged; continued growth is considered the ideal scenario. The concept of keeping the scale of the economy within the limits of the ecosystem is not considered legitimate.[34]

Finally, it has also been argued that if we are to be fair to our descendants, the present economic values and costs of water (and other natural resources) should also include the value and potential cost to future generations.[35] When considering future impacts of current water policy, what we do today could either result in a variety of problems or pave the way for a more secure and prosperous future.

Ownership

The concept of ownership is very important to water allocation challenges. Ownership of water determines access and use, and it is important to recall that competition for water can be very rigorous and can have both economic and social motivations. Ownership is assumed in the neoclassical economic approach to water allocation.

Several questions were posed at the beginning of this chapter: *Does water belong to everyone? If not, who owns it?* To answer these questions, it is necessary to first explain the consequences of the answers. If water does belong to everyone, then we all must have some agreed-upon minimum level of access. If it does not belong to everyone, then owners must still make water available to everyone somehow, because it is essential to human survival.

At the beginning of this chapter we also asked, *Since water is so vital to human existence, is it logical and ethical to assign ownership to water? If so, under what circumstances is ownership valid, and how does this ownership ensure that all humans have access to necessary water supplies?* It was long ago decided that ownership of water is logical and ethical. What we are required to establish is how water is claimed and who sells it. We must also know who can buy it, and at what price. We must have water, but other questions arise from that. Is it best for us, individually, and also for society to claim common ownership? Perhaps we should agree to private ownership regimes, or some combination of the two? These questions are answered by modern society in several ways. Economics shapes some of those answers that ultimately design society and subsequently guide the way we allocate water.

Internationally, water has been acknowledged as a basic human right. This assumption drives a plea by the United Nations for governments and mankind to work to prevent the levels of global water stress predicted for the next twenty-five years. Mikhail Gorbachev wrote in 2000, "Without water security, social, economic, and national stability are imperiled—a consequence that is magnified where water flows across borders and becomes crucial in regions of religious, territorial, or ethnic tension."[36] Obviously, ownership and how it is determined is paramount, and decisions about this can stem from using a range of methods, including deliberation and debate at one end and war and violence at the other.

However, the world as a whole is now more prosperous than at any other time in human history, and the most recent improvements are attributed to globalization efforts that have increased standards of living in most developed, industrial nations. High praise is given to private enterprise and free markets. It is therefore not surprising that there is now speculation that greater privatization of the water business, whose customers worldwide are usually served by some type of public utility, would improve service and lower costs.[37]

Privatization—which means private water markets and private investors taking responsibility for municipal water utilities—is being contemplated and used in some parts of the world to tackle the challenges of allocation.[38] Examples across the planet show that water from privately owned companies can improve service and cost. But examples also exist of the opposite outcome. This debate has generally not been settled in the United States, where no national water policy exists and state and local entities often have powerful representation in the federal scheme.

In the United States, most water is publicly owned by municipal utility companies. Roughly 90 percent of U.S. tap water treatment facilities are publicly owned, as are 99 percent of sewage-treatment facilities. However, as of this writing, privately owned international companies are entering the U.S. marketplace, purchasing various systems that serve a few cities nationwide. A British company, Thames Water, now owns the water company serving Elizabeth, New Jersey. Atlanta, Indianapolis, and Milwaukee have all signed contracts with the French company Suez Lyonnaise des Eaux. Lyonnaise will run either the wastewater or the water supply components of their municipal systems.[39]

U.S. water utilities are facing daunting challenges, as noted above. It is costly to provide water for growing cities that may have neglected maintenance on pipes and fittings in old systems or that might need to construct new systems for unprecedented inmigration and other causes of population growth. Privatization is being examined as one potential way to solve these pressing problems. The question becomes, Will privatization result in the customer actually getting better value at lower costs, when local water utilities are taken over by private, profit-motivated concerns? And will everyone get water? If not, why not, and what are their alternatives?

One argument for privatization is supported using the concept of efficiency. As we will describe in the third part of the chapter, "Water-Management Problems," the government institutions involved in water allocation can be highly inefficient due to a number of factors, including overlapping jurisdictions that require sophisticated levels of cooperation that are not always present or possible. By contrast, profit-driven private companies must incorporate efficiency into their operations, or they will not make money. In the case of privatization of water systems, capital investment is minimal because the municipality has already provided the system. Even if extensive repair or overhaul is needed, this is still usually far less than the cost of the initial installation. Therefore, costs should be minimal, and privatized systems should be profitable shortly after taking over from a public concern. Furthermore, private companies can be expected to continue to strive for efficiency, and citizens should expect the same or better service for a reasonable price.[40]

In Buenos Aires, a private French company has taken over municipal water operations and the citizens are very satisfied. The firm has fixed leaks, extended service, shed inefficient staff, and improved revenue collections, which has provided more service for more people at a lower cost. Another French company successfully runs the water system in Berlin, also with satisfactory results for citizens.

However, in Great Britain, political hostility to private water companies is growing, due to rate increases being linked to direct, personal benefits for private water executives. In Cochambamba, Bolivia, a privatized water program has been criticized for being extremely insensitive to local needs. In February 2000, protests and riots in Bolivia over steep water price increases rocked the national government.[41]

The argument against privatization notes that water customers will never be buyers in a traditional, neoclassical market model because there is no opportunity to purchase water from a variety of potential sellers. Because there will always be only one set of water pipes in place for a community, there is no way a customer can take his or her business elsewhere.[42] The costs of running a single municipal water facility make it highly impractical for companies to construct separate, unrelated systems. This makes competition—which acts to benefit the customer—very difficult. Therefore, some degree of regulation by government—representing and acting in the customer's interest—seems beneficial for citizens, even if some form of privatization is used.

Critics of privatization also argue against selling water on the open market, either directly or through the use of regional water brokers selling surplus water to private or public interests. They worry that commodification of water will not allow equitable distribution to a thirsty world. Theorists say that if the world does not reexamine its current growth trends and the policies that encourage them, a mass diversion of water will ultimately be needed. Privatizing water supplies will do little to encourage a reexamination of current growth policies, because the dominant attitude benefits private firms and regional supply brokers.[43]

The infrastructure that might be required for massive diversion to swelling cities is staggering. This gives great cause for concern that private corporations or brokers might deliver water only to those who can pay for it, such as wealthy cities, water-intensive industries, and individuals.[44] Critics also worry about the potential impact of massive water-diversion projects upon global ecosystems, and they worry further that there will be very little chance of protecting ecosystems in the face of economic imperatives to continued growth.

Pricing

Once ownership is determined, it is necessary to establish the rest of the allocation equation. That is, the price of water must be set, and that price must enable everyone to have clean, potable water, if water is indeed a basic international human right.

It has been noted that the problem in the United States is that everyone expects better water service, but they do not expect to have to pay a lot to get it, regardless of who owns it.[45] This is very evident in the West, where federal subsidies support an affordable price for water in an area that is actually deprived of an abundant supply. Normally, a weak supply would force high demand and high prices. However, federal water supply systems, constructed across the region, have made water available for agricultural expansion and municipal growth. This would not have been possible without the federal dams, levees, and canals.

It is important to note that because of local political power and western lobbying at the federal level, these supply systems were financed by taxpayers across the entire United States and not just by the residents of the region. The application of prior appropriation laws to mining and agricultural interests created tremendous wealth and power, which also greatly influenced political decisions. This resulted in water policy that was designed to encourage the growth and settlement of the West. Expensive water would have certainly hindered rapid settlement efforts.

Some of the water demand challenges faced by growing U.S. cities could be alleviated by conservation techniques, especially in the West. Manipulating water prices is a very easy way to promote conservation, which would help offset the costs of providing water to arid or drought-stricken regions. This has been successfully used in some places, but conservation is not the norm. There are even a few U.S. cities that do not meter water, which leads to very wasteful water practices.[46]

Water is usually priced according to the costs involved in storing, transporting, and treating it, which results in rather inexpensive prices for U.S. consumers. This method is criticized by some who argue that the true cost of developing water is usually hidden, or not reflected accurately, when water is priced this way. Most things that are pumped out of the ground, such as oil and water, are not priced for their value. Rather, they are priced for the cost of getting them out of the ground and distributing them. This pricing standard makes the water itself essentially free.[47]

Environmental degradation is not usually factored into the cost of water. For example, the cleanup of the pesticide runoff from irrigation that has degraded a riparian habitat is not included in the price of water, and this is unlikely to change soon in the West. Existing contracts ensure that federal subsidies for agricultural water will continue far into the future, providing little incentive to price water to encourage conservation,[48] or to help with environmental cleanups or preservation efforts.

Now we turn to the special challenges of water management.

Water-Management Problems: The Water Industry, Environmental Interests, and Alternative Approaches

The Water Industry

Water-management policy, decided by politics and the political will, is what determines the standards used to identify efficiency and to determine what is equitable in water questions. The political will of a governing body is formed in many ways, including large donations to political campaigns by vested interests and the influence of grassroots movements. When politicians make laws under the influence of vested interests—ranging from mining companies to environmentalists—they often write the laws in ways favorable to those interests.

At first glance, there is "a bewildering variety to human approaches to water management."[49] Unfortunately, because of the complex web of interests involved with water, it is difficult to write legislation that is clear and easily understood by the average citizen. These interests can also make it difficult to write legislation that is simple to implement.[50]

Those who make water policy are members of a group known as the water industry. This group is composed of a combination of private interests and public agencies. The water industry manages our water and has designed an elaborate and intricate system to address water problems.[51]

Private Interests: Agricultural, Municipal, and Industrial Competition

The private groups in the water industry reflect a range of interests, such as agriculture, ranching, mining, energy, navigation,

recreation, and urban-development. These groups are all benefi-
ciaries of water development, and they often receive subsidies
and benefit from water infrastructure facilities. Outcomes of
water policy often reflect the relative access, economic resources,
and organizational skills that these different groups enjoy.[52]

"The agricultural wing of the water industry has long maintained a special place in the politics of water."[53] Agriculture has
dominated lobbying and political organizations in the water industry for many decades. However, beginning in the 1980s, agricultural dominance of water policy has been mitigated by increasing urban demands for water. A new competition for water
emerged from urban interests. Such competition had a great impact on agriculture, and eventually the farming interests suffered
a loss of influence in water issues. Agriculture maintained the status of a major force, but it was no longer "first among equals in a
water industry seeking to contend with a changing agenda."[54]

Political influence and priorities shifted with the growth of
cities and suburbs. Simultaneously, a breathtaking evolution in technology and industry was speeding up the transition to an information and service economy. The gentrification of agricultural land to
accommodate expanding metropolitan areas—especially in the
West and the South but to some extent all over the nation—also affected the water industry. In 1988, it was noted, "Water has become
central to these plans of the urban-development complex. It is priced
so that developments do not have to pay their way. It is made available from distant places so there is no mechanism to link development to what the resources of an area can support. And through its
oversizing and dependence on increased sales, the water system has
been structured so that growth follows the water."[55]

Water—simply because rural areas have it and urban
areas want it—has a great potential for rural/urban
conflict. For example, in Arizona, during the passage
of the Arizona Groundwater Management Act in 1980,
rural farmers felt as though mining interests and
urban municipalities ganged up on them to unfairly
take some of their water rights. In many parts of the
West, as states become more urbanized, agriculture's
political influence will wane, and this cannot help but
become a point of division in rural-urban relations.

In most Western states, farmers use a majority of the

water, but produce only a small percentage of the personal income and job opportunities in a state. The transfer of water from agricultural to municipal use is inevitable, due to the population projections that guarantee increased water demand. The only place it can come from is the farm, and the issues involved will be where the water will go, where it will come from, and at what price.

At various places in the development of the West, the transferring of water from one groundwater basin or region to another has been an issue in water politics. Most of the conflicts and issues have been resolved either through the courts or the state legislatures. Most of the resolutions have been to the benefit of the municipality or other interest desiring to transfer the water, sometimes with provisions to protect interests within the region from which the water is exported, sometimes not. This is something rural landowners and farmers will be concerned about in the future.

It can be argued that supporting and maintaining agriculture serves important needs, such as diversification of a state's economy, which benefits both rural and urban areas. The question is one of state goals and allocation decisions. Agriculture will certainly become increasingly irrelevant to state economies that pursue continued growth of urban areas. A population of millions could eventually blanket Western valleys, or add to the steady sprawl of cities along the front slope of the Rocky Mountains. That kind of future will require transfers of water from agriculture to municipalities with varying degrees of compensation. What farmers can expect in the way of compensation and benefits will depend upon their strength in the political process, and the willingness of the cities to help maintain part of the state's rural heritage.[56]

Public Interests: Local, State, and Federal Responsibilities

Public agencies have long dominated the business of supplying water. These agencies exist at a variety of government levels, from municipal sewer and water departments to county water authorities to regional irrigation districts to departments in federal executive agencies.[57]

Local and State Responsibilities

The water laws in each state are different from the laws in every other state. At the local and state level, water agencies are organized in many ways.[58] Each agency has different powers, ranging from the ability to levy taxes and charge user fees to the ability to make land-use decisions. These powers can often result in water agencies becoming de facto land planners for their jurisdictions.[59]

At the local level, it is sometimes obvious who wins and who loses as a result of water policy. Because of this, water politics tend to be more intense at the local level than at the federal level. Local laws, agencies, court decisions, county ordinances, and regulation of irrigation districts all specify detailed allocation of water use. Such specifications can range from the amount of water allowed within a water right to the season and purpose of use to the point of diversion to the regulation of irrigation.[60]

Yet it is not uncommon for local water issues to be fought at the federal level due to the pervasive role of the federal government, primarily in water-pollution policy. For example, the recent emphasis on the control of non–point source pollution probably makes local upstream-downstream conflicts more pronounced in the East. However, they will need to be resolved within a federal framework.[61]

An interesting example of state, local, and federal control and cooperation occurred in the early 1970s. A small western city was ordered to suspend springtime sluicing operations on a dam for their municipal reservoir. The operation was designed to alleviate silt buildup behind the dam, but it was causing water downstream to fail water quality standards, and it was possibly interfering with fish spawning beds. Various state and federal agencies were sympathetic, but they were unable to help because of their own policies or because they did not have any money. Meanwhile, the silt load behind the dam increased and, in consequence, the reservoir storage area shrank. After ten years of "addressing" the issue, city officials ended up with a federal permit in hand authorizing them to do what they had originally done: sluice the reservoir in the spring. The only difference was that now they had to submit monthly reports to the EPA.[62]

Additional confusion results from the fact that state laws

encompass county and municipal ordinances, and states coordinate those laws, direct them, and sometimes override them. Agency goals at different levels of government—and the laws they are responsible for administering—may conflict with one another. This can create confusion that has real consequences, as described in the above example.[63]

Federal Roles

A very strong demand continues to exist for local and state control of water resources. Still, Americans have neglected to take responsibility for control of our water, calling on the federal government to help when we get into trouble.[64]

The federal influence over local water issues, nationwide, has resulted in arguments for the need to clarify and improve federal water policy. However, this does not necessarily mean we should have a "national water policy." The argument against doing so is persistent.[65] Federal policy is a different thing from a "national water policy." Federal policy is narrower in scope, restricted to addressing the federal interest in any given problem area. It does not claim to solve national problems. Some scholars argue that, given the scope of the geography of the United States, there is no reason to believe there are "national" water problems. The water problems on the two sides of the 100th meridian require different solutions. Hence, federal policy must be able to deal with specific regional problems, not national water problems.[66]

Peter Rogers identifies the overarching issues on the topic of water in the United States as:

1. The role of the federal government in establishing coherent policies;
2. The interagency conflicts and overlaps of jurisdiction;
3. The importance of budget considerations;
4. The need for information, research, and education; and
5. The coordination of state and federal efforts.

"Despite the shortcomings of the policymaking process, the current condition of America's water is relatively good. How good it remains, however, will depend to a large degree on our ability to make the technical, economic, political, and bureaucratic adjustments" that are needed to keep it that way.[67]

Environmental Interests

In addition to the water industry, which encompasses both private and public interests, there are also environmental interests in the water-policy arena. This section describes a few of these groups and their roles. Please see Chapter 6 for a more complete list and description of organizations.

Examples of environmental interests in water exist at every level of government and society. These actors emerged to fill a void. For the first time in history, we recognize mankind's power to harm the planet in many different ways. Global economic business interests have formidable resources, but these interests rarely take environmental issues seriously. Certainly technology will be developed to help with some environmental problems, but technological innovation cannot be counted upon to provide a sufficient response to all the threats we face. In light of this void, environmental interests have entered the water-policy arena.

One example of a governmental environmental water interest is the EPA, established in 1970 as an independent agency of the federal government. The mission of the EPA is "to protect human health and to safeguard the natural environment—air, water, and land—upon which life depends."[68] The agency is concerned with water in many ways. The EPA Office of Water has several departments that address such issues as groundwater and drinking water, wastewater management, wetlands, oceans, and watersheds. It also has a water-policy staff and houses the American Indian Environmental Office. In addition, it has a department dedicated to water science and technology.[69] Finally, it has an entire list of environmental programs, dedicated to problems ranging from fish consumption advisories to dredged material management.[70]

In contrast, Great Lakes United is an example of a societal environmental water interest. This is a private, "international coalition dedicated to preserving and restoring the Great Lakes–St. Lawrence River ecosystem."[71] Member organizations include very many interest groups, such as local community associations, environmentalists, labor unions, and tribal interests in both the United States and Canada. The organization has been active since 1982. It is impressive because it works to protect the Great Lakes by encouraging activism and communication among the various interested groups. They have education programs to enable communities to focus on local and regional water issues and to help develop relevant policy initiatives. Their goal is to keep the Great Lakes healthy for people, wildlife, and future generations.[72]

Notes

1. Charles W. Howe, *Natural Resource Economics: Issues, Analysis, and Policy* (New York: John Wiley, 1979), 1.

2. Peter Rogers, *America's Water: Federal Roles and Responsibilities* (Cambridge: MIT Press, 1996), 75–77.

3. Ibid.

4. Ibid.

5. "Whose Water Is It Anyway? New Book Examines Negotiating Water Rights." *Economic and Political Weekly,* October 28, 2000: 1, as reprinted on the IFPRI Website (online; available: http://www.ifpri.org/pressrel/2000/072000.htm#top; accessed July 2, 2001); David H. Getches, *Water Law in a Nutshell* (St. Paul, MN: West Publishing Co., 1997), 2.

6. Getches, *Water Law in a Nutshell,* 2–4.

7. Ibid., 4, 15–19.

8. Ibid., 18–20, 4–5.

9. Richard A. Wehmhoefer, "Water in the Southwest," in *Water and the Future of the Southwest,* ed. Zachary A. Smith (Albuquerque: University of New Mexico Press, 1989), 20–21.

10. Getches, *Water Law in a Nutshell,* 4–6, 15.

11. Charles F. Wilkinson, *Crossing the Next Meridian: Land, Water, and the Future of the West* (Washington, DC: Island Press, 1992), 12; Getches, *Water Law in a Nutshell,* 74.

12. Wilkinson, *Crossing the Next Meridian,* 231–233.

13. Ibid.

14. Getches, *Water Law in a Nutshell,* 74.

15. Wilkinson, *Crossing the Next Meridian,* 235.

16. Wehmhoefer, "Water in the Southwest," 22–23.

17. Getches, *Water Law in a Nutshell,* 6.

18. Ibid., 8.

19. Getches, *Water Law in a Nutshell,* 190.

20. Ibid., 190–191.

21. Ibid., 214–215.

22. Ibid., 215.

23. Getches, *Water Law in a Nutshell,* 12; Wilkinson, *Crossing the Next Meridian,* 267–268.

24. Rogers, *America's Water,* 92.

25. Ibid., 172.

26. Donald J. Pisani, *Water, Land, and Law in the West: The Limits of Public Policy, 1850–1920* (Lawrence: University Press of Kansas, 1996), 7; Rogers, *America's Water,* 152.

27. N. Gregory Mankiw, *Principles of Economics* (Orlando, FL: Dryden Press, Harcourt Brace College Publishers, 1998), 4.

28. S. V. Ciriacy-Wantrup, *Resource Conservation: Economics and Policies* (Berkeley and Los Angeles: University of California Press, 1952), 199–203.

29. Peter Montague, "Sustainable Development, Part 2," *Rachel's Environment and Health Weekly,* no. 625, November 19, 1998 (online; available: http://www.rachel.org/bulletin/index.cfm?St=2; accessed November 30, 2002), 1.

30. Ibid.

31. Mankiw, *Principles of Economics,* 5.

32. Rogers, *America's Water,* 152.

33. Ibid.

34. Montague, "Sustainable Development," 2–4.

35. Rogers, *America's Water,* 152.

36. Mikhail Gorbachev, "Out of Water: The Distant Alarm Comes Closer," *Civilization: The Magazine of the Library of Congress,* October/November 2000: 82.

37. Douglas B. MacDonald, "The Water Bill—We Pay It: The Question Is, Who Writes It?" *Civilization: The Magazine of the Library of Congress,* October/November 2000: 92.

38. Rogers, *America's Water,* 13.

39. MacDonald, "The Water Bill," 92–94.

40. Ibid.

41. Ibid., 93.

42. Ibid., 92–93.

43. Maude Barlow, "Water Privatization and the Threat to the World's Most Precious Resource: Is Water a Commodity or a Human Right?" *IFG Bulletin: Special Water Issue,* Summer 2001: 1–2.

44. Ibid.

45. MacDonald, "The Water Bill," 93.

46. Zachary A. Smith, *The Environmental Policy Paradox,* 2nd ed. (Englewood Cliffs, NJ: Prentice Hall, 1995), 118.

47. Ibid., 118–119; William Ashworth, *Nor Any Drop to Drink* (New York: Summit Books, 1982), 75.

48. Smith, *The Environmental Policy Paradox,* 118–119.

49. Ashworth, *Nor Any Drop to Drink,* 125.

50. Rogers, *America's Water,* 152.

51. Robert Gottlieb, *A Life of Its Own* (Orlando, FL: Harcourt Brace Jovanovich, 1988), xi.

52. Ibid., xii, Rogers, *America's Water,* 164.

53. Gottlieb, *A Life of Its Own,* 79.

54. Ibid., 80.

55. Ibid., 116.

56. Grenetta Thomassey Fink and Zachary A. Smith, "Arizona Government and Politics," in *Uniting a Diverse Arizona: Background Report Prepared by Northern Arizona University,* ed. Kathryn Cruz Uribe, Margot Nason, and Frances Julia Riemer (Flagstaff: Seventy-Fifth Arizona Town Hall, October 31–November 3, 1999), 93–95.

57. Gottlieb, *A Life of Its Own,* xii.

58. Ashworth, *Nor Any Drop to Drink,* 125.

59. Gottlieb, *A Life of Its Own,* xii.

60. Rogers, *America's Water,* 152–153; Ciriacy-Wantrup, *Resource Conservation,* 288–289.

61. Rogers, *America's Water,* 152–153.

62. Ashworth, *Nor Any Drop to Drink,* 127–128.

63. Ibid., 126–127.

64. Donald Worster, *Rivers of Empire: Water, Aridity, and the Growth of the American West* (New York: Pantheon Books, 1985), 335.

65. Rogers, *America's Water,* 152–153.

66. Ibid., 7–8.

67. Ibid., ix.

68. U.S. Environmental Protection Agency Website, "About EPA: Our Mission" (online; available: http://www.epa.gov/epahome/aboutepa.htm; accessed November 30, 2002), 1.

69. U.S. Environmental Protection Agency Website, "Office of Water: Office of Water Organizational Chart" (online; available: http://www.epa.gov/water/programs/index.html; accessed November 30, 2002), 1.

70. U.S. Environmental Protection Agency Website, "Office of Water: Office of Water Environmental Programs" (online; available: http://www.epa.gov/water/programs/orgchart.html; accessed November 30, 2002), 1.

71. "Who Is Great Lakes United?" Great Lakes United Website (online; available: http://www.glu.org/organizational/whosglu.htm; accessed November 30, 2002), 1.

72. Ibid.

3

A History of
Key People and Events

In this chapter we provide a history of water policy, with a focus on key people and events. The first part, "The Government Framework," is a short discussion of federalism, pluralism, and elitism. The second part, "General History of U.S. Water Management: People and Events," covers people and policies in water management generally. It provides a history that presents events and laws that should be noted for their special significance and effect upon water policy. A bibliography of suggested readings that provide additional biographical information on all the key people mentioned in this chapter is included in Chapter 7, "Selected Print and Nonprint Resources."

Federalism provides the framework for all water-management systems, laws, and policies in the United States. Federalism, pluralism, and elitism are all very relevant to the study of U.S. public policy and therefore to water management and other environmental policy matters. Below we summarize these concepts. This information will give the reader a better understanding of the later discussion of the history of water management in the second part of the chapter.

The Government Framework

Federalism

The term "federalism" refers to a system of government that creates a relationship between national and state interests. It is a dual system of government, with power shared between national and state levels. Both levels claim sovereignty, each with authority over citizens and resources within their boundaries. This sovereignty cannot be taken away by another government. Each state is a sovereign government within a separate, national sovereign government. The U.S. government is designed as a federalist system, and the biggest challenge in this kind of system is to coordinate actions between the two levels of government.[1]

In a federal system, in general, state and local governments provide for the needs of citizens in very important and often very direct ways. For example, as Lewis Lipsitz and David Speak put it, police and fire protection, building codes, driver's licenses, and public health inspections are all things that come under the jurisdiction and responsibility of state and local entities. On the other hand, the federal government is responsible for matters such as foreign affairs, interstate commerce, and national security and defense.[2]

Federalism is an important point of departure in any discussion of policymaking, especially for environmental policy. Public policy in general is often formulated in an intergovernmental context, and this is certainly the case in the environmental arena. This is largely because environmental problems do not obey boundaries. Pollution emanating from a plant upstream will not stop at a state border downstream. Growth issues do not stop at the edges of one bulging city. They have implications for all sorts of land-use, wildlife, and resource-scarcity concerns that often have an impact on an entire region. Therefore, the debate has become one of how we are to best protect the environment and balance that protection with the other needs of society. Is it best to turn to the federal government to answer this question? Or should state and local governments take the lead role in environmental issues, such as water policy?

It has been argued that the common-pool nature of pollution problems (see Chapter 1) is what initially got the national government involved in pollution control and other environmental issues, and this is largely true. The U.S. federal government took an early lead role in health and safety issues regarding water as well as in navigation and commerce, but its initial steps were cautious and controversial. Most environmental issues were the responsibility of state and local governments because environmental protection was not a high national political priority.[3]

However, as the following general history will demonstrate,

there has always been a federal presence in water issues in the United States. The difference through time has only been a question of scale: How intrusive is the federal government, and how much funding does it contribute to the ability to comply with the regulation or law?

In the late 1960s and early 1970s, modern environmental policy developed rapidly, as environmental protection became more of a national political concern. During the last half of the twentieth century, new, unprecedented challenges became evident. Groundbreaking research and subsequent publications, such as the book *Silent Spring* by Rachel Carson on the dangers of DDT, helped to bring widespread attention to various problems and environmental issues. In 1969, Congress enacted a series of laws to regulate environmental protection and quality standards from the national level. As a result, a majority of the federal environmental responsibilities were centralized in the Environmental Protection Agency (EPA).[4]

During these years, environmental problems seemed fairly clear and obvious. For example, Los Angeles was choking in smog; the Cuyahoga River, near Cleveland, Ohio, caught fire several times; and Lake Erie was ultimately declared dead. Acid rain, endangered species, ecology, and pollution became part of the vernacular. Environmental quality improved significantly over the next twenty-five years. These positive gains were made with few questions about cost, as long as water and air were getting cleaner. At the start of the twenty-first century, however, arguments are being made that environmental innovation comes more from state and local governments than from Washington, D.C. Some are calling for greater local control of environmental policy.[5]

Some reasons for these calls for local control are obvious and were reported to you in Chapter 2. Economic concerns have grown in relation to environmental policy issues, and costs are now very much involved in water-policy discussions. Also, implementation of national laws can be difficult, given the need for intergovernmental communication and coordination. Government bureaucratic systems do not always make government-to-government communication and coordination swift or easy. Another concern is the fact that local entities are more familiar with their own environmental and water issues. Outside help can seem like outside interference if local voices are not listened to when efforts are made to solve water problems.

However, there are also important reasons to maintain a federal presence in environmental and water policy. For example, interstate pollution and other issues that require cross-border solutions are often best resolved with the coordinating federal influence that might come with federal funding efforts. Also, public land policy mandates a federal role in local issues that involve public lands. In addition, problems may be ignored if an area with an environmental problem does not have the political will to solve it. This can happen, for example, when local jobs and economies are threatened by attempts to stop or curtail polluting industries. In such situations, problems may grow and have an impact on other areas that *do* have the political will to correct them but cannot do so without the cooperation of the original area. In this instance, the federal government can be viewed as a positive force, passing legislation that at least sets minimum standards and regulates the most egregious violations of common-pool resource protection. It has been argued, and we agree, that the EPA has been very effective in pollution control and that the significant improvements in water quality at the end of the twentieth century would not have been realized if states had had sole responsibility for pollution control.

Pluralism and Elitism

The term "pluralism" refers to the presence of various influential groups in the federalist system. These groups communicate with legislatures and policymakers. The point of this communication is to sway governments to make policy decisions that reflect the group's agenda and interests. In the United States, it is assumed that anyone can approach his or her elected officials with a problem or request, and anyone is free to collect groups of people who are of a similar opinion. An example of this would be the American Association of Retired Persons (AARP). This group is interested in things that concern senior citizens, such as social security policy. Therefore, the AARP communicates to various legislators and policymakers on this and other subjects. Another example is the Sierra Club, a group with environmental interests that consistently communicates to state and national government entities in the hopes of influencing the creation of environmental policy.

The concept of pluralism stands in stark contrast to the idea of elitism, which is also a concern in the federalist system. Those who hold that the United States is an elitist system believe that the U.S. people are largely excluded from policy decisionmaking. Rather, the real power is thought to be in the hands of an elite, which includes major financial and corporate institutions, key politicians, leading military officials, and the top members of the national bureaucracy, according to Lipsitz and Speak. In an elitist system, these actors have all the information and resources needed to create policy, and they will do so according to their best interests. The voice of the people ends at the ballot box.[6]

Pluralism and elitism are two different ways to view the dynamics of the federalist system in the United States. Both have legitimate elements and arguments, and both can be used to examine how water policy is formed. Everything that was discussed in Chapter 2 is related to federalism, pluralism, or elitism—water rights and laws, economic concerns, ownership, pricing, private interests, public interests, and environmental interests. The following discussion of significant events in water management should help to illustrate how this is so.

General History of U.S. Water Management: People and Events

1700s–1800s

Water issues have always been important, providing challenges to the earliest societies. Prior to the formation of the United States, some of the first governmental functions on the continent were related to water. Most Native American tribes had formal ways to manage water resources, including irrigation systems. Spanish explorers and subsequent settlers improved tribal irrigation techniques as they moved into the deserts of the West. The colonies assumed responsibility for the regulation of fisheries, harbors, and waterways as the roots of the U.S. system took hold. [7]

This official, authoritative presence is not surprising, considering that water matters involve basic survival. However, eventually water came to be tied to the ways and means of making a living, first in the agrarian community and then in industrial society. This added economic aspect also served to strengthen the presence of the federal government in water issues.[8]

In 1797, Congress provided money to improve navigation,

which was vital to the exploration of the continent, providing transportation and opportunities for commerce and trade. However, as noted above, in a federalist system, it was controversial for Congress to assume this role and to allocate federal money for water issues. The traditional, federalist position holds that there should be very little national presence in local issues, and with the adoption of the U.S. Constitution, water was formally declared to be a local issue. [9]

However, during the Revolutionary War, George Washington had a favorable experience with engineers, and this led to an early federal presence in water-resources management. In 1802, an engineering school was established at the U.S. Military Academy at West Point, and it was the only source of trained engineers for the United States until the nineteenth century. Because of this, the army engineers were called upon to establish the majority of the civil works required for a new, growing nation.[10]

Despite federal water expertise, a traditional, federalist attitude continued to be the prevailing political sentiment. An example of this attitude is demonstrated by the fact that President James Madison rejected federal funding for the Erie Canal in 1811. The canal was eventually built by the state of New York between 1817 and 1825.[11]

However, in 1824 the Supreme Court ruled, in *Gibbons v. Ogden,* that the federal government was legally responsible for navigation because of the commerce clause in the U.S. Constitution. The federal government, according to Chief Justice John Marshall's majority opinion, had the power to regulate commerce and that power included a similar authority over navigation. This led to a continued but cautious federal presence in water policy. It also strengthened the authority Congress had given the military in 1820 to survey the Mississippi and Ohio Rivers. In the same year as the *Gibbons v. Ogden* ruling, Congress appropriated money for improvements to navigation on the Mississippi and Ohio Rivers, following the 1820 surveys.[12]

Then, with expansion into the West, irrigation also became a federal concern because early expeditions reported that settlement of large portions of the area would be impossible unless water could be provided on a large scale. As Mark Reisner explains it, before the federal government could take action in the West, however, a survey of this vast region was needed. To solve that problem, Major John Wesley Powell, an officer of the Union

Army during the Civil War, led an expedition to do this survey work. Powell later became the first director of the U.S. Geological Survey (USGS). Despite the fact that Powell lost an arm in the war, in 1869 the Powell Geographic Expedition set out on a courageous and productive trip to the West, starting at the Green River in Wyoming. The exploration was successful, producing a survey of the region, including information from a trip down the wild rapids of the untamed Colorado River, and the first river expedition through the Grand Canyon to provide survey and mapping information.[13]

In 1871, the federal government stepped in on the topic of food protection. A joint resolution of Congress provided for the preservation and protection of food fisheries through the establishment of the U.S. Fish and Fisheries Commission. Then, in 1873, the Timber Culture Act was passed, which promoted the planting of trees to increase precipitation. In the 1800s it was an accepted theory of rainmaking that the presence of more trees would increase the rainfall. The main idea of this and related theories was that when a region was settled, precipitation would increase because it would "follow the plow."[14] This idea was prominent in efforts to settle the land west of the 100th meridian.

In 1877, the Desert Land Act was passed. The act offered land grants as incentives to irrigate and settle the arid West. Instead, it led to tremendous land speculation and resulted in very little sustained irrigation. It has been estimated that nearly 95 percent of the claims made under the act were fraudulent.[15]

In 1879, Major Powell gave his survey report to Congress, "Report on the Lands of the Arid Region of the United States, with a More Detailed Account of the Lands of Utah," which had been published in 1876. Powell presented a plan to develop the arid West that was considered radical at the time.[16] He advocated that settlers work within the environmental constraints of the region. For example, he suggested that rangelands be developed as communal pastures to make the best use of scanty grasses. He also urged that forested mountain highland areas be designated as political units according to the watershed they were in and managed cohesively. He strongly encouraged riparian irrigation in lowlands, using cooperative labor and farms.[17]

Major Powell's survey information was used extensively, but his management recommendations for the area were largely ignored. The West was developed with boundaries that followed rivers for convenience and then jutted out in straight lines that often cut watersheds and mountain ranges into pieces. Powell considered that the aridity of the region was formidable and that the one thing that really mattered was water. He did not believe the theory that precipitation would follow the plow, and he had personally witnessed the climatic oddities of the West, including drought. It made sense to him to organize states around watersheds, with each major river—from headwaters to delta—being designated as a state or a region within a state.[18] History has shown that if Powell had been taken seriously, some of the problems of the modern West, such as endangered species and watershed degradation, may have been averted.

Instead, the region was settled with a zeal for expansion rather than with the thoughtful, cautious approach advocated by Major Powell. The prevailing attitudes of vested interests won, and reclamation efforts to harness the available water in the region were seriously discussed. The federal government was considered to be the appropriate level of government to "correct" the water situation in the West and to get irrigation going on the scale necessary to provide family-sized farming opportunities. This was an important shift in attitude, and a paradox became evident, one that continues into modern times: Politicians from the area were hostile to Powell's report and recommendations, claiming that the region was not arid and encouraging settlement on a grand scale. Yet when it came time to build the reclamation projects that were being advocated, the politicians from the West insisted it would be impossible to bring about farming and other settlement efforts, on the scale desired by the nation, without federal government involvement, according to Reisner. The costs of making the desert bloom could only be paid with federal participation.[19]

Eventually, concern for waterways and navigation also resulted in an additional role for the federal government in flood control, and the Army Corps of Engineers was dominant in the initial efforts in this direction. In 1879, Congress responded to devastating floods on the Mississippi River by establishing the Mississippi River Commission to develop a comprehensive flood-control program for the river.[20]

Legislation enacted toward the end of the 1800s continued to demonstrate a growing federal presence. In 1884, dams were authorized on the Mississippi River for private power development, although the rights to control navigation on the river were reserved to the federal government. In 1891, the Payson Act was passed, which authorized the president to reserve public forest lands from being sold in order to protect future water supplies. In 1894, the Carey Irrigation Act granted 160-acre tracts of public lands to states for irrigation purposes.[21]

In 1899, a series of additional laws were passed regarding water matters. Congress allocated money to establish federal standards for bridges over navigable streams, rivers, and harbors. Also, regulations were passed to authorize the issuing of permits for private development at mineral springs, which had become popular tourist attractions. The law required developers to operate their businesses in compliance with federal standards. Finally, the Rivers and Harbors Act (also known as the Refuse Act) prohibited "the discharge of solid materials into navigable streams."[22] Waste was becoming a problem in the growing cities of the United States, where more people and new industries added to the tonnage and frequency of disposal. Rivers were becoming clogged with trash, making safe passage difficult for ships and barges.

1900–1920

One exception to the failure of private irrigation efforts in the West was evident in work done by the Mormons in Utah. Peter Rogers notes that in 1847, the Mormons began irrigation projects, and in fifteen years, they had reclaimed 150,000 acres. Reisner adds that by 1902, they had 6 million acres under full or partial irrigation in several western states. That same year, based on observation of the Mormon experience, the United States began its own irrigation program and established the Reclamation Service, which later became the U.S. Bureau of Reclamation. Because of the work of the bureau, states such as California, Arizona, Nevada, and Idaho became wealthy and now support millions of people, sometimes in places that would have only supported thousands, at most, without irrigation. The difference was made by providing irrigation on a scale that was only possible with the backing of the federal government.[23]

By the turn of the century, most of the land in the contiguous United States had been settled, and the nation was progressing into an industrial age. As Carolyn Merchant puts it, this industrialization required stocks of natural resources, a situation that caught the attention of scientists, writers, and politicians of the time. Resource development had been left to individuals and private enterprise, for the most part, and common-pool resource problems were not the main concern of those developers. This was challenged by Progressive Era politics, which advocated natural resource conservation through government regulation.[24] The forces of pluralism began a major challenge to the elitist tendencies of the day, and the idea of centralized federal regulation began to challenge the federalist, state-based viewpoint.

A conservation consciousness was beginning to take shape in the United States at about this time. The demand for reliable sources of water in the West was at the center of the new debate, which alerted the general population to concerns about the protection of watersheds and about the depletion of forests and the deterioration of rangelands, among other issues. In response, a nationwide focus on conservation took shape in various ways. Engineers designed impressive, state-of-the-art dams and irrigation systems, making precious water available to the arid West. Ranchers planted new forage mixtures and fenced in their rangelands in an effort to conserve and efficiently use scarce grazing areas. Schoolchildren planted trees, Audubon Societies promoted efforts to save endangered species of birds, and women's clubs across the nation took responsibility for cleaning up city streets and harbors.[25]

President Theodore Roosevelt was an enthusiastic supporter of conservation, and all these unrelated interests were united under the banner of conservation during his presidency. Merchant writes that conservation was defined as "the use of natural resources for the greatest good of the greatest number for the longest time." She also notes, however, that eventually the conservation movement splintered into two main camps.[26]

The first was the utilitarian conservation movement, whose principles were best described by the above definition. This camp regarded natural resources as something to be conserved and made available for use by humans as needed. The idea was economically based, regarding nature as something to be tamed and completely controlled by humans. Progress into the industrial age was a signal of victory over nature. Technology provided lifestyles that included such things as better homes, plumbing, heating and cooling, and transportation, to name just a few. Nature made all this possible, but we could not do these things without first taming nature and then continuing to fight against the elements.

Utilitarian conservationists eventually become known simply as conservationists, and they were ranged against the second camp, the preservationists. Preservationists held a very different viewpoint. They saw technological progress as something that threatened nature and therefore threatened humanity. Teeming cities, rapid settlement efforts, floods of immigrants, and fast-moving technological change all forced the open land and forests to recede. Wilderness was no longer threatening, for technology and urban life kept the elements at bay. Soot, garbage, and noise posed a larger threat than the change of seasons or a severe storm. They saw the wilderness vanishing, and voiced their concern in the literature and art of the day.[27]

Interestingly, other vested interests also supported the idea of wilderness preservation, but this was because they saw it as an opportunity. Railroad promoters supported the politics of preservation, seeing opportunity in the idea of federal parks being established for tourists. Also, city planners in the East promoted western migration to clean out the cities, using the magic of advertising to lure the poor to the West with promises of land ownership and all the opportunity that came with it. Politicians seized the romantic appeal of wilderness, campaigning to the preservationists for votes.[28]

In 1905, President Roosevelt created the U.S. Forest Service in the U.S. Department of Agriculture (USDA). He named a close friend, forester Gifford Pinchot, as its chief. Pinchot was the ultimate utilitarian conservationist, and he proved to be a major figure of the times. The establishment of the Forest Service mandated the wholesale transfer of the national forests from the Department of the Interior to the USDA. When that was done, Pinchot had accomplished a key step toward implementing his philosophy of conservation.[29]

Charles Wilkinson describes the Pinchot philosophy as striving to make the forest produce the most amount of whatever crop or service was considered to be most useful while keeping it producing for generations of people and trees—the greatest good for the greatest number. This policy was meant to discourage any waste of forest resources, but the dominant use was clearly timber production. Managing forest land meant growing trees as crops for use by homebuilders. This was certainly a priority for Pinchot, but in the process of carrying out this goal, he angered private interests by advocating and accomplishing the designation of 148 million acres of forest land as national forest.[30] Ironically, despite his forethought in setting aside vast amounts of land for protection, environmentalists at the turn of the twenty-first century severely criticize his utilitarian emphasis and the influence it continues to wield. Modern environmentalists believe his philosophy is partially responsible for justifying the commodification of nature, for using the forest as a crop rather than appreciating it for its intrinsic value.

Pinchot is credited with coining the catchphrase "wise use," meaning that the wise use of resources requires federal oversight of public lands to protect them from unwise use. This concept came from Pinchot's observation that natural resources were being consumed at an alarming rate by business and that the future of the land was not adequately being contemplated. Years later, this phrase was co-opted by various interests, such as miners, timber companies, ranchers, and land barons. At the end of the twentieth century, these interests employed the phrase "wise use" to mean that federal involvement in public land policy prevented the best use of private and public land because federal regulations intending to protect the environment were a hardship on profit-making enterprises.[31]

The federal presence in water management and policy continued to grow, as Rogers explains. The Reclamation Act of 1906 authorized "the sale of surplus power from reclamation projects" funded by the federal government. In the same year, the General Dam Act was passed to regulate "private dam construction on navigable streams." An amendment to this act was passed in 1910, placing "additional restrictions on dams on navigable streams." The Withdrawal Act was also passed in 1910, authorizing the president to "withdraw public lands from sale for irrigation, waterpower, and other purposes." The following year, the Weeks Act authorized "the purchase of forest land to preserve streamflow."[32]

In 1912, the Public Health Service Act established the Public Health Service and gave it the authority to study stream pollution. That same year, the Supreme Court, in *Winters v. United States*, enunciated what has come to be called the *Winters* Doctrine, declaring that the federal government is assumed to have "reserved prior rights" to water for lands that it reserved for Indian tribes and for other federal uses.[33]

During this time, a battle was brewing between the conservationists and the preservationists. John Muir, a famous wilderness expert of the day, was regarded as the ultimate preservationist. In 1892, he participated in the formation of the Sierra Club. In his work and writings, Muir expressed preservationist arguments, believing in the "redemptive powers of nature" and asserting that "wilderness deserved to exist for its own sake." In 1912, the contrast between the conservationist and preservationist positions became glaringly evident in arguments over a proposal by San Francisco to build a dam to provide water to the city from the Hetch Hetchy Valley, located in Yosemite National Park 200 miles away.[34] After a bitter fight, in which Pinchot favored the dam and Muir opposed it, the Raker Act was passed in 1913, and Congress authorized the city of San Francisco to build Hetch Hetchy Dam.[35]

1920–1960

From 1921 through 1933, there was a twelve-year political backlash against the Progressives. Yet federal involvement in water policy was reinforced by continued legislation dealing with public health, flood control, regulation of nonfederal power, and the sale of power from federal projects (see Chapter 4). Then, in 1922, the Colorado River Compact was negotiated at the state level. Arizona, California, Colorado, Nevada, New Mexico, Utah, and Wyoming apportioned Colorado River waters among themselves. A total of 18 million acre-feet of water per year was allocated to the seven states, even though as a result the Colorado River ran several million acre-feet less water during most years. This was the first time in U.S. history that more than two or three states made a treaty among themselves, and it was also the first time a group of states divided an interstate river among themselves for consumptive uses. It is notable, however, that this was not actually accomplished without federal involvement, and a final agreement was not reached until 1963, after a battle waged between Arizona and California before the Supreme Court. With settlement of *Arizona v. California* (373 U.S. 546 [1963]), the dispute over apportionment of water between the final two states involved in the compact was resolved. California was allocated 4.4 million acre-feet of the river, and Arizona received 2.8 million acre-feet. With this resolution, the compact finally went into effect.[36]

Despite this example of interstate agreement, federal involvement in water policy continued to expand. The Rivers and Harbors Act of 1925 authorized the Army Corps of Engineers to do a twenty-year survey of all navigable rivers, except the Colorado, to develop plans covering navigation, flood control, irrigation, and power production. In 1928, Congress authorized the construction of Hoover Dam. The sale of electric power from the dam was to help pay for construction costs. According to Daniel Beard, by 1936, with the help of the New Deal under President Franklin D. Roosevelt, Hoover, Bonneville, Fort Peck, Shasta, and Grand Coulee Dams were all under construction in the United States. In addition, the twenty-year Tennessee Valley Authority (TVA) project was well underway, in the process of building twenty dams on the Tennessee River.[37]

Also in 1936, the first nationwide Flood Control Act was passed and placed under the jurisdiction of the Army Corps of Engineers. An important innovation here was the requirement that a cost-benefit analysis be done, for the first time for a federal water project. The next year, the Water Facilities Act authorized the USDA to provide irrigation facilities to local interests. With the Flood Control Act of 1938, Congress authorized flood-control projects to be 100 percent funded by the federal government. Then, in 1939, the Reclamation Project Act authorized the secretary of the interior to plan and build projects that serve multiple purposes, such as a dam that provides municipal water supplies and hydroelectricity in addition to irrigation.[38] The federal presence in water issues was, by now, firmly established.

In 1944, the Army Corps of Engineers and the Bureau of Reclamation agreed to develop the Missouri River according to the Pick-Sloan Plan.[39] Beard points out that as a result, by 1967 the Missouri River Basin had twenty-two dams, drowning more than a million acres of fertile bottomlands.[40] Flood control, power development, navigation, pollution control, and fish and wildlife management continued to be the focus of federal water laws passed during the 1940s and early 1950s (see Chapter 4). In 1954, multiple use was included in the Flood Control Act, expanding the use of flood-control reservoirs to include recreation. By 1958, federal jurisdiction over boating regulations had been established through the passage of the Federal Boating Act, which included recreational use of reservoirs. In the same year, the Water Supply Act ensured that planning of future multiple-purpose projects would include urban and industrial water supplies.[41]

1960–1970

New challenges had become evident by the 1960s. In 1961, the Delaware River Basin Compact was negotiated among Delaware, New Jersey, New York, and Pennsylvania. This compact established and gave broad powers to the Delaware River Basin Commission, and the states involved expressed concern for future municipal water supplies, water quality, and recreational needs. In the same year, the U.S. Senate issued a report on national water resources. The report predicted a water crisis for the nation and emphasized that pollution was an important future cost facing the federal government.[42]

President Lyndon Johnson reiterated this concern when he spoke to Congress and cited pollution as the major natural resource problem facing the nation in 1966. The Clean Water Restoration Act was passed the same year, dramatically increasing funding for clean water programs. It also increased federal participation to 50 percent of state or local construction costs involved in clean water programs.[43]

In 1964, the Glen Canyon Dam was built, creating Lake Powell and drowning a wilderness desert canyon.[44] Even though others were proposed, this dam became the final one in the long-term effort to tame the Colorado River. Despite this engineering accomplishment, problems with dams became evident. The first was their effect on species preservation. The second problem is discussed below in the section covering the 1970s.

In 1965, the Anadromous and Great Lakes Fish Act was passed. The act promoted the preservation and development of fish resources in areas where it was becoming difficult for various species to sustain survival. ("Anadromous" refers to fish that migrate from saltwater to freshwater for spawning, such as salmon.) The National Wild and Scenic Rivers Act became law in 1968, prohibiting dams on designated "wild and scenic" rivers. That same year, the first barge transport of salmon and juvenile steelhead trout was made around the lower Snake River dams in an attempt to preserve fish runs endangered by construction of the dams. In 1970, the National Marine Fisheries report estimated that as much as 70 percent of Idaho salmon smolts (young salmon in the stage of their first migration to the sea) were killed each year from dam-produced nitrogen in the lower Snake River.[45]

In 1968, a study of estuaries was authorized by the Estuarine Protection Act. The study was directed to determining whether a nationwide system of protected estuarine areas should be established for the purposes of protecting those areas from environmental degradation and protecting their species from potential extinction. An oil spill occurred in 1969 off the coast of Santa Barbara, California, caused by the blowout of an oil platform operated by a federal lessee. In reaction to this tragedy, the Water Quality Improvement Act was passed in 1970 to regulate oil-spill prevention measures, cleanup methods, and the consequences for violating the regulations.[46]

It is not difficult to see how these events and policy decisions, among others, would bring environmental issues into the public debate. President Nixon issued Executive Order 11472 in 1969, establishing a cabinet-level Committee on the Environment to advise him on matters of environmental quality. This committee was terminated by Executive Order 11541 in 1970, the same year Nixon signed the National Environmental Policy Act (NEPA) of 1969 into law. NEPA required environmental impact statements for "any significant federal action" on development projects. It also established the Council on Environmental Quality (CEQ).[47]

1970–1990

The 1970s produced an important series of environmental policy decisions and legislation. In 1970, President Nixon established the EPA to "consolidate federal environmental control programs." In 1972, the Clean Water Act allocated $18 billion in grants that would pay up to 75 percent of the cost of constructing and installing municipal sewage-treatment plants. In 1974, the Safe Drinking Water Act was passed. This was the "first comprehensive federal drinking water legislation," but it only allocated a small amount of grant money to municipalities. However, in 1977, amendments were passed to the Clean Water Act allocating additional grant money to state and local entities.[48]

One problem with dams, their effect on species preservation, has already been mentioned. A second problematic area for dams is safety, and safety concerns emerged dramatically in the 1970s. In 1976, the Teton Dam in Idaho collapsed, killing eleven people and causing millions of dollars in damage. The following year, the Kelly Barnes Dam in Georgia failed, killing thirty-nine people. The nation was shaken by these sad events, and President Jimmy Carter called for inspections by the Army Corps of Engineers of all "high hazard" dams in the nation. In 1987, after nearly a decade of inspections, one-fifth of the dams built by the Bureau of Reclamation and one-third of those built by the Army Corps of Engineers were classified as unsafe. By that time, the bureau had constructed 275 dams and the corps had built 554 dams across the country.[49]

In the 1980s, deformities among birds in the Kesterson National Wildlife Refuge in California were tied to tainted runoff from excessive irrigation of desert soils. The costs associated with attempting to clean up this area and save species from extinction were tremendous. The California farmers using the irrigation provided by the Central Valley Project had repaid only 4 percent of the $950 million cost (only $38 million) of building the Central Valley Project. U.S. taxpayers were footing the bill not only for the cleanup and species-protection efforts but for the balance of the construction costs as well.[50]

In 1981, amendments to the Clean Water Act were enacted reducing federal funding to 50 percent of the cost of construction of new water-pollution control facilities. The language of the legislation reflected a shifting policy attitude. Cost was becoming a very big factor in federal efforts, due to a recession that led to staggering interest rates and concerns about unemployment. The amendments encouraged innovative solutions from state and local governments, meaning that the federal government wanted local entities to get used to finding at least partial funding for their local clean water projects. The same year, the Water Resources Council was "zero-budgeted," that is, Congress appropriated no money for its annual operation. This cutoff of funding effectively dismantled the council.[51]

Yet despite this concern for cost issues and a growing backlash in the federal government against the environmental movement, the federal government remained very much involved in the water-policy arena. This involvement did not necessarily mean broad environmental protection, however, as had been the case in previous decades. Still, water issues were considered important, and in 1982, an executive reorganization in President Ronald Reagan's administration included the creation of the cabinet-level Council on Natural Resources. Also, the Office of Water Policy was created within the Department of Interior. However, the Reclamation Reform Act of 1982 offered another glimpse at changing political attitudes and priorities. This act increased the upper limits on the amount of farm property eligible for federally subsidized water for irrigation of crops to 960 acres, favoring the interests of private farmers. As private farms became larger, they were less and less likely to be family farms. By this time, agribusiness was firmly planted in the rural areas of the nation, and agribusiness was now eligible for federal water subsidies.[52]

In 1986, amendments were passed to the Safe Drinking Water

Act. The key changes were regulatory, setting standards for eighty-three contaminants and requiring filtration for most surface drinking water sources. In the same year, the Water Resources Development Act was passed. New water resources projects totaling $16.5 billion were authorized, with the federal government sharing the costs, paying up to 100 percent of the cost of some projects. The next year, however, amendments to the Clean Water Act further reduced federal grant money for local and regional projects. Cost sharing was to be "phased out over five years and replaced by revolving loan funds."[53]

Unfortunately, environmental and water-related challenges persisted. In 1988, coho salmon were declared to be extinct in the Snake River, unable to overcome the threats to their survival from dam construction, according to Beard.[54] And the decade ended with the infamous *Exxon Valdez* oil spill off the coast of Alaska in 1989. In 1991, after two years of litigation, a plea settlement was reached on the charges arising from the spill, and the Exxon Shipping Company pled guilty to violating the Clean Water Act, the Refuse Act, and the Migratory Bird Treaty Act.[55]

1990–2001

In 1990, the American Fisheries Society reported that 214 salmon species in the West were facing extinction from water-development projects in the region. Species extinction generally and the plight of the salmon in the Northwest specifically were very hot topics in the 1990s.

For example, in 1992, the federal government mandated that up to 1.2 million acre-feet of water was to be diverted from the Central Valley Project in California in order to restore streamflows in an attempt to bring back various fish populations that had been decimated by water diversions out of their habitats.[56] However, in 1994, for the first time in history, the Columbia River was closed to commercial salmon fishing in fear of the depletion or extinction of various species. The 130 dams on the river were considered to be the biggest factor in salmon population declines. In 1997, the National Marine Fisheries Service (NMFS) issued a biological study "confirming that water diversions from the Columbia River jeopardize salmon survival." Authorities recommended a change in dam operations to increase the chances of salmon survival, and this was significant because the NMFS has authority over the Army Corps of Engineers. This study and the resulting opinion directed the corps to "deny new permits for new water diversion facilities." It also recommended revisiting "existing permits that deplete streamflows during the salmon migration season."[57]

Attention to flood-control efforts was also paramount in the early 1990s. In 1992, a federal Task Force on Floodplain Management concluded that despite investments in flood control exceeding $25 billion, flood-damage costs were steadily rising, costing over $2 billion annually as of 1992. Tragically, during the following year, devastating floods on the Mississippi River illustrated the need for floodplain management. Beard notes that after the floods, entire towns were relocated to higher ground rather than being rebuilt on the floodplain.[58]

Another important focus during the last decade of the twentieth century was drinking water safety. In 1992, the EPA added twenty-three chemicals to the Safe Drinking Water Act standards, bringing the total number of federal drinking water standards to eighty-four. In 1995, the EPA released its study "Strengthening the Safety of Our Drinking Water." The study included a model for partnership with private water suppliers to upgrade drinking water quality. In 1996, President Bill Clinton signed amendments to the Safe Drinking Water Act into law. The amendments included protections for local drinking water sources and also established the first Safe Drinking Water Revolving Loan Fund. This fund helped states and communities afford to upgrade aging drinking water systems.[59]

In 1997, Maryland and the USDA formed a partnership to expand the USDA's Conservation Reserve Program (CRP). This program allowed up to 100,000 acres of sensitive riparian lands along Maryland streams and rivers to be set aside to protect water quality. That same year, the Association of Metropolitan Water Agencies, made up of the largest municipal drinking water agencies around the nation, applauded the new CRP for giving farmers incentives to set aside land that would provide "a natural barrier between farmland and water supplies for community drinking water systems."[60] Also in 1997, the United States and Canada signed an agreement to protect public health by "virtually eliminating persistent toxic substances from the Great Lakes by the year 2006."[61]

The 1990s also brought concerns about wetland areas to the attention of the public. Wetlands were no longer considered to be mere wasteland, or useless swamps. They were now appreciated for their role in providing specialized habitats and for their value for naturally cleaning freshwater. Whenever a wetland is filled, section 404 of the Clean Water Act requires developers to create a "mitigation marsh" on an acre-for-acre basis to prevent further loss of national wetland resources. The Army Corps of Engineers has jurisdiction in wetland policy and is the agency that grants permits for these land exchanges, which are accomplished through mitigation banks that are usually created by states for this purpose. In 1995, the first privately held wetland mitigation bank was created in Illinois.[62]

In 1996, however, North Carolina agriculture experts claimed that constructing and maintaining wetlands was too expensive, despite evidence that man-made wetlands were the best technology available to deal with the "wastewater produced by livestock confinement facilities."[63] On a more encouraging note, though, in 1999, a Bureau of Reclamation project created wetlands near Cortez, Colorado. This action reflected a "shift away from dam-building and toward conservation."[64]

Toward the turn of the century, very few water-policy initiatives were accomplished independently. Almost every action in the water-policy arena required intergovernmental efforts. This was reflected in the key federal policy decisions and legislation of the time. For example, in 1997, the EPA released its "first comprehensive assessment of U.S. watersheds" and made the data available on the Internet.[65] In 1998, the Western Water Policy Review Advisory Commission issued a report requested by Congress, "Water in the West: The Challenge for the Next Century." The report described the impact of population growth, social conflicts, declining groundwater levels, and damaged river ecosystems on water-policy issues in the West.[66]

Later that year, in celebration of the twenty-fifth anniversary of the Clean Water Act, President Clinton's budget proposal included a multimillion-dollar increase for fiscal year 1999, and a multibillion-dollar increase over five years, in funds for restoration and protection efforts. This budget proposal was known as the Clean Water Action Plan. The plan required massive intergovernmental efforts and is still being implemented as of 2002.[67] In 1999, in the largest single rural wastewater project in U.S. history, the USDA promised to spend over $200 million in funding "for clean water improvements in rural communities in 44 states and Puerto Rico."[68]

The EPA reported in 2000 that 1999 had been a record year

for the number of enforcement actions and penalties, including prison terms, for environmental crimes. This flurry of activity happened after several troubling incidents in 1998. That year, nearly one-third of the 1,062 beaches reporting to the EPA had at least one health advisory or closing. Also, 2,506 food-consumption advisories or bans had been issued because local fish were too contaminated to eat.[69] These problems struck at the heart of everyday living, and in such cases the public expects action.

However, in 2000, a report issued by the Environmental Working Group Report charged that poor water quality in the United States remained a problem, but that the continuing problems were due to regulators' failure to maintain Clean Water Act permits. These permits are the legal foundation for improving the quality of the nation's waters, yet at the time of the report, 25 percent of all major permits were expired nationally, and as a result, clean water laws could not be enforced.[70]

There have been some environmental victories at the start of the twenty-first century. For example, the Water Resources Development Act of 2000 approved a comprehensive Everglades restoration plan, establishing federal and state cost-sharing requirements. After years of work involving local, state, and federal governments; tribal governments; scientists; and environmental groups, the act authorized projects to restore, preserve, and protect the south Florida ecosystem and water supply.[71] Also in 2000, a settlement between the U.S. Department of Justice and Colorado resolved claims filed in 1979 by the U.S. Forest Service. The Forest Service had asserted "reserved instream flow water rights on 303 stream segments in the Rio Grande National Forest and Gunnison National Forest." The 2000 agreement was the first time that state and local water users "agreed that the federal government has reserved water rights for instream flows in national forests."[72]

However, farmers have had a difficult time with some controversial issues at the turn of the century. First, in 2000, the Bureau of Reclamation "ordered water managers on the middle Rio Grande to keep enough water in the river for the endangered silvery minnow." Critics charged that farmers were being abandoned and that the Bureau was no longer honoring irrigation as a part of its mission. Then, in April 2001, the Bureau of Reclamation shut off irrigation water to 90 percent of the 220,000-acre Klamath Project because endangered suckers in Upper Klamath Lake and coho salmon in the Klamath River would face death if water levels were to fall below a certain depth. The following July, Secretary of the Interior Gale Norton authorized a limited release of Klamath Project water to farmers, hoping to defuse the increasing tension, but the release was less than 20 percent of the water that had been provided in past years.[73] In August, the water was withheld again, and as of January 2002, the farmers were still facing severely reduced irrigation allotments.

The future holds promise of more controversy, stemming from various water interests in many locations and at every level of government.

Notes

1. Lewis Lipsitz and David M. Speak, *American Democracy* (New York: St. Martin's Press, 1993), 118–119.

2. Ibid.

3. Jonathan H. Adler, "Reinvigorating Environmental Federalism," in *Environmental Briefing Book* (Washington D.C.: Competitive Enterprise Institute, 1999), 23.

4. Ibid.

5. Ibid.

6. Lipsitz and Speak, *American Democracy*, 14–15.

7. Mark Reisner, *Cadillac Desert* (New York: Penguin Books, 1986), 2; Peter Rogers, *America's Water: Federal Roles and Responsibilities* (Cambridge: MIT Press, 1996), 46.

8. Rogers, *America's Water*, 46.

9. Ibid., 47, 219.

10. Ibid., 47.

11. Ibid., 47, 234.

12. Ibid., 48, 219–220.

13. Reisner, *Cadillac Desert*, 26–37.

14. Rogers, *America's Water*, 220; Reisner, *Cadillac Desert*, 5.

15. Rogers, *America's Water*, 48–49; Reisner, *Cadillac Desert*, 46.

16. Reisner, *Cadillac Desert*, 47.

17. Carolyn Merchant, *Major Problems in American Environmental History*, ed. Carolyn Merchant (Lexington, MA: D.C. Heath and Company, 1993), 339, 344–345.

18. Reisner, *Cadillac Desert*, 49.

19. Rogers, *America's Water*, 48–49; Reisner, *Cadillac Desert*, 51–53.

20. Rogers, *America's Water*, 48.

21. Ibid., 221.

22. Ibid.

23. Ibid., 235; Reisner, *Cadillac Desert*, 2–3.

24. Merchant, *Major Problems in American Environmental History*, 338.

25. Ibid., 338.

26. Ibid.

27. Ibid., 338, 383.

28. Ibid., 383.

29. Reisner, *Cadillac Desert*, 84; Charles F. Wilkinson, *Crossing the Next Meridian: Land, Water, and the Future of the West* (Washington, DC: Island Press, 1992), 91.

30. Wilkinson, *Crossing the Next Meridian*, 129, 125.

31. Mark Dowie, *Losing Ground* (Cambridge: MIT Press, 1997), 16–18, 93–98.

32. Rogers, *America's Water*, 222.

33. Ibid.

34. Dowie, *Losing Ground*, 16–17.

35. Rogers, *America's Water*, 222.

36. Norris Hundley Jr., *Water and the West: The Colorado River Compact and the Politics of Water in the American West* (Berkeley and Los Angeles: University of California Press, 1975), 334; Colorado State University Website, "Colorado Water Knowledge" (online; available: http://waterknowledge.colostate.edu/1963_az.htm; accessed December 1, 2002), 1.

37. Rogers, *America's Water*, 223; Daniel P. Beard, "Water Policy for the Next Generation," *World Rivers Review* 11, no. 3 (July 1996): 4–5.

38. Rogers, *America's Water*, 52, 224.

39. Ibid., 225.

40. Beard, "Water Policy for the Next Generation," 2.

41. Rogers, *America's Water*, 226–227.

42. Ibid., 227.

43. Ibid., 228.

44. Beard, "Water Policy for the Next Generation," 2.

45. Rogers, *America's Water*, 228; Beard, "Water Policy for the Next Generation," 2.

46. Rogers, *America's Water*, 228.

47. Ibid.

48. Ibid., 229.

49. Bureau of Reclamation Pacific Northwest Region Website, "The Failure of Teton Dam" (online; available: http://www.pn.usbr.gov/dams/teton.shtml; accessed December 1, 2002), 1; Georgia USGS Website, "Toccoa Flood" (online; available: http://ga.water.usgs.gov/news/

historical-toccoa/; accessed December 1, 2002; Beard, "Water Policy for the Next Generation," 2.

50. Beard, "Water Policy for the Next Generation," 2.

51. Rogers, *America's Water*, 229.

52. Ibid.

53. Ibid., 229–230.

54. Beard, "Water Policy for the Next Generation," 2.

55. "Exxon to Pay Record One Billion Dollars in Criminal Fines and Civil Damages in Connection with Alaskan Oil Spill," EPA press release, March 13, 1991, on EPA History Office Website (online; available: http://www.epa.gov/history/topics/valdez/02.htm; accessed January 21, 2002).

56. Beard, "Water Policy for the Next Generation," 2–3.

57. "National Marine Fisheries Service Confirms That Columbia River Diversions Harm Salmon," U.S. Water News Online Website, June 1997 (online; available: http://www.uswaternews.com/archives/arcpolicy/7natmar6.html; accessed January 19, 2002).

58. Beard, "Water Policy for the Next Generation," 3.

59. "President Clinton Signs Legislation to Ensure Americans Safe Drinking Water," EPA press release, August 6, 1996, on EPA History Office Website (online; available: http://www.epa.gov/history/topics/sdwa/05.htm; accessed January 20, 2002).

60. "Drinking Water Suppliers Applaud Buffer Initiative," U.S. Water News Online Website, June 1997 (online; available: http://www.uswaternews.com/archives/arcpolicy/7driwat6.html; accessed January 19, 2002).

61. "U.S., Canada Move to Eliminate Toxics in Great Lakes," EPA press release, April 7, 1997, on EPA History Office Website (online; available: http://www.epa.gov/history/topics/canada/04.htm; accessed January 14, 2002).

62. "Illinois Entrepreneur Forms Wetland Mitigation Bank," U.S. Water News Online Website, September 1995 (online; available: http://www.uswaternews.com/archives/arcpolicy/5ilentrep.html; accessed January 11, 2002), 1.

63. "Wetlands Considered Unaffordable by Hog Producers," U.S. Water News Online Website, February 1996 (online; available: http://www.uswaternews.com/archives/arcpolicy/6wethog.html; accessed January 11, 2002).

64. "Wetlands Creation Marks Shift in Water Management Strategy," U.S. Water News Online Website, August 1999 (online; available: http://www.uswaternews.com/archives/arcpolicy/9wetcre8.html; accessed January 11, 2002).

65. "EPA Assesses U.S. Watersheds; Gives Citizens Access to National and Local Water Quality Data," EPA press release, October 2, 1997, on EPA History Office Website (online; available: http://www.epa.gov/history/topics/water/02.htm; accessed January 14, 2002).

66. "Presidential Advisory Commission Releases Final Report on Western Water Resources," U.S. Water News Online Website, July 1998 (online; available: http://www.uswaternews.com/archives/arcpolicy/8preadv7. html; accessed January 22, 2002).

67. "The Clean Water Action Plan," Clean Water Initiative Website, revised April 5, 2000 (online; available: http://www.cleanwater.gov/news/fact_sheet.html; accessed December 22, 2001).

68. "Rural Areas to Get Millions for Clean Water Projects," U.S. Water News Online Website, May 1999 (online; available: http://www.uswaternews.com/archives/arcpolicy/9rurare5.html; accessed December 28, 2001).

69. "The Clean Water Action Plan."

70. "Clean Water Report Card: Failing Grades," Friends of the Earth Environmental Working Group Website (online; available: http://www.ewg.org/reports/reportcard/home.html; accessed December 28, 2001).

71. Rescuing an Endangered Ecosystem—The Journey to Restore America's Everglades Website, "Water Resources Development Act of 2000" (online; available: http://www.evergladesplan.org/wrda2000/wrda.cfm; accessed December 1, 2002).

72. "Historic Water Rights Settlement Reached in Colorado," Department of Justice press release, March 15, 2000 (online; available: http://www.usdoj.gov/opa/pr/2000/March/129enrd.htm; accessed January 9, 2002).

73. "Feds Set Aside Irrigation Water to Save Minnow," U.S. Water News Online Website, August 2000 (online; available: http://www.uswaternews.com/archives/arcpolicy/tfedset8.html; accessed January 3, 2002). "Feds Reclose Klamath Headgates," Fox News Website, Friday, August 24, 2001 (online; available: http://www.foxnews.com/story/0,2933,32774,00. html; accessed January 20, 2002).

4

Chronology: A Detailed History of U.S. Water Policy

This chapter is a history of U.S. water policy in chronological order. The first part covers federal policies, and the second is a review of local and state policies. The following lists are a compilation of earlier works and various sources. They present timelines that give dates; locations, policies, or laws; and short descriptions.[1]

Federal Water Policy

1783   The Treaty of Independence, signed between France and England, acknowledges the independence of the United States and provides that navigation of the Mississippi River is to remain free of charge.

1785   The Virginia and Maryland Compact regulates the use of fisheries on the Chesapeake Bay and in the Potomac Estuary.

1787   The U.S. Constitution signed in Philadelphia. Water becomes a state matter, following traditional federalism—a state-based view.

In Philadelphia, the Northwest Ordinance is passed, declaring that all U.S. inland waterways should be "common highways and forever free."

1797   Congress, in its first appropriation for water, allocates $3,500 to provide lighthouses, buoys, and other navigational improvements.

1802   The Army Corps of Engineers is established at the U.S. Military Academy at West Point, New York.

1820   Congress, now moved to Washington, D.C., gives money to the U.S. military to survey the Mississippi and Ohio Rivers.

1822   Congress gives money to the Army Corps of Engineers to do rivers and harbors work.

1824   The U.S. Constitution, Article 1, section 8, is known as the commerce clause. It gives Congress the authorization "[t]o regulate commerce with foreign nations, and among the several states, and with Indian Tribes." In *Gibbons v. Ogden*, the Supreme Court rules that this federal power to regulate commerce carries a similar authority over navigation. The decision leads to continued but cautious involvement by the federal government in water-related matters.

       Congress appropriates money for navigation improvements on the Mississippi and Ohio Rivers, following the 1820 surveys.

1826   Congress passes the first of many Rivers and Harbors Acts giving authority to the Army Corps of Engineers for water work.

1849   Congress passes an act to drain Louisiana swamplands, which allows Louisiana to sell swamps and lands subject to flooding, then use revenues to construct levees and drains.

1850   Congress passes the Swamp Act, which encourages the draining of wetlands and extends to all states the privileges that Louisiana had been granted the prior year.

1868   A joint resolution of Congress extends survey work and examinations of U.S. rivers and harbors.

1871   A joint resolution of Congress creates the U.S. Fish and Fisheries Commission, which provides for preservation and protection of food fisheries.

1873   Congress passes the Timber Culture Act, which promotes tree planting. One reason for this is to increase precipitation (an accepted theory of rainmaking in the 1800s).

1877   Congress passes the Desert Land Act, which authorizes sales of 640-acre land tracts to persons willing to irrigate them within three years. This leads to tremendous land speculation in the West.

1879   In reaction to dramatic Mississippi River floods in the 1870s, the Mississippi River Commission is established by Congress to develop a comprehensive flood-control program.

Geological Survey and Public Lands Commission is established by Congress to enhance efforts to settle the "dry half" of the country. Various interests push for increased federal involvement in regional development projects for the West.

John Wesley Powell, the first director of the U.S. Geological Survey, issues a report to Congress on the arid regions of the United States.

1884   A Congressional act authorizes dams on the Mississippi River for private power development at St. Cloud and Brainerd, Minnesota. However, Congress reserves navigation rights.

1891   The Payson Act authorizes the president to protect future water supplies by reserving public forest lands from being sold.

1894   The Carey Irrigation Act grants 160-acre tracts of public lands to states for the purpose of irrigation.

1899   Congress allocates money to establish federal standards for bridges over navigable streams, rivers, and harbors.

1899, Congress passes a law regulating mineral springs. The
cont. law authorizes permits for private development at mineral springs according to federal standards.

The Rivers and Harbors Act (Refuse Act) prohibits the dumping of solid materials into navigable streams.

1902 The Reclamation Act (Newlands Act) establishes a reclamation fund for irrigation development, using proceeds from sales of public lands in sixteen western states. It also establishes the Reclamation Service, which is later reorganized as the Bureau of Reclamation.

1905 The U.S. Forest Service is created in the Department of Agriculture (USDA). Chief Forester Gifford Pinchot introduces policy to limit permits for waterpower to fifty years, charging fees to private interests and eliminating congressional giveaways.

1906 Congress passes the Reclamation Act of 1906, funded by the federal government, to sell surplus power.

The General Dam Act is passed to regulate private dam construction on navigable streams.

1910 Congress passes an amendment to the General Dam Act, placing additional restrictions on dams on navigable streams.

The Withdrawal Act authorizes the president to withdraw public lands from sale for several purposes, including irrigation and waterpower.

1911 The Weeks Act authorizes the purchase of forest land by the federal government to preserve streamflow.

1912 The Public Health Service Act is enacted to establish the Public Health Service, giving it authority to study stream pollution.

In *Winters v. United States*, the Supreme Court enunciates the *Winters* Doctrine, which states that the federal government is assumed to have reserved prior rights to water for lands that it has set aside for Indian tribes and other federal uses.

1913   Congress passes the Raker Act, which authorizes the city of San Francisco to build Hetch Hetchy Dam in Yosemite National Park.

1914   Public Health Service is authorized to adopt and regulate drinking water standards for interstate carriers of water.

1917   Flood-control work is authorized in the federal budget for the Mississippi and Sacramento Rivers. This is the first federal construction for flood control.

1920   The Federal Water Power Act abolishes the Waterways Commission. The act empowers the Federal Power Commission, upgraded from a cabinet-level committee, to regulate nonfederal power and sell power from federal projects.

1922   The Colorado River Compact apportions the Colorado River waters among seven states, Arizona, California, Colorado, Nevada, New Mexico, Utah, and Wyoming. The compact allocates a total of 18 million acre-feet of river water per year to the seven states, even though as a result the Colorado runs several million acre-feet less each year. This is the first time in U.S. history that more than two or three states make a treaty among themselves and also the first time a group of states divide an interstate river among themselves for consumptive uses. Final agreement is not reached until 1963, after a Supreme Court battle between Arizona and California.

1924   The Oil Pollution Act prohibits the discharge of oil into navigable waters along the coasts.

The Fact Finders Act requires the secretary of the interior to have detailed information available on reclamation projects before submitting those projects to Congress for approval.

1925 The Rivers and Harbors Act authorizes the Army Corps of Engineers to do a survey of all navigable rivers, except the Colorado, to develop plans covering navigation, flood control, irrigation, and power production. Ultimately, the survey took over twenty years to accomplish this work.

1928 An Act of Congress authorizes the construction of Hoover Dam. The sale of electric power by utility companies is included in the plan, and the revenue from these sales help pay for the construction of the dam.

1933 The Public Works Administration is established as part of Franklin D. Roosevelt's New Deal. This allows the financing of several sewage treatment plants.

The Tennessee Valley Authority (TVA) Act establishes the TVA, charged with developing the Tennessee Valley with public water and power works.

1934 National resources are considered a crucial element of economic recovery and planning to overcome the Great Depression. The National Resources Board is created. The board emphasizes water resources development coordination and eventually becomes the National Resources Planning Board (NRPB).

1936 Civil engineering projects are underway in various locations. Hoover, Bonneville, Fort Peck, Shasta, and Grand Coulee dams all under construction in the United States. In addition, the TVA is well underway, in the midst of a twenty-year project to build twenty dams on the Tennessee River.

The Flood Control Act of 1936, the first nationwide flood control act, is passed. Section 1 requires cost-benefit analysis for the first time for federal water projects. The Army Corps of Engineers and the USDA each have jurisdiction over portions of the projects.

1937 With the Water Facilities Act, the Department of Agriculture is authorized to provide irrigation facilities to farming interests.

1938   With the Flood Control Act of 1938, Congress authorizes flood-control work projects to be entirely funded by the federal government.

1939   With the Reorganization Act, Congress restricts the president from transferring any functions performed by the Army Corps of Engineers to any other government entity.

The Reclamation Project Act authorizes the secretary of the interior to plan and build projects that serve multiple purposes, such as a dam that may provide municipal water supplies and hydroelectricity in addition to irrigation.

In a three-way agreement in the executive branch, the Departments of War, Interior, and Agriculture agree to provide voluntary consultation services for river-basin surveys.

1943   Congress dismantles the National Resources Planning Board (NRPB) and prevents successor agencies from picking up its functions.

Presidential Executive Order 9384 directs all public works construction agencies to submit annual, long-range programs to the Bureau of the Budget. This is an attempt by President Roosevelt to retain the powers of the newly dismantled NRPB.

The three-way agreement in the executive branch among the Departments of War, Interior, and Agriculture is replaced by the creation of the Federal Inter-Agency River Basin Committee (FIARBC).

1944   The Pick-Sloan Plan outlines an agreement between the Army Corps of Engineers and Bureau of Reclamation to develop the Missouri River jointly. By 1967, the Missouri River Basin has twenty-two dams, drowning over a million acres of fertile bottomlands.

A joint resolution of Congress authorizes the Fish and Wildlife Service to survey marine and freshwater fisheries.

1945 The Flood Control Act of 1945 authorizes flood-control reservoirs to provide power facilities.

1946 A presidential memorandum from President Harry Truman coordinates federal power development under the Department of Interior.

With the Legislative Reorganization Act, Congress consolidates several standing committees in both houses to dictate the disposition of water bills. This is still in effect, with minor changes made in 1961.

1948 The Water Pollution Control Act provides technical assistance to municipalities to control pollution. It also provides construction loans, but money is never appropriated. Public Health Service abatement procedures for interstate waters is also part of the act, but enforcement will not happen without state consent.

1950 The Dingell-Johnson Act authorizes redistribution of federal excise taxes to states to provide for fish restoration and management.

1952 With the Saline Water Act, Congress funds research on desalination.

1954 President Dwight D. Eisenhower reorganizes the FIARBC. It becomes the Inter-Agency Committee on Water Resources (IACWR), with subcabinet-rank members.

The Small Watershed Act establishes a watershed-protection program in the Soil Conservation Service.

The Flood Control Act of 1954 expands the use of flood-control reservoirs to include recreational purposes.

1955 A report by the President's Advisory Committee on Water Resources Policy recommends more executive-level control by using a board of review and by making IACWR a permanent cabinet subcommittee. The report also introduces the importance of water quality and the environment.

1956   With the passage of the Small Reclamation Projects Act, the secretary of the interior is authorized to provide local entities with construction loans for the rehabilitation of small irrigation projects.

With the Upper Colorado Storage Project, Congress bans reservoirs in national parks, and irrigation is limited to use on basic agricultural commodities.

The Federal Water Pollution Control Act strengthens the 1948 Water Pollution Control Act and adds $50 million annually for direct grants to construct sewage treatment plants. The act also strengthens enforcement procedures.

1958   United States Study Commissions are established to present two comprehensive river basin plans in Texas and the Southeast.

The Federal Boating Act establishes federal jurisdiction over boating rules and regulations.

The Water Supply Act ensures that the planning of future multiple-purpose projects includes urban and industrial water supplies.

1961   The Senate issues a report on national water resources. The report predicts a water crisis, emphasizes pollution as an important future cost, and strongly recommends comprehensive river-basin planning.

The Delaware River Basin Compact, among Delaware, New Jersey, New York, and Pennsylvania, establishes the Delaware River Basin Commission, which has broad powers. This is done out of concern for municipal water supplies, water quality, and recreational needs in the four-state area.

Amendments to the Federal Water Pollution Control Act of 1956 authorize an additional $100 million annually in grants for the construction of sewage treatment plants.

1962   The Rivers and Harbors Act expands the authority of the

1962, Army Corps of Engineers to include development of
cont. recreation areas in water projects.

1964 The Water Resources Research Act establishes research institutes in each state, with $100,000 grants for each.

The Land and Water Conservation Fund Act allows for the funding of outdoor recreation facilities, using the sale of admission stickers.

The Glen Canyon dam is built in Page, Arizona. This project creates Lake Powell but drowns a unique wilderness desert canyon.

1965 The Water Resources Planning Act establishes the Water Resources Council. This authorizes the formation of river-basin commissions and prohibits the study of inter-basin water transfers.

The Water Project Recreation Act is enacted, recognizing recreation as a legitimate purpose for inclusion in multi-purpose reservoir projects.

The Anadromous and Great Lakes Fish Act is passed to promote the preservation and development of fish resources. ("Anadromous" refers to fish, such as salmon, that migrate from saltwater to freshwater for spawning.)

The Water Quality Act establishes the Federal Water Pollution Control Administration (FWPCA) in the Department of Health, Education, and Welfare. The act requires states to set a timetable for the creation of water quality standards for all of their interstate water sources. It also increases the construction grant program for states to $150 million annually.

1966 In a speech to Congress, President Lyndon B. Johnson cites pollution as the most important natural resource problem facing the nation.

An executive reorganization transfers the FWPCA to the Department of the Interior.

The Clean Waters Restoration Act dramatically increases funding for clean water programs, with federal participation paying for up to 50 percent of state or local costs.

1968   The Estuarine Protection Act mandates a study of estuaries to determine if a nationwide system of estuarine areas should be established.

With the National Wild and Scenic Rivers Act, Congress passes legislation that prohibits dams on designated "wild and scenic" rivers.

The first barge transport of juvenile steelhead trout and salmon is made around the lower Snake River dams in Idaho. This is an attempt to preserve natural fish runs endangered by the construction of the dams on the river.

A congressional white paper reflects hearings on twenty bills filed regarding a national environmental policy during the 90th Congress.

1969   President Richard Nixon's Executive Order 11472 establishes a cabinet-level Committee on the Environment for advice on environmental matters. The committee will be terminated by Executive Order 11541 in 1970.

1970   President Nixon signs into law the National Environmental Policy Act of 1969 (NEPA). This groundbreaking legislation requires environmental impact statements for significant federal action on development projects. It also establishes the Council on Environmental Quality (CEQ).

The Water Quality Improvement Act regulates oil spills in reaction to a 1969 Santa Barbara oil spill, caused by blowout of an oil platform operated by a federal lessee.

A National Marine Fisheries report estimates that as much as 70 percent of Idaho salmon smolts (young salmon in the stage of their first migration to the sea) are killed from nitrogen in the lower Snake River. The nitrogen is produced as a result of dam construction.

1970,   President Nixon establishes the Environmental Protec-
cont.   tion Agency (EPA) for the purpose of consolidating fed-
        eral environmental control programs under the jurisdic-
        tion of one agency.

1972   The Clean Water Act is passed. This is crucial water-
        pollution legislation, allocating $18 billion in grants that
        pay up to 75 percent of the costs of municipal sew-
        age treatment plants and interceptor wastewater flow
        sewers.

1974   The Safe Drinking Water Act is passed. This is the first
        comprehensive national drinking water legislation. How-
        ever, it only allocates a small amount of grant money to
        municipalities to help implement the legislation.

1976   The collapse of the Teton Dam in Idaho kills eleven
        people and causes an estimated $1 billion in damage.

1977   The failure of the Kelly Barnes Dam in Georgia kills
        thirty-nine people. President Jimmy Carter calls for
        inspections of all "high hazard" dams in the nation.

        Amendments to the Clean Water Act give additional
        grant money to state and local entities.

1980s   Bird mutations and deformed birds are found at Kester-
        son National Wildlife Refuge in California. The muta-
        tions are found to be related to tainted runoff resulting
        from excessive irrigation of desert soils in the region.

        During the 1980s, it becomes known that California farm-
        ers using irrigation provided by the Central Valley Proj-
        ect have repaid only 4 percent of the $950 million capital
        cost (only $38 million). U.S. taxpayers have been footing
        the bill for the balance.

1981   Amendments to the Clean Water Act reduce federal
        funding to 50 percent of costs for clean water projects.
        They also reflect a shift in federal attitudes, encouraging
        innovative solutions from state and local governments
        for funding.

The Water Resources Council is "zero-budgeted"; that is, Congress appropriates no money for its annual operation.

1982   An executive reorganization creates the Council on Natural Resources as a cabinet-level position.

An executive reorganization creates the Office of Water Policy within the Department of Interior.

The Reclamation Reform Act revises to 960 acres the upper limits on the amount of farm property eligible for federally subsidized water for irrigation of crops.

1986   Amendments are made to the Safe Drinking Water Act. The key changes are regulatory, setting standards for eighty-three contaminants and requiring most surface drinking water sources to be subject to filtration.

The Water Resources Development Act authorizes new projects totaling $16.5 billion. The federal government shares project costs, paying up to 100 percent of the cost of some projects.

1987   Amendments to the Clean Water Act make additional reductions in federal grant money for local and regional projects. Cost sharing is to be phased out and replaced by revolving loan funds over five years.

After inspections by the Bureau of Reclamation and the Army Corps of Engineers, one-fifth of the dams built by the Bureau of Reclamation and one-third by the Army Corps of Engineers are classified as unsafe. The bureau had constructed 275 dams; the corps had built 554 dams across the country.

1988   Coho salmon are declared extinct in the Snake River in Idaho, unable to overcome various threats to their survival from dam construction.

1989   The *Exxon Valdez* oil spill contaminates the Alaska coast.

1991   An American Fisheries Society report states that 214

1991, salmon species in the West are facing extinction from
cont.   water-development projects in the region.

1988,   In a series of legislation, the Water Resources Develop-
1990,   ment Act provides for the conservation of water and the
1992   development of water resources. The legislation author-
        izes the Army Corps of Engineers to cònstruct various
        projects for improvements to rivers and harbors in the
        United States.

1992   The EPA adds twenty-three chemicals to the Safe Drink-
        ing Water Act standards, bringing the total number of
        federal drinking water standards to eighty-four.

        The federal government attempts to restore decimated
        fish populations, diverting up to 1.2 million acre-feet of
        water from the Central Valley Project in California back
        to their original water sources.

        A federal Task Force on Floodplain Management con-
        cludes that despite U.S. investment exceeding $25 billion,
        flood-damage costs are steadily rising. The task force
        determines that the federal government is spending over
        $2 billion annually on flood-damage repairs.

        The Reclamation Projects Authorization and Adjustment
        Act authorizes additional appropriations for the construc-
        tion of the Buffalo Bill Dam and Reservoir in Cody,
        Wyoming, as well as other water projects across the nation.

1993   Devastating floods along the Mississippi River illustrate
        the need for floodplain management. Entire towns are
        relocated to higher ground rather than being rebuilt on
        the floodplain.

1995   The EPA issues its study "Strengthening the Safety of Our
        Drinking Water." The study includes a partnership with
        private water suppliers to upgrade drinking water qual-
        ity across the nation.

        In policy changes affecting the Army Corps of Engineers,
        the corps is authorized to issue new general permits for

the construction or expansion of single-family homes in wetland areas. In addition, for the first time ever, an appeal process is proposed in which landowners would be allowed to procedurally challenge a corps wetland jurisdiction decision or permit denial.

1996   Amendments to the Safe Drinking Water Act are signed into law by President Bill Clinton. These amendments provide strengthened protections for clean, safe tap water.

1997   The United States and Canada sign a plan to protect public health by attempting to eliminate persistent toxic substances from the Great Lakes by the year 2006.

The EPA releases its first comprehensive study of U.S. watersheds and makes the data available on the Internet.

In Centerville, Maryland, the state of Maryland and the USDA form a partnership to expand the USDA's Conservation Reserve Program (CRP). This agreement allows up to 100,000 acres of sensitive riparian lands to be set aside for the purpose of protecting water quality in the region.

In what is known as the Buffer Initiative, the Conservation Reserve Program gives farmers incentives to set aside environmentally sensitive land to provide a natural barrier between farmland and water supplies for community drinking water systems.

1998   President Clinton's budget proposes a $568 million increase in fiscal year 1999 and a total increase of $2.3 billion over the next five years to restore and protect U.S. waters. The plan, known as the Clean Water Action Plan, is unveiled in Baltimore, Maryland.

The Western Water Policy Review Advisory Commission issues a report to Congress, "Water in the West: The Challenge for the Next Century." The report describes the impact of population growth, declining groundwater levels, damaged river ecosystems, and social conflicts over water policy.

1998, President Clinton signs the National Drought Policy Act
cont. of 1998. The law is intended to educate and prepare citizens for drought.

1999 The USDA funds over $200 million for clean water improvements intended for rural communities in forty-four states and Puerto Rico. This is the largest single rural wastewater project in U.S. history.

In Cortez, Colorado, a Bureau of Reclamation project creates new wetlands, reflecting a shift away from dam building and toward conservation in national policy initiatives.

2000 It is reported that the EPA had a record number of enforcement actions and penalties during 1999. Defendants are sentenced to prison for environmental crimes.

The EPA announces a plan to clean the Hudson River of contamination by polychlorinated biphenyls, or PCBs.

In an effort to reduce cancer risks, the EPA proposes reducing the limits for the amount of arsenic allowed in drinking water to one-tenth the current federal standard.

The Bureau of Reclamation orders water managers on the middle Rio Grande to maintain water levels in the river to help restore endangered silvery minnow populations. Critics charge that farmers are being abandoned and that the bureau no longer considers irrigation as a part of its legitimate mission.

In Anderson, California, the Saeltzer Dam is dismantled in order to restore a creek to increase salmon populations to a yearly estimated number of 13,000 salmon. The project costs about $5.8 million.

The Water Resources Development Act of 2000 approves a comprehensive Everglades restoration plan. The act establishes federal-state cost-sharing requirements and authorizes projects to restore, preserve, and protect the south Florida ecosystem and the freshwater supply that is vital to its survival.

Local and State Water Policy

1652   Boston, MA: The Private Water Works Company is chartered. Wooden conduits are used to supply water to the citizens of Boston.

1682   Philadelphia, PA: The first public water wells in the United States are sunk.

1704   Boston, MA: Private capital is invested for sewer. Francis Thrasker builds a city sewer using personal financing.

1707   New Orleans, LA: The first levees are constructed to hold back the waters of the Mississippi delta.

1709   Boston, MA: A municipal act is passed to regulate drains and common shores; a fee is charged for the use of drains.

1741   New York, NY: New York City passes a law requiring the city to install pumps, passing the expense on to the users.

1754   Bethlehem, PA: Hans Christopher Christiansen builds the first municipal waterworks.

1769   New York, NY: New York City builds trunk sewer lines.

1774   New York, NY: Christopher Colles constructs a public waterworks and distribution system for New York City.

1784   Virginia: George Washington assumes the presidency of the Potowmack Canal Company.

1795   Boston, MA: The privately owned Aqueduct Corporation is given authority to pipe water from Roxbury, at a distance of four miles.

1801   Philadelphia, PA: Benjamin Latrobe builds a municipal water works and distribution system that includes two large steam pumps.

1804   Paisley, Scotland: The first public water supply filtering system is built. It uses sand and gravel for filtration.

1817   Boston, MA: Water is piped forty miles to 800 families for a fee of $10 a year each (roughly $1,000 in today's terms) using a pine pipeline.

1817–   Cincinnati, OH: The city awards the Cincinnati Manu-
1819   facturing Company a ninety-nine-year monopoly to use horse-driven water pumps to supply water to the region.

1817–   New York: Governor De Witt Clinton of New York builds
1825   the 364-mile Erie Canal, which runs from Albany to Buffalo.

1818   Philadelphia, PA: For the first time in the United States, cast-iron pipes are used to replace wooden pipes.

1820   Lowell, MA: The city develops waterpower for the textile industry.

1823   Boston, MA: The city repeals the 1709 municipal act and resumes public control over privately operated sewer systems.

1827   Chelsea, England: James Simpson builds a prototype for the slow sand filter that he designed.

       Greenock, Scotland: Robert Thom installs reverse-flow filters to service the city; such filters are still used in modern-day plants.

1832   New York, NY: Polluted city wells are cited as the cause of a cholera epidemic that takes 3,500 lives in the city. In response, the Croton Aqueduct is built. Costing $13 million, it will be completed in 1842.

       Richmond, VA: The city attempts to filter the public water supply but fails. Not until 1872, forty years later, will such an attempt be successful.

1837 Philadelphia, PA: With a water supply at 3.1 million gallons a day (mgd), Philadelphia provides 19,600 users with 158 gallons of water per capita per day.

1840s Various locations: It is discovered that water softening can be accomplished using lime and soda ash.

1842 Chicago, IL: The Chicago Hydraulic Company is awarded a seventy-year charter to supply water to the city.

1843 Hamburg, Germany: Hamburg becomes the first city to have a comprehensive sewer system in place.

1844 Boston, MA: A local ordinance prohibits baths without a doctor's order because of excessive wastewater in the city.

1847 Utah: The Mormons begin irrigation, and within fifteen years they have 150,000 acres under irrigation for farming in this arid region.

1848 Boston, MA: The fourteen-mile municipal Cochichuate Aqueduct is completed, at a cost of $4 million.

1850 Lowell, MA: James B. Francis invents the Francis turbine, which boosts the efficiency of waterpower and is still in use today.

1851 Chicago, IL: In response to a deadly typhoid epidemic of 1848, Chicago's private water company is replaced by a municipal utility.

1857 New York, NY: Julius W. Adams designs a city sewer system for New York based on the model of Hamburg's system.

Anaheim, CA: Several thousand acres are under irrigation by German farmers on the Santa Ana River.

1858 Chicago, IL: Citywide sewers are in place in the city.

1862 New York, NY: The city installs a billion-gallon reservoir in Central Park.

1869   Massachusetts: The State Board of Health begins serious investigation into water waste treatment methods.

1870   Greeley, CO: The Greeley Colony, a cooperative agricultural enterprise, has 32,000 acres of land under irrigation. The Colony was founded by Nathan Meeker, agricultural editor of the *New York Tribune,* with the support of Horace Greeley.

1872   Augusta, ME: The State Insane Asylum opens the first sewage farm in the United States.

1874   New York, NY: The water supply is filtered in the city.

1876   Missouri: James P. Kirkwood reports to the State Health Board on evidence that streams cleanse themselves naturally.

1880s   Lawrence, MA: Sewage treatment is enhanced by the installation of an intermittent filtration system.

1880   Memphis, TN: The first separate sewers are installed in Memphis to remove sewage from stormwater.

1882   Appleton, WI: The first hydroelectric plant, generating 12.5 kilowatts of power, goes on-line in Wisconsin.

1887   New York, NY, and Kansas City, MO: Chemical precipitation is used to handle sewage treatment in New York and water purification (using alum) in Kansas City.

1889   Boston, MA: A sanitary engineering program is added at the Massachusetts Institute of Technology.

1895   Niagara Falls, NY: Niagara Falls generates 11,200 kilowatts of hydroelectric power.

1896   Louisville, KY: Chlorine disinfection experiments are performed on polluted water.

1902   Middelkerke, Belgium: Permanent chlorination of the city water supply is established.

Little Falls, NJ: The first municipal rapid sand filtering plant is opened. The plant is still in operation today.

1903   Boston, MA: A pollution research laboratory is opened at the Massachusetts Institute of Technology.

1905   Oberlin, OH: The first municipal water-softening plant is opened in Ohio.

1907   Oregon: A network is started to irrigate the arid Klamath Basin in order to establish a fertile, productive farming region.

1908   Jersey City, NJ: The first continuous application of chlorine to a city water supply system is done in New Jersey.

1914   Milwaukee, WI: Research is conducted on activated sludge. This large-scale work leads to the opening of the world's largest sewage-treatment plant by 1924.

1916   San Marcos, TX: The city installs the first activated sludge plant to improve waste treatment.

Chicago, IL: Lake Michigan pumping stations add chlorine to the water for treatment.

1917   Chicago, IL: Chemical conditioning of sludge is used in wastewater treatment.

1920s   Various locations: Taste and odor in water are addressed by using activated carbon. Oxidation ponds and stabilization lagoons are also being widely used for water treatment.

1921   Milwaukee, WI: Vacuum filtration of sludge is successfully implemented to treat wastewater.

1932   Chicago, IL: A sludge incinerator is installed for wastewater treatment.

1945   Various locations: Fluoride is introduced into water supplies to reduce tooth decay.

1945– Various locations: Most notable water policy during this
1985   period is at the federal level and is outlined in the first
       part of this chapter.

1985   Boston, MA: The Massachusetts Water Resource Author-
       ity (MWRA) is formed. The authority provides water and
       sewer services, funded primarily through user fees.

1987   Boston, MA: The Boston region begins work to come into
       compliance with 1972 federal water laws.

1989   Boston, MA: The MWRA opens the Deer Island waste-
       water treatment plant, at a cost of $3.8 billion, to protect
       Boston Harbor against pollution from metropolitan sew-
       ers.

1994   Washington, Oregon, and British Columbia, Canada: The
       Columbia River is closed to commercial salmon fishing to
       protect species. The 130 dams on the river are cited as a
       factor in salmon population declines.

1995   Louisiana: The Louisiana Mineral Board lifts the ban on
       oil and gas drilling in Lake Pontchartrain.

       Rosemont, IL: Illinois private interests form a wetland
       mitigation bank, which allows a designated wetland to
       be developed if a new wetland is constructed elsewhere.
       The Army Corps of Engineers grants permits for these
       exchanges, usually for state banks.

1996   Kenansville, NC: North Carolina agriculture experts
       claim that constructing and maintaining wetlands is too
       expensive, despite evidence that man-made wetlands are
       the best available technology to deal with wastewater
       produced by livestock.

1997   Washington, DC: The National Rural Water Association
       and the Ground Water Protection Council, together rep-
       resenting over 17,000 rural communities and state
       groundwater protection agencies, propose to Congress
       the prevention of groundwater contamination, using
       Superfund reform.

Portland, OR: The National Marine Fisheries Service confirms that diversions of water from the Columbia River harm salmon habitat and have a direct impact on the species. Most diverted water is used for irrigation purposes.

Miami, FL: A $25 million federal grant is made to help Florida acquire 31,000 acres of private land in the Everglades.

Grand Junction, CO: Fifteen endangered Colorado fish species climb the Redlands fish ladder on the Gunnison River near Grand Junction, along with 15,000 other native fish. The Bureau of Reclamation built the ladder to allow rare fish to migrate around a twelve-foot-high diversion dam.

1998   Various locations: During the year, nearly one-third of the 1,062 beaches reporting to the EPA have at least one health advisory or closing. In addition, 2,506 advisories are issued because local fish are too contaminated to eat.

1999   Hartford, CT: Methyl tertiary butyl ether, or MTBE, is widely blamed for contaminating water supplies in Connecticut and other states.

2000   The Environmental Working Group, affiliated with the national organization known as Friends of the Earth, issues a report charging that poor water quality in the United States is due to failure by regulators to maintain Clean Water Act permits, which are the legal foundation for improving the quality of the nation's waters. Twenty-five percent of all major permits nationally have expired, and clean water laws cannot be enforced.

Washington State: After a four-year study, federal officials delay a decision on breaching dams in Washington State to help salmon, and the government asks people in the region to help them decide.

Washington, DC: The U.S. Department of Justice and the State of Colorado agree to a settlement that resolves

2000,   claims filed in 1979 by the U.S. Forest Service for reserved
cont. instream flow water rights on 303 stream segments in the
Rio Grande National Forest and Gunnison National Forest. This is the first time that state and local water users agree that federal government has reserved water rights for instream flows in national forests.

Washington, DC: The federal government decides not to go ahead with the proposed breaching of four dams on the Snake River for a period of eight years while other measures are implemented to protect the salmon. If those measures fail, the dams may be breached.

2001   Wyoming and Nebraska: The Supreme Court approves water settlement between Wyoming and Nebraska regarding flows of the North Platte River.

Klamath Falls, OR: In April, the Bureau of Reclamation shuts off irrigation water to 90 percent of the 220,000-acre Klamath Project because endangered suckers in Upper Klamath Lake and coho salmon in the Klamath River face death if water levels fall below a certain depth.

2002   In July, Secretary of the Interior Gale Norton authorizes a limited release of water to farmers—less than 20 percent of the water provided in past years—hoping to defuse the building tension over irrigation. In August, the water is withheld again.

Notes

1. The following sources were used to compile this list: We relied heavily on Peter Rogers, *America's Water: Federal Roles and Responsibilities* (Cambridge: MIT Press, 1996), especially the appendixes; and we also relied on David H. Getches, Robert A. Williams, and Charles F. Wilkinson, *Cases and Materials on Federal Indian Law,* 4th ed. (St. Paul, MN: West Publishing Co., College and School Division, 2000); Daniel P. Beard, "Water Policy for the Next Generation," *World Rivers Review* 11, no. 3 (July 1996): 1–3; Peter H. Gleick, "Making Every Drop Count," *Scientific American,* February 2001: 41–45; "Turbine," in *Encyclopædia Britannica Online* (online;

available:http://www.eb.com:180/bol/topic?eu=108534& sctn=12; accessed January 28, 2002); U.S. Environmental Protection Agency History Office Websites (online; available: http://www.epa. gov/history/topics/drink/02.htm;http://www.epa.gov/history/topics/sdwa/05.htm#fact; http://www.epa.gov/history/topics/sdwa/05.htm#fact; accessed January 15, 2002); U.S. Water News Websites (online; available: http://www.uswaternews.com/archives/arcpolicy/9rurare5.html;http://www.uswaternews.com/archives/arcpolicy/7vicpre11.html; http://www.uswaternews.com/archives/arcpolicy/8newnat9.html; http://www.uswaternews.com/archives/arcpolicy/9wetcre8.html; http://www.uswaternews.com/archives/arcpolicy/5lamorat.html; http://www.uswaternews.com/archives/arcpolicy/5wesug.html; http://www.uswaternews.com/archives/arcpolicy/5ilentrep.html; http://www.uswaternews.com/archives/arcpolicy/6wethog.html; http://www.uswaternews.com/archives/arcpolicy/9bresna9.html; accessed January 15, 2002); EPA Office of Water Website (online; available: http://www.epa.gov/ow/liquidassets/execsumm.html; accessed January 8, 2002); State of Wyoming Office of the Governor Website (online; available: http://www.state.wy.us/governor/press_releases/2001/november_2001/watersettlement.html; accessed January 26, 2002); U.S. Department of Justice Website (online; available: http://www.usdoj.gov/opa/pr/2000/March/129enrd.htm; accessed January 10, 2002); Environmental Working Group Website (online; available: http://www.ewg.org/reports/reportcard/home.html; accessed January 16, 2002); Fox News Website, Friday, August 24, 2001 (online; available: http://www.foxnews.com/story/0,2933,32774,00.html; accessed January 20, 2002).

5

Freshwater Facts and Data

This chapter provides a convenient reference section for statistics and data on topics related to water supply and demand. The first part, "Reference Facts and Figures," presents information about where our freshwater supply comes from, how much is available and where, who uses water, and how much is used. The second part, "Policy References," highlights important water policy information for both the United States and for the international arena, including treaties and other formal agreements on freshwater topics.

Reference Facts and Figures

Water Supply Statistics

Water is vital to life on earth because of its unique physical properties. Water is the only substance that exists in all three physical states—as a gas, a solid, or a liquid—depending upon the climatic conditions that prevail. However, water also greatly influences exactly what climatic conditions do prevail, as will be explained in the following section. Water is a gas (water vapor) above its boiling point of 100°C or 212°F. It is a solid (ice) below its freezing point of 0°C or 32°F, and it exists as a liquid between those extremes, which is the temperature range that fosters most forms of life on earth (100°C to 0°C, or 212°F to 32°F). These extreme boiling and melting points allow water to exist on the planet, taking the form of oceans, lakes, rivers, and other water sources that

93

support vast numbers of plant and animal species. Water is also the only common substance that expands when it freezes instead of contracting. Because of this, ice floats, which means that the seas do not freeze solid from top to bottom.[1]

Climate

The relationship between water and heat makes possible the hydrologic cycle, described in detail in Chapter 1. When solar energy vaporizes water during evaporation, a water molecule absorbs large amounts of heat without appreciably changing its own temperature. This means that large amounts of heat are released when water vapor condenses and falls back to earth in the form of precipitation. The storage and release of heat during the evapotranspiration process is an important means of heat distribution across the planet. It is also an effective cooling process for plants and animals; for example, when perspiration evaporates from your skin, you feel cooler. The ability of liquid water to store heat without drastic temperature changes prevents large bodies of water from heating up or cooling down too rapidly. This protects living things from shocking temperature changes and allows the earth to maintain a moderate range of climate.[2]

Water vapor is water stored in the atmosphere as a gas, but the atmosphere also holds water in a liquid form as drops. Either these drops are either too small or lightweight to fall as precipitation, or they are buoyed by winds. This liquid in the atmosphere is humidity, and the amount of humidity present annually in a region influences what kind of vegetation is able to flourish there. Lack of humidity makes a region more arid, which also means that the region regularly expects low precipitation.[3]

Climate is the determining factor for how much water is available in a region, and climates are traditionally classified according to the amount of seasonal or annual heat and moisture present in any given region.[4] Table 5.1 presents a general idea of these climatic regions and shows where water is abundant or scarce.

One important climatic change is drought, which can be defined in several ways. A meteorological drought is a period when the precipitation is less than usual. An agricultural drought is a period when there is not enough precipitation for crops. A hydrological drought is a period "when less water is available than usual from the sum of precipitation and stream flow."[5] All refer to conditions where the climate is more arid than normal in a given region.

Table 5.1
Vegetation Associated with Climatic Regions

Climatic Region	Vegetation
Superhumid	Rain forest
Humid	Forest
Subhumid	Grassland
Semiarid	Steppe
Arid	Desert

Source: D. I. Blumenstock and C. W. Thornthwaite, "Climate and the World Pattern," in *Climate and Man: The 1942 Yearbook of Agriculture* (Washington, DC: Department of Agriculture, Government Printing Office, 1942), 98–127.

Evaporation and Precipitation

Water is returned to the atmosphere in the evapotranspiration process from bodies of water, land, and plant tissues (see Table 5.2). According to the USGS, 280 cubic miles of water evaporate or transpire into the atmosphere each day.[6] (A cubic mile is an imaginary cube, or a square box, measuring one mile on each side. A cubic mile of water is the equivalent of more than one trillion gallons.)[7] Condensation occurs, and the resulting precipitation infiltrates the soil and either produces soil moisture or continues to move deep underground to form groundwater. Otherwise, it runs off rapidly to become surface water runoff, which fills lakes, rivers, and reservoirs. The water we use for drinking, irrigation, industry, and other uses comes from these primary sources—groundwater or surface water runoff. The hydrologic cycle continually collects, purifies, and distributes this water. [8]

About 3,100 cubic miles of water is in the atmosphere at any one time. Most of this is in the form of water vapor, and if it fell as precipitation all at once, the earth would only be covered with about one inch of water, according to the USGS.[9]

There are many forms of precipitation, coming from several kinds of storms across the planet. The combination of the storms' type and form and the season in which they occur enables us to classify hydrologic regions or units (see Table 5.3). Patterns of water movement and storage are the basis for these regional classifications, which are characterized by precipitation activity, runoff, and stream behavior.[10] Each hydrologic unit is identified by a unique, two-to-eight-digit hydrologic unit code (HUC).[11]

Table 5.2
Evapotranspiration

Evapotranspiration Factors	Properties/Characteristics
Energy available for evaporation	Properties of the incoming energy:
	Latitude
	Elevation
	Time of day
	Time of year
	Degree of cloud cover
	Temperature of water
	Temperature of substrate
	Temperature of adjacent air
	Properties of the water:
	Depth
	Color/turbidity
	Color of bottom (if shallow)
	Properties of a wetted surface:
	Color
	Roughness
	Temperature
	Exposure to advection of warm air
	Orientation with respect to solar radiation
Water present	Characteristics of the hydrology:
	Frequency of supply of water to a wetted surface
	Supply of soil water by capillary action
	Characteristics of the body of water:
	Basin depth
	Basin volume
	Stagnant/flowing water
Vapor Pressure Gradient	Wind
	Elevation
	Atmospheric pressure
	Extent of gradient
	Continuity of gradient
	Air temperature at surface
	Air temperature above surface
	Relative humidity at surface
	Relative humidity above surface
	Exposure of evaporating surface
Atmospheric factors that interact with vegetation	Seasonal characteristics:
	Form of precipitation
	Leaf condition

Evapotranspiration Factors	Properties/Characteristics
Atmospheric factors that interact with vegetation, *cont.*	Storm characteristics:
	Amount
	Intensity
	Duration
	Frequency
	Time of day
Vegetative	Characteristics affecting interception:[a]
	Type of vegetation
	Tree
	Shrub
	Grass
	Deciduous/evergreen foliage
	Density of vegetative canopy
	Position of tree crown in canopy
	Bark roughness
	Branching habit of vegetation
	Number of vegetative layers (in the forest)
	Cutting history and land use of the area

[a]Interception is a process in which the downward movement of precipitation is interrupted and redistributed; the amount of water lost to soil moisture by this process is expressed as a percent of the total water that falls.

Source: Adapted with permission from Peter E. Black, *Watershed Hydrology* (Chelsea, MI: Ann Arbor Press, 1996), 99, 424. Copyright CRC Press, Boca Raton, Florida.

Precipitation is sampled infrequently, and the potential for error must be kept in mind when using precipitation data for research and management. Assessing water resources for a country as large as the United States includes figuring out how much water enters the geographic boundaries in a given time period; for example, it would include figuring out how much precipitation occurs annually. Rain gauges provide a good measure of the amount of precipitation for a given spot, but to effectively measure and collect data on precipitation for the entire United States requires many gauges over a large geographic area, which is expensive. Although there are more than 6,000 rain gauges in the federal networks, it has been argued that this is not enough. Evaporation is sampled and measured even less frequently than precipitation.[12]

Also noted in Chapter 1, oceans represent about 97 percent of global water supplies. Of the remaining 3 percent of freshwater, more than half is unavailable for human use because it is locked in glaciers or permanent snowfields. Our major sources of fresh-

Table 5.3
Hydrologic Units in the United States

Regions	Divides the nation into 21 major geographic areas, or regions.
Subregions	Divides the 21 regions into 222 subregions: "A subregion includes the area drained by a river system, a reach of a river and its tributaries in that reach, a closed basin(s), or a group of streams forming a coastal drainage area."
Accounting units	Divides the subregions into accounting units. "These 352 hydrologic accounting units nest within, or are equivalent to, the subregions."
Cataloging units, also sometimes called "watersheds"	Divides subregions into the smallest hydrologic units: "A cataloging unit is a geographic area representing part or all of a surface drainage basin, a combination of drainage basins, or a distinct hydrologic feature. ... There are 2150 Cataloging Units in the Nation."

Source: Based on USGS Website, "USGS: Science for a Changing World—Water Resources: Hydrologic Unit Maps" (online; available: http://water.usgs.gov/GIS/huc.html; accessed June 30, 2002), 1. Adapted from P. R. Seaber, F. P. Kapinos, and G. L. Knapp, Hydrologic Unit Maps: U.S. Geological Survey, Water-Supply paper 2294, 1987.

water from precipitation—surface water and groundwater aquifers—make up less than 1.5 percent of the total global water supply.[13] Comprehensive studies on the global freshwater supply estimate the total annual precipitation on the planet to be 125,971 cubic miles. Seventy-eight percent of this precipitation falls on the world's oceans and is therefore unavailable for human consumption. Only 1.7 percent of this precipitation, or 2,159 cubic miles, is available for human use.[14] The USGS estimates that the forty-eight contiguous states of the United States receive approximately four cubic miles of precipitation each day.[15] Table 5.4 summarizes these facts.

In 1970, studies showed that one-third of this precipitation was diverted and captured for human use. Unfortunately, as much as two-thirds of the water available from precipitation is affected by pollution, according to the studies. The actual percentage of freshwater precipitation used for human consumption was only 1 percent of the total global precipitation annually. The studies concluded that even though this seems like a very small amount, the global water-resource base was not inadequate.

Table 5.4
Precipitation Facts

Total Global Water Supply	
Oceans	97%
Freshwater (lakes, rivers, streams, and groundwater)	3%: 1.5% permanent snowfields + 1.5% accessible
Total Annual Global Precipitation	
Total precipitation	125,971 cubic miles[a]
Precipitation over oceans	78%
Precipitation available for human use	1.7% (2,159 cubic miles)
Total Daily Precipitation	
48 contiguous U.S. states	4 cubic miles per day

[a] 1 cubic mile = 1 trillion + gallons of water

Source: Based on Ralph A. Wurbs, "Managing Our Precious Liquid Asset," *World and I* 15, no. 10 (October 2000): 133; Peter Rogers, *America's Water: Federal Roles and Responsibilities* (Cambridge: MIT Press, 1996), 37–38; USGS Website, "USGS: Science for a Changing World—Water Resources: Hydrologic Unit Maps" (online; available: http://water.usgs.gov/GIS/huc.html; accessed June 30, 2002), 1.

However, if usage were to double over the next twenty years and if nothing were to be done to reduce water pollution, the world-wide resource could become "severely stressed."[16] The natural purification of the water supply is adequate and works well, unless we pollute water faster than it is naturally cleansed or add chemicals that cannot be broken down by the action of bacteria.[17] Table 5.5 is an example of the kind of monitoring being done to watch the quality of global freshwater supplies. The parameters that are measured in monitoring include the physical and chemical breakdown of the water; the levels of major ions, metals, nutrients, and organic contaminants that are found in the water; the microbiology; and the date range in which the data was collected.

Quality concerns are not limited to surface water resources. Such concerns are prevalent in relation to groundwater resources, as well. It is difficult to clean both surface water and groundwater sources that have been polluted or contaminated, but threats of groundwater pollution raise serious concerns in the general U.S. population because many, many people rely not on a public water supply system but on self-supplied, untreated well water for their personal water supplies.[18] According to the USGS, of the 43 million Americans who supplied their own water at home in 1990, nearly 99 percent of them used groundwater. During the same year, about 20 percent of our total water withdrawals were from groundwater sources, and roughly 80 percent were from

Table 5.5

Classification of Water Quality Parameters

	Physical/Chemical Properties (electrical conductivity, Suspended solids, pH, biological oxygen demand [BOD], chemical oxygen demand [COD])	Major Ions (alkalinity, sodium, magnesium, sulfate, chloride, potassium, calcium)	Metals (aluminum, nickel, chromium, manganese, iron, copper, zinc, arsenic, selenium, cadmium, mercury, lead)	Nutrients (nitrogen, ammonia, phosphorus)	Organic Contaminants (lindane, alpha-BHC, mirex, aldrin, endrin, PCBs, and others)	Microbiology (total coliform, fecal coliform, fecal streptococci)	Date Range
AFRA	2,024	3,921	970	1,914	4	339	1978–2000
AMRA	33,269	35,260	31,333	27,224	3,593	9,389	1978–1999
EMRA	12,427	15,362	10,115	8,503	366	3,081	1978–2002
EURA	129,562	128,271	140,378	104,378	13,036	21,979	1978–2001
SEAA	79,256	102,911	20,096	56,387	267	16,264	1978–1999
WPRA	58,478	41,583	48,738	70,047	6,605	9,953	1978–2002
Total	315,016	327,308	251,630	268,453	23,871	60,805	1978–2002

Global Regions Defined:

AFRA: Ghana, Kenya, Mali, Senegal, Uganda, United Republic of Tanzania, Democratic Republic of Congo

AMRA: Argentina, Bolivia, Brazil, Canada, Chile, Colombia, Cuba, Ecuador, Guatemala, Mexico, Panama, Peru, United States, Uruguay

EMRA: Egypt, Iran, Jordan, Pakistan, Morocco, Sudan, Tunisia

EURA: Austria, Belgium, Denmark, Finland, France, Germany, Grand Duchy of Luxembourg, Greece, Hungary, Ireland, Israel, Italy, Lithuania, Netherlands, Norway, Poland, Portugal, ussian Federation, Spain, Sweden, Switzerland, Turkey, United Kingdom

SEAA: Bangladesh, Cambodia (in progress), India, Indonesia, Lao People's Democratic Republic (in progress), Sri Lanka, Thailand, Vietnam (in progress)

WPRA: Australia, China, Fiji, Hong Kong, Japan, Republic of Korea, Malaysia, New Zealand, Philippines, and Papua New Guinea

Note: The numbers in the columns represent the total number of data points used to collect information for each region.

Source: Environment Canada Website, "United Nations Environment Programme: GEMS/WATER" (online; available: http://www.cciw.ca/gems/gems-e.html; accessed July 1, 2002), l; e-mail communications with Kelly Hodgson, environmental analyst at the United Nations Environment Programme GEMS Water Programme Office, November 26, 2002.

Table 5.6
Groundwater Use

Groundwater Use	Percentage
Irrigation	64
Public uses	19
Industry/mining	8
Domestic	4
Livestock	3
Commercial	1
Power production	<1

Source: USGS Website, "Groundwater Use in the United States" (online; available: http://ga.water.usgs.gov/edu/wugw. html; accessed July 17, 2002), 1.

surface water.[19] Of the 338 billion gallons of freshwater used each day, about 79 billion gallons came from groundwater sources, according to the USGS.[20] Table 5.6 shows the breakdown of uses for this groundwater.

Every year, the USGS monitors groundwater levels using thousands of wells across the nation. Groundwater data are collected and stored as a continuous record, and these data can also be accessed as discrete groundwater level measurements. Data from many of these continuous record stations are sent to USGS offices across the nation, and the USGS website provides access to real-time groundwater data. The website also provides a groundwater site inventory, which "consists of more than 850,000 records of wells, springs, test holes, tunnels, drains, and excavations in the United States." Site information also includes the well's "latitude and longitude, depth, site use, water use, and aquifer."[21]

Global Resource Base Measurements

Huge amounts of water are involved in the hydrologic cycle and it can be difficult to precisely measure. According to studies done by Swedish scientists Malin Falkenmark and Gunnar Lindh, the sun evaporates 108,675 cubic miles of water from the seas and 17,513 cubic miles from the land. Most of the seawater returns to the sea because oceans cover seven-tenths of the earth's surface. The remaining evaporated moisture from both the sea and the land, amounting to 27,349 cubic miles returns as precipitation over land. Of that, 9,836 cubic miles becomes surface water runoff or groundwater.[22] The USGS estimates that the total water supply of the world is 326 million cubic miles.[23]

As noted earlier, assessing water resources for a country includes figuring out how much water enters the geographic boundaries in a given time period. Runoff is another valuable measurement, because runoff crosses borders: It is water in motion and is also known as overland flow.[24] The flow of rivers is often measured in terms of the "cubic feet of water that pass a certain point in one second." One cubic foot per second is about 449 gallons per minute, or 646,315 gallons per day. An acre-foot of water is the amount required to cover one acre, or 43,560 square feet, to a depth of one foot. This equals 43,560 cubic-feet, or slightly more than 325,851 gallons—often rounded to 325,900 gallons. An acre-foot generally represents the "personal water needs of a family of five for one year."[25] In the United States, the flow of water in streams is recorded continuously, using a system of 6,800 sites across the nation. Not only is the flow rate measured on a daily basis, but the quality is also measured at 550 stations nationwide.[26] Figure 5.1 shows one such model of river runoff data collection, from the Yuba River in California.

Table 5.7 gives another example of the use of statistical information for rivers. It summarizes data for the three major river basins in the western United States.

Another way to measure water is in inches. An inch of rain is the amount needed to cover one acre to a depth of one inch, and it equals 27,143 gallons and weighs over 100 metric tons.[27] Table 5.8 presents in great detail the normal annual rainfall, in inches, for a sampling of cities in the United States and its territories during a thirty-year period. The table shows the rainfall for at least one city in each state, and some states are represented by several cities, if they are geographically large or heavily populated. (The entire compilation is not presented here. The entire chart can be seen on the website cited in the table.) The table shows that there are interesting variations in precipitation, both in the monthly fluctuations in individual locations and in the differences in monthly and annual precipitation in different regions of the nation. It serves to illustrate the vast amount of land and the diverse climates encompassed by the United States.

In the United States, surface water data is also monitored annually by the USGS. These time-series data describe stream levels, reservoir and lake levels, streamflow, surface water quality, and precipitation. The data are collected by automatic recorders

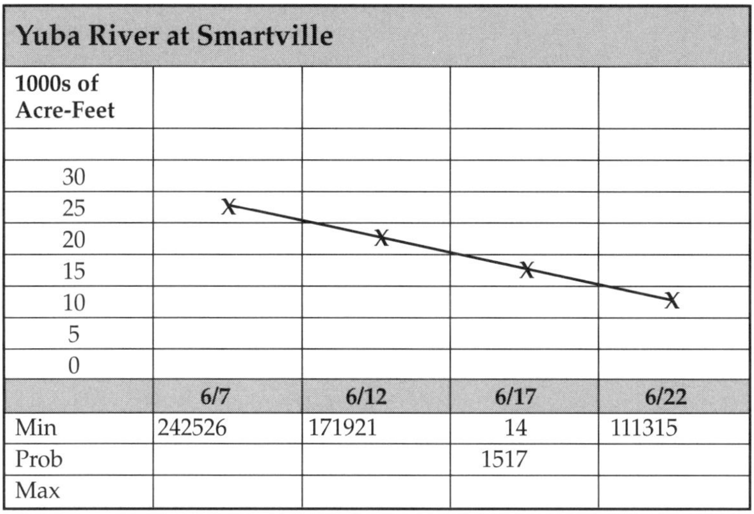

Yuba River at Smartville

1000s of Acre-Feet

	6/7	6/12	6/17	6/22
Min	242526	171921	14	111315
Prob			1517	
Max				

Figure 5.1 River Runoff Data. *Source:* From the graph Yuba River at Smartville, California Department of Water Resources Website, California Hydrologic and Water Supply Conditions. Snowmelt Runoff Forecast link to Adobe Acrobat report Forecast of Runoff Volumes for the Snowmelt Season (online; available: http://watersupplyconditions.water.ca.gov/hydrowatersupply.htm; accessed July 1, 2002), 2.

Table 5.7
Columbia, Missouri, and Colorado River Basins

	Columbia River Basin	Missouri River Basin	Colorado River Basin
River length (miles)	1,214	2,315	1,450
Average annual runoff (acre-feet)	182.5 million	61.5 million	15 million
Average flow at river mouth (acre-feet)	185 million	52	0
Reservoir storage, active capacity (acre-feet)	41 million	75 million	58.9 million
Basin size (square miles)	258,500	530,000	235,000
Irrigated land (acres)	7 million	14.1 million	2.2 million
Hydropower capacity (megawatts)	22,000	3,300	3,786

Source: High Country News, *Western Water Made Simple* (Washington, DC: Island Press, 1987), 4. Reprinted by arrangement with Island Press and High Country News. © 1987 High Country News.

Table 5.8
Normal Monthly Precipitation in Inches

Normals 1961–1990	No. of Years	JAN	FEB	MAR	APR	MAY	JUN	JUL	AUG	SEP	OCT	NOV	DEC	Annual
Birmingham, AL	30	5.10	4.72	6.19	4.96	4.85	3.73	5.25	3.59	3.93	2.81	4.33	5.12	54.58
Huntsville, AL	30	5.17	4.87	6.62	4.93	5.08	4.13	4.85	3.47	4.08	3.25	4.86	5.87	57.18
Mobile, AL	30	4.76	5.46	6.41	4.48	5.74	5.04	6.85	6.96	5.91	2.94	4.10	5.31	63.96
Anchorage, AK	30	0.79	0.78	0.69	0.67	0.73	1.14	1.71	2.44	2.70	2.03	1.11	1.12	15.91
Barrow, AK	30	0.17	0.15	0.17	0.20	0.16	0.28	0.94	0.96	0.60	0.45	0.25	0.16	4.49
Fairbanks, AK	30	0.47	0.40	0.37	0.32	0.61	1.37	1.87	1.96	0.95	0.90	0.80	0.85	10.87
Little Rock, AR	30	3.91	4.36	5.31	6.21	7.02	7.84	8.19	8.06	7.41	6.30	5.21	4.28	74.10
Flagstaff, AZ	30	2.04	2.09	2.55	1.48	0.72	0.40	2.78	2.75	2.03	1.61	1.95	2.40	22.80
Phoenix, AZ	30	0.67	0.68	0.88	0.22	0.12	0.13	0.83	0.96	0.86	0.65	0.66	1.00	7.66
Tucson, AZ	30	0.87	0.70	0.72	0.30	0.18	0.20	2.37	2.19	1.67	1.06	0.67	1.07	12.00
Fresno, CA	30	1.96	1.80	1.89	0.97	0.30	0.08	0.01	0.03	0.24	0.53	1.37	1.42	10.60
Los Angeles, CA	30	2.92	3.07	2.61	1.03	0.19	0.03	0.01	0.14	0.45	0.31	1.98	2.03	14.77
Sacramento, CA	30	3.73	2.87	2.57	1.16	0.27	0.12	0.05	0.07	0.37	1.08	2.72	2.51	17.52
San Diego, CA	30	1.80	1.53	1.77	0.79	0.19	0.07	0.02	0.10	0.24	0.37	1.45	1.57	9.90
San Francisco, CA.	30	4.06	2.95	3.07	1.29	0.25	0.15	0.04	0.07	0.26	1.26	3.21	3.10	19.71
Colorado Springs, CO	30	0.29	0.40	0.94	1.19	2.15	2.25	2.90	3.02	1.33	0.84	0.47	0.46	16.24
Denver, CO	30	0.50	0.57	1.28	1.71	2.40	1.79	1.91	1.51	1.24	0.98	0.87	0.64	15.40
Grand Junction, CO	30	0.56	0.48	0.90	0.75	0.87	0.50	0.65	0.81	0.82	0.98	0.71	0.61	8.64
Hartford, CT	30	3.41	3.23	3.63	3.85	4.12	3.75	3.19	3.65	3.79	3.57	4.04	3.91	44.14

City		Jan	Feb	Mar	Apr	May	Jun	Jul	Aug	Sep	Oct	Nov	Dec	Annual
Washington, D.C. (Dulles AP)	30	2.70	2.81	3.17	3.11	4.02	3.92	3.49	3.94	3.36	3.20	3.30	3.22	40.24
Wilmington, DE	30	3.03	2.91	3.43	3.39	3.84	3.55	4.23	3.40	3.43	2.88	3.27	3.48	40.84
Jacksonville, FL	30	3.31	3.93	3.68	2.77	3.55	5.69	5.60	7.93	7.05	2.90	2.19	2.72	51.32
Key West, FL	30	2.01	1.80	1.71	1.75	3.46	5.09	3.61	5.03	5.85	4.42	2.84	2.02	39.59
Miami, FL	30	2.01	2.08	2.39	2.85	6.21	9.33	5.70	7.58	7.63	5.64	2.66	1.83	55.91
Orlando, FL	30	2.30	3.02	3.21	1.80	3.55	7.32	7.25	6.78	6.01	2.42	2.30	2.15	48.11
Tallahassee, FL	30	4.77	5.56	6.21	3.74	4.75	6.93	8.82	7.53	5.58	2.92	3.87	5.03	65.71
Tampa, FL	30	1.99	3.08	3.01	1.15	3.10	5.48	6.58	7.61	5.98	2.02	1.77	2.15	43.92
Atlanta, GA	30	4.75	4.81	5.77	4.26	4.29	3.56	5.01	3.66	3.42	3.05	3.86	4.33	50.77
Savannah, GA	30	3.59	3.22	3.78	3.03	4.09	5.66	6.38	7.46	4.47	2.39	2.19	2.96	49.22
Hilo, HI	30	9.88	10.29	13.92	15.26	9.91	6.20	9.71	9.34	8.53	9.60	14.51	12.04	129.19
Honolulu, HI	30	3.55	2.21	2.20	1.54	1.13	0.50	0.59	0.44	0.78	2.28	3.00	3.80	22.02
Des Moines, IA	30	0.96	1.11	2.33	3.36	3.66	4.46	3.78	4.20	3.53	2.62	1.79	1.32	33.12
Sioux City, IA	30	0.55	0.71	1.96	2.34	3.67	3.71	3.27	2.97	2.88	1.94	1.08	0.78	25.86
Boise, ID	30	1.45	1.07	1.29	1.24	1.08	0.81	0.35	0.43	0.80	0.75	1.48	1.36	12.11
Pocatello, ID	30	1.04	0.92	1.26	1.20	1.35	1.02	0.65	0.67	0.85	0.91	1.16	1.11	12.14
Chicago, IL	30	1.53	1.36	2.69	3.64	3.32	3.78	3.66	4.22	3.82	2.41	2.92	2.47	35.82
Peoria, IL	30	1.51	1.42	2.91	3.77	3.70	3.99	4.20	3.10	3.87	2.65	2.69	2.44	36.25
Springfield, IL	30	1.51	1.77	3.24	3.68	3.62	3.43	3.52	3.29	3.33	2.60	2.53	2.73	35.25
Fort Wayne, IN	30	1.87	1.91	2.90	3.38	3.44	3.59	3.45	3.37	2.67	2.49	2.79	2.89	34.75
Indianapolis, IN	30	2.32	2.46	3.79	3.70	4.00	3.49	4.47	3.64	2.87	2.63	3.23	3.34	39.94
Topeka, KS	30	0.95	1.04	2.46	3.08	4.45	5.54	3.59	3.89	3.81	3.06	1.93	1.43	35.23
Wichita, KS	30	0.79	0.96	2.43	2.38	3.81	4.31	3.13	3.02	3.49	2.22	1.59	1.20	29.33

Table 5.8, continued

Normals 1961–1990	No. of Years	JAN	FEB	MAR	APR	MAY	JUN	JUL	AUG	SEP	OCT	NOV	DEC	Annual
Louisville, KY	30	2.86	3.30	4.66	4.23	4.62	3.46	4.51	3.54	3.16	2.71	3.70	3.64	44.39
Paducah, KY	30	3.27	3.90	4.92	5.01	4.94	4.05	4.19	3.34	3.69	3.00	4.32	4.68	49.31
New Orleans, LA	30	5.05	6.01	4.90	4.50	4.56	5.84	6.12	6.17	5.51	3.05	4.42	5.75	61.88
Shreveport, LA	30	3.88	3.92	3.59	3.75	5.18	4.29	3.67	2.43	3.12	3.73	4.45	4.10	46.11
Boston, MA	30	3.59	3.62	3.69	3.60	3.25	3.09	2.84	3.24	3.06	3.30	4.22	4.01	41.51
Worcester, MA	30	3.68	3.46	3.95	3.91	4.33	3.88	3.85	3.82	4.01	4.32	4.49	4.05	47.75
Baltimore, MD	30	3.05	3.12	3.38	3.09	3.72	3.67	3.69	3.92	3.41	2.98	3.32	3.41	40.76
Portland, ME	30	3.53	3.33	3.67	4.08	3.62	3.44	3.09	2.87	3.09	3.90	5.17	4.55	44.34
Detroit, MI	30	1.76	1.74	2.55	2.95	2.92	3.61	3.18	3.43	2.89	2.10	2.67	2.82	32.62
Grand Rapids, MI	30	1.83	1.42	2.63	3.37	3.13	3.68	3.19	3.57	4.24	2.81	3.32	2.85	36.04
Marquette, MI	30	2.17	1.73	2.77	2.64	3.03	3.48	2.88	3.41	4.08	3.61	2.89	2.61	35.30
Minneapolis–St. Paul, MN	30	0.95	0.88	1.94	2.42	3.39	4.05	3.53	3.62	2.72	2.19	1.55	1.08	28.32
Duluth, MN	30	1.22	0.80	1.91	2.25	3.03	3.82	3.61	3.99	3.84	2.49	1.80	1.24	30.00
Jackson, MS	30	5.24	4.70	5.82	5.57	5.05	3.18	4.51	3.77	3.55	3.26	4.81	5.91	55.37
Tupelo, MS	30	4.89	4.72	6.07	5.25	5.72	3.84	4.30	3.05	3.60	3.42	4.85	6.16	55.87
Kansas City, MO	30	1.09	1.10	2.51	3.12	5.04	4.72	4.38	4.01	4.86	3.29	1.92	1.58	37.62
St. Louis, MO	30	1.81	2.12	3.58	3.50	3.97	3.72	3.85	2.85	3.12	2.68	3.28	3.03	37.51
Billings, MT	30	0.90	0.64	1.16	1.74	2.57	1.99	0.94	1.01	1.36	1.14	0.84	0.79	15.08
Helena, MT	30	0.63	0.41	0.73	0.97	1.78	1.87	1.10	1.29	1.15	0.60	0.48	0.59	11.60
Missoula, MT	30	1.24	0.79	0.97	0.96	1.78	1.78	0.91	1.20	1.12	0.74	0.81	1.16	13.46
Lincoln, NE	30	0.54	0.72	2.09	2.76	3.90	3.89	3.20	3.41	3.48	2.12	1.27	0.88	28.26

City														
Omaha, NE	30	0.65	0.78	2.13	2.74	4.36	3.90	3.27	3.22	3.65	2.41	1.35	0.93	29.39
Scottsbluff, NE	30	0.50	0.47	1.09	1.58	2.77	2.64	2.06	1.07	1.10	0.81	0.62	0.56	15.27
Concord, NH	30	2.51	2.53	2.72	2.91	3.14	3.15	3.23	3.32	2.81	3.23	3.66	3.16	36.37
Mt. Washington, NH	30	7.94	8.56	8.97	8.17	7.51	7.82	7.08	8.24	7.38	7.19	10.38	9.72	98.96
Atlantic City, NJ	30	3.46	3.06	3.62	3.56	3.33	2.64	3.83	4.14	2.93	2.82	3.58	3.32	40.29
Newark, NJ	30	3.39	3.04	3.87	3.84	4.13	3.22	4.50	3.91	3.66	3.05	3.91	3.45	43.97
Albuquerque, NM	30	0.44	0.46	0.54	0.52	0.50	0.59	1.37	1.64	1.00	0.89	0.43	0.50	8.88
Roswell, NM	30	0.35	0.46	0.33	0.46	1.04	1.61	1.71	2.58	2.02	1.05	0.52	0.45	12.58
Las Vegas, NV	30	0.48	0.48	0.42	0.21	0.28	0.12	0.35	0.49	0.28	0.21	0.43	0.38	4.13
Reno, NV	30	1.07	0.99	0.71	0.38	0.69	0.46	0.28	0.32	0.39	0.38	0.87	0.99	7.53
Albany, NY	30	2.36	2.27	2.93	2.99	3.41	3.62	3.18	3.47	2.95	2.83	3.23	2.93	36.17
Buffalo, NY	30	2.70	2.31	2.68	2.87	3.14	3.55	3.08	4.17	3.49	3.09	3.83	3.67	38.58
New York (JFK AP), NY	30	3.17	3.02	3.59	3.90	3.80	3.65	3.80	3.41	3.30	2.88	3.65	3.42	41.59
Syracuse, NY	30	2.34	2.15	2.77	3.33	3.28	3.79	3.81	3.51	3.79	3.24	3.72	3.20	38.93
Cape Hatteras, NC	30	5.30	4.12	4.29	3.53	4.00	4.11	4.98	6.00	5.27	4.98	4.97	4.54	56.09
Charlotte, NC	30	3.71	3.84	4.43	2.68	3.82	3.39	3.92	3.73	3.50	3.36	3.23	3.48	43.09
Raleigh, NC	30	3.48	3.69	3.77	2.59	3.92	3.68	4.01	4.02	3.19	2.86	2.98	3.24	41.43
Bismarck, ND	30	0.45	0.43	0.77	1.67	2.18	2.72	2.14	1.72	1.49	0.90	0.49	0.51	15.47
Fargo, ND	30	0.67	0.45	1.06	1.82	2.45	2.82	2.70	2.43	1.99	1.68	0.73	0.65	19.45
Cleveland, OH	30	2.04	2.19	2.91	3.14	3.49	3.70	3.52	3.40	3.44	2.54	3.17	3.09	36.63
Columbus, OH	30	2.18	2.24	3.27	3.21	3.93	4.04	4.31	3.72	2.96	2.15	3.22	2.86	38.09
Toledo, OH	30	1.75	1.73	2.66	2.96	2.91	3.75	3.27	3.25	2.85	2.10	2.81	2.93	32.97
Youngstown, OH	30	2.13	2.03	3.11	3.06	3.52	3.94	4.07	3.32	3.48	2.62	3.11	2.93	37.32
Oklahoma City, OK	30	1.13	1.56	2.71	2.77	5.22	4.31	2.61	2.60	3.84	3.23	1.98	1.40	33.36

Table 5.8 continued

Normals 1961–1990	No. of Years	JAN	FEB	MAR	APR	MAY	JUN	JUL	AUG	SEP	OCT	NOV	DEC	Annual
Tulsa, OK	30	1.54	1.97	3.46	3.72	5.60	4.44	3.09	3.12	4.70	3.66	3.13	2.16	40.59
Eugene, OR	30	7.91	5.64	5.52	3.11	2.16	1.43	0.51	1.08	1.67	3.41	8.32	8.61	49.37
Portland, OR	30	5.35	3.85	3.56	2.39	2.06	1.48	0.63	1.09	1.75	2.67	5.34	6.13	36.30
Salem, OR	30	5.92	4.50	4.17	2.42	1.88	1.34	0.56	0.76	1.55	2.98	6.28	6.80	39.16
Erie, PA	30	2.22	2.28	3.00	3.24	3.44	4.09	3.43	4.06	4.39	3.77	4.02	3.59	41.53
Harrisburg, PA	30	2.84	2.93	3.28	3.24	4.26	3.85	3.59	3.31	3.51	2.93	3.52	3.24	40.50
Philadelphia, PA	30	3.21	2.79	3.46	3.62	3.75	3.74	4.28	3.80	3.42	2.62	3.34	3.38	41.41
Pittsburgh, PA	30	2.54	2.39	3.41	3.15	3.59	3.71	3.75	3.21	2.97	2.36	2.85	2.92	36.85
Majuro, Marshall Islands, PC	30	8.43	6.15	8.28	10.28	11.18	11.59	13.00	11.52	12.42	13.84	12.80	11.85	131.34
Pago Pago, Amer. Samoa, PC	30	12.59	12.76	11.26	12.04	9.92	7.38	6.28	6.71	6.69	10.79	10.84	14.54	121.80
Wake Island, PC	30	1.16	1.60	2.23	2.51	1.74	2.29	4.02	6.16	5.07	4.33	2.79	1.78	35.68
Guam, PC	30	5.55	5.11	4.45	4.71	7.10	6.49	11.78	14.59	15.02	12.74	9.06	6.44	103.04
San Juan, PR	30	2.81	2.15	2.35	3.76	5.93	4.00	4.37	5.32	5.28	5.71	5.94	4.72	52.34
Providence, RI	30	3.88	3.61	4.05	4.11	3.76	3.33	3.18	3.63	3.48	3.69	4.43	4.38	45.53
Charleston, SC	30	3.36	3.06	4.30	2.44	3.53	5.83	6.05	7.31	4.67	2.78	2.29	2.90	48.52
Columbia, SC	30	4.42	4.12	4.82	3.28	3.68	4.80	5.50	6.09	3.67	3.04	2.90	3.59	49.91
Greenville-Spartanburg AP, SC	30	4.10	4.41	5.39	3.86	4.42	4.77	4.63	3.95	3.96	3.99	3.65	4.14	51.27
Rapid City, SD	30	0.39	0.52	1.03	1.89	2.68	3.06	2.04	1.67	1.23	1.10	0.56	0.47	16.64
Sioux Falls, SD	30	0.51	0.64	1.64	2.52	3.03	3.40	2.68	2.85	3.02	1.78	1.09	0.70	23.86
Chattanooga, TN	30	4.89	4.81	6.03	4.31	4.37	3.52	4.85	3.53	4.15	3.22	4.61	5.17	53.46
Memphis, TN	30	3.73	4.35	5.41	5.46	4.98	3.57	3.79	3.43	3.53	3.01	5.10	5.74	52.10
Nashville, TN	30	3.58	3.81	4.85	4.37	4.88	3.57	3.97	3.46	3.46	2.62	4.12	4.61	47.30

Location	Years	Jan	Feb	Mar	Apr	May	Jun	Jul	Aug	Sep	Oct	Nov	Dec	Annual
Austin, TX	30	1.71	2.17	1.87	2.56	4.78	3.72	2.04	2.05	3.30	3.43	2.37	1.88	31.88
Brownsville, TX	30	1.56	1.06	0.53	1.56	2.94	2.73	1.90	2.77	6.00	2.80	1.51	1.25	26.61
Dallas–Fort Worth, TX	30	1.83	2.18	2.77	3.50	4.88	2.98	2.31	2.21	3.39	3.52	2.29	1.84	33.70
Houston, TX	30	3.29	2.96	2.92	3.21	5.24	4.96	3.60	3.49	4.89	4.27	3.79	3.45	46.07
Waco, TX	30	1.65	2.09	2.33	3.19	4.58	3.28	1.99	1.68	3.52	3.36	2.43	1.86	31.96
Milford, UT	30	0.63	0.71	1.17	1.03	0.74	0.48	0.78	0.94	0.96	0.84	0.78	0.70	9.76
Salt Lake City, UT	30	1.11	1.23	1.91	2.12	1.80	0.93	0.81	0.86	1.28	1.44	1.29	1.40	16.18
Lynchburg, VA	30	2.86	3.04	3.47	3.09	3.91	3.45	4.16	3.59	3.24	3.70	3.14	3.23	40.88
Norfolk, VA	30	3.78	3.47	3.70	3.06	3.81	3.82	5.06	4.81	3.90	3.15	2.85	3.23	44.64
Richmond, VA	30	3.24	3.16	3.61	2.96	3.84	3.62	5.03	4.40	3.34	3.53	3.17	3.26	43.16
Burlington, VT	30	1.82	1.63	2.23	2.76	3.12	3.47	3.65	4.06	3.30	2.88	3.13	2.42	34.47
Seattle, WA	30	5.35	4.03	3.77	2.51	1.84	1.59	0.85	1.22	1.94	3.25	5.65	6.00	38.00
Spokane, WA	30	1.98	1.49	1.49	1.18	1.41	1.26	0.67	0.72	0.73	0.99	2.15	2.42	16.49
Charleston, WV	30	2.91	3.04	3.63	3.31	3.94	3.59	4.99	4.01	3.24	2.89	3.59	3.39	42.53
Green Bay, WI	30	1.15	1.03	2.05	2.40	2.82	3.39	3.10	3.50	3.47	2.23	2.16	1.53	28.83
Milwaukee, WI	30	1.60	1.45	2.67	3.50	2.84	3.24	3.47	3.53	3.38	2.41	2.51	2.33	32.93
Cheyenne, WY	30	0.40	0.39	1.03	1.37	2.39	2.08	2.09	1.69	1.27	0.74	0.53	0.42	14.40
Sheridan, WY	30	0.73	0.64	0.97	1.72	2.39	2.25	0.88	0.82	1.37	1.18	0.83	0.70	14.48

Source: From "Normal Monthly Precipitation, Inches," on the University of Utah Department of Meteorology Website (from National Weather Service data) (online; available: http://www.met.utah.edu/ jhorel/html/wx/climate/normrain.html; accessed July 1, 2002), 1.

or manual measurements by field personnel at sites across the nation. They are then relayed to offices where they are stored and processed. Daily summary data are collected and stored in the database. If the data are sent using the Geostationary Operational Environmental Satellite (GOES) system, they can be processed automatically and are often available online within minutes at the USGS website. The USGS publishes the daily data in annual water-data reports.[28]

Water Demand Statistics

Water-Resource Problems

As noted earlier, there is plenty of freshwater on earth for human use. Despite this fact, water supply and access problems still exist under certain conditions, making it difficult to keep up with demand. This is because the earth's regions vary considerably in average annual precipitation, precipitation patterns, and evaporation rates. G. Tyler Miller outlines four basic water-resource problems that exist for the planet as a result; they are summarized here:

1. *Too little precipitation annually.* At least eighty arid and semiarid countries, mostly in Asia and Africa, contain almost 40 percent of the world's population. These countries experience serious periodic droughts and have a difficult time producing enough food. Many people in these places spend hours daily obtaining water, and often the water sources are polluted streams and rivers.

2. *Too much precipitation for part of the year; too little the rest of the year.* Some countries get enough annual precipitation annually, but, unfortunately, most of it comes during one time of the year. For example, countries like India or Bangladesh can receive nearly 90 percent of their annual precipitation during the monsoon season. During this time, usually between June and September, the massive downpour of rain runs off too rapidly to be captured and used. These heavy rains can also lead to devastating periodic floods.

3. *Adequate precipitation that runs off too far away from agricultural and population centers.* Some areas receive enough water, but in the wrong place. One example of this situation is South America, which has the largest annual runoff of any continent on earth. The problem is that 60 percent of this runoff flows through the Amazon River, which is far away from most of the people living on the continent.

4. *Lack of sanitary drinking water.* Drinking contaminated water is the most prevalent health hazard to a vast number of people in the world. In 1980, the World Health Organization (WHO) estimated that 70 percent of people living in rural areas of less-developed countries and 25 percent of people in their urban areas did not have access to adequate safe drinking water. As a result, approximately 25 million deaths occur every year from dysentery, cholera, and other waterborne diseases that are actually preventable.[29]

In addition, two other problems result from the use of water for irrigation: the buildup of mineral salts in the soil (salinization) and the waterlogging of soil to the point that agricultural land becomes unproductive. Irrigation water that flows over and into the ground dissolves salts, making the water saline. When this saline water evaporates into the atmosphere, it leaves behind a high concentration of salts in the topsoil. This is salinization, and if the salts are not flushed or drained from the soil, the buildup leads to wasteful water use. It can also stunt and eventually kill crops, resulting in unproductive farmland.[30]

But as Miller also notes, waterlogging often accompanies salinization. If farmers apply heavy amounts of irrigation water to wash or leach salts deeper into the soil, water can accumulate underground and gradually raise the water table. If no drainage is provided, the roots of plants can drown in saline water. It is estimated that one-tenth of all irrigated land worldwide is affected by waterlogging.[31]

Water Distribution

Peter H. Gleick notes that studies estimate that in the year 2025, most of the world—approximately 60 percent—will have an abundant water supply, with "abundant" meaning that more than 450,000 gallons will be available annually per person. Water-distribution problems will be limited to particular seasons and regions for this segment of the world's population. The other 40 percent of the world should expect water in amounts that will leave them with water supplies that are "limited," "scarce," or "stressed." And nearly every region, including some with generally abundant precipitation, such as the United States and China, has areas prone to severe water shortages. All of Australia is prone to these shortages.[32] Table 5.9 shows how these classifications compare to the "abundant" category.

For additional information about global water distribution, please see Chapter 1.

Table 5.9
Projected World Water Supply, 2025

Category	Gallons per person	% World population	Problems	Examples of Regions included in category
Abundant	Over 450,000	59.3	Limited to regions and/or seasons	Most of North and South America; large parts of Asia, Europe, and Australia; some areas of Africa
Limited	260,000 to 450,000	32.6	Constraints on agricultural supplies	Parts of Africa and southern Asia; some parts of Europe and South America
Scarce	130,000 to 260,000	5.3	Persistent restrictions on agriculture and industry	Parts of Africa and the Middle East
Stressed	Less than 130,000	2.8	Potentially serious threats to human health, agriculture, and industry	Parts of Africa and the Middle East

Source: Based on the map "Where the Water Will Be in 2025," in Peter H. Gleick, "Making Every Drop Count," *Scientific American,* February 2001, 42–43.

Withdrawal and Consumption of Water

There are two methods of measuring water use: measuring withdrawal and measuring consumption. "Withdrawal" refers to taking water from a surface or groundwater source; the water is then moved to the place where it will be used. Water is said to be "consumed" when, after it has been withdrawn, it is no longer available for reuse in the local region. This loss can be due to several factors: because it has evaporated; because it is being stored in the living matter of humans, animals, or plants; because it has been contaminated; or because it has seeped into the ground. Up to 90 percent of water withdrawn on the planet is returned to rivers and other water sources and is not consumed.[33] The USGS reports that in the United States in 1990, approximately 339,000 million gallons per day of freshwater was withdrawn, which is about one quarter of the national renewable supply. In addition, nearly 220 billion gallons per day (bgd) was returned to surface water sources after being used.[34]

The demand for water at the end of the twentieth century did not increase as rapidly as had been anticipated. The total amount

Table 5.10

Per Capita and Total Global Water Withdrawals, 1900–2000

Year	Per Capita Withdrawals	Total Withdrawals
1900	Approximately 100,000 gallons per person	Approximately 100,000 gallons per person
1940	Over 100,000 gallons per person	Approximately 150,000 gallons per person
1960	Just under 200,000 gallons per person	Approximately 250,000 gallons per person
1980	Just under 200,000 gallons per person	Approximately 300,000 gallons per person
2000	Approximately 180,000 gallons per person	Approximately 500,000 gallons per person

Source: Based on the graph "Annual Global Water Withdrawals" in the map "Where the Water Will Be in 2025," in Peter H. Gleick, "Making Every Drop Count," *Scientific American,* February 2001, 42.

of water withdrawn globally increased fourfold from 1940 to 1984, and the average withdrawal per person doubled.[35] To compare this to a more extended time period: From 1900 to 2001, the amount withdrawn globally increased ninefold, but the water use per person still only doubled from the start of the century (see Table 5.10). Gleick points out two factors to explain this: First, people know how to use water more efficiently as time goes on, and secondly, communities have adjusted their priorities for water use.[36]

It has been estimated that of the annual freshwater budget for the United States, Americans use slightly over 94 bgd for consumptive purposes. However, a total of up to 1,400 bgd of freshwater exist because it does not evaporate from the gross water budget; therefore, one might assume there would be no reason to expect water shortages.[37] Unfortunately, that assumption is incorrect because of four additional problems noted by Peter Rogers. These problems are somewhat related to the four global problems listed above, but they are specific to U.S. water use:

1. *Actual diversions of water amount to about 400 bgd.* Most of this water is returned to water sources quickly, but it can be degraded in quality and it may also be returned to a different location. An example is groundwater that is used by a city that is then disposed of into a surface stream. Even though it is returned to the hydrologic cycle for use, it may not be useful—practically or economically—in that same year in that particular region of the country.

2. *The interyear fluctuations in precipitation diminish the average figure of 1,400 bgd.* The amount of precipitation available in an average year actually translates into 675 bgd.

3. *Available rainfall and surface water varies widely by region.* On

average, there is plenty of water statistically for all consumptive uses in the United States, but large parts of the nation may face serious shortages at any given time due to the random nature of precipitation and seasonal variability.

4. *Water that runs to the sea is not "wasted."* Instream water requirements are significant for the breeding habitats of fish and wildlife and the protection of riparian ecology. These habitats and ecosystems could be destroyed if adequate water flows are not provided for rivers, estuaries, and wetlands. Only recently have instream flows become legally considered beneficial uses of water.[38]

Experts worry that despite positive changes and trends in annual water use per person, improvements in water use may not keep pace with expected population growth.[39] Table 5.11 shows U.S. water withdrawals for 1995.

U.S. domestic withdrawals are staggering when compared to domestic withdrawals around the world. Approximately 340 liters, or 90 gallons, of the daily U.S. withdrawal is used for mundane daily activities. The is roughly three times the average domestic use per person in other nations around the world, and as much as twenty times the amount used in less-developed countries.[40] (See Chapter 1 for additional U.S.-global comparisons of water use.)

Most withdrawn freshwater goes to home use, private business and public use, irrigation, industrial processing, and cooling electric power plants. However, an estimated 75 percent of the water withdrawn annually for irrigation is consumed and subsequently lost for reuse in the region from which it is taken. Worldwide, the greatest demand on freshwater supplies, in terms of both withdrawal and consumption, comes from irrigation.[41] The cooling of electric power plants have similar withdrawal rates, but the consumption rate is low.

Table 5.12 shows worldwide annual withdrawal figures as percentages of each nation's available water. The internal availability of water per person per year is also shown, which gives an idea of the aridity of a region and the resulting scarcity or abundance of water. When the percentage of withdrawals is looked at in relation to the availability, one can get some idea of how efficiently water is managed.

Development
Massive and extensive development technology has been applied to U.S. freshwater resources, especially in the West. Development

Table 5.11
U.S. Water Withdrawals, 1995

Type of Use	Billion Gallons per Day	Percentage
Irrigation	134	39%
Power generation	132	39%
Public supply	40.2	12%
Industry/mining	23.3	7%
Livestock	5.5	1%
Domestic	3.4	1%
Commercial	2.9	1%

Source: Based on "Water Withdrawals in the U.S. in 1995," USGS Website (online; available: http://ga.water.usgs. gov/edu/ graphicshtml/totpie95.html; accessed July 3, 2002), 1.

Table 5.12
Worldwide Water Scarcity

Country	Internal Water Availability (cm/person/year)[a]	Withdrawal as Percentage of Country's Available Water[b]
Canada	109,510	1
Panama	60,760	1
Nicaragua	46,730	1
United States	10,060	19
China	2,520	16
India	2,270	21
Peru	1,840	—
Haiti	1,500	—
South Africa	1,400	18
Poland	1,290	30
Kenya	610	—
Tunisia	490	53
Israel	370	88
Barbados	200	52
Libya	170	374
Malta	60	92
Egypt	40	97

[a]Internal availability excludes river flow from other countries, renewable water only.

[b]Available water includes river inflow (renewable + net river inflow).

Source: World Resource Institute, *World Resources: An Assessment of the Resource Base That Supports the Global Economy* (New York: Basic Books, 1986), 1:67, as cited on "Worldwide Water Scarcity," on ITT Industries Website (online; available: http:// www.itt.com/waterbook/scarcity_countries.asp; accessed July 3, 2002), 1.

Table 5.13
Ten Highest Dams in the United States

Dam Name	State	River	Owner	Height (feet)	Date completed
Oroville	California	Feather	California DWR	770	1968
Hoover	Nevada	Colorado	Bureau of Reclamation	730	1936
Dworshak	Idaho	N. Fork Clearwater	Corps of Engineers	717	1973
Glen Canyon	Arizona	Colorado	Bureau of Reclamation	710	1964
New Bullards Bar	California	North Yuba	Yuba County Water Agency	645	1969
Seven Oaks	California	Santa Ana	Corps of Engineers	632	1999
New Melones	California	Stanislaus	Bureau of Reclamation	625	1979
Mossyrock	Washington	Cowlitz	City of Tacoma	606	1968
Shasta	California	Sacramento	Bureau of Reclamation	602	1945
Don Pedro	California	Tuolumne	Turlock and Modesto Irrigation Districts	585	1971

Source: "Dam, Hydropower, and Reservoir Statistics," USSD Website (online; available: http://www.uscid.org/~uscold/uscold_s.html; accessed July 27, 2002), 1.

Table 5.14
Ten Largest Man-Made Reservoirs in the United States

Dam Name	Reservoir	Location	Owner	Acre-Feet	Completed
Hoover	Lake Mead	Nevada	Bureau of Reclamation	28,255,000	1936
Glen Canyon	Lake Powell	Arizona	Bureau of Reclamation	27,000,000	1964
Oahe	Lake Oahe	South Dakota	Corps of Engineers	19,300,000	1966
Garrison	Lake Sakakawea	North Dakota	Corps of Engineers	18,500,000	1953
Fort Peck	Fort Peck Lake	Montana	Corps of Engineers	15,400,000	1957
Grand Coulee	Franklin Delano Roosevelt Reservoir	Washington	Bureau of Reclamation	9,562,000	1942
Libby	Lake Koocanusa	Montana	Corps of Engineers	5,809,000	1973
Shasta	Lake Shasta	California	Bureau of Reclamation	4,552,000	1945
Toledo Bend	Toledo Bend Reservoir	Louisiana	Sabine River Authority	4,477,000	1966
Fort Randall	Lake Francis Case	South Dakota	Corps of Engineers	3,800,000	1954
Flaming Gorge	Flaming Gorge Reservoir	Utah	Bureau of Reclamation	3,788,900	1964
Oroville	Lake Oroville	California	California DWR	3,540,000	1968

Source: "Dam, Hydropower, and Reservoir Statistics," USSD Website (online; available: http://www.uscid.org/~uscold/uscold_s.html; accessed July 27, 2002), 1.

Table 5.15
Ten Largest Hydroelectric Projects in the United States

Dam Name	River	Location	Megawatts
Grand Coulee	Columbia	Washington	6,180
Chief Joseph	Columbia	Washington	2,457
John Day	Columbia	Oregon	2,160
Bath County P/S	Little Back Creek	Virginia	2,100
Robert Moses–Niagara	Niagara	New York	1,950
The Dalles	Columbia	Oregon	1,805
Luddington	Lake Michigan	Michigan	1,657
Raccoon Mountain	Tennessee River	Tennessee	1,530
Hoover	Colorado	Nevada	1,434
Pyramid	California Aqueduct	California	1,250

Source: "Dam, Hydropower, and Reservoir Statistics," USSD Website (online; available: http://www.uscid.org/~uscold/uscold_s.html; accessed July 27, 2002), 1.

is done to control water supplies and to make them more accessible to humans for use in their daily routines. One of the most recognized products of development technology is a dam, which is made from earth, rock, or concrete and is "usually constructed on rivers to store water in a reservoir."[42] Other examples of development technology are levees, canals, wells, and aqueducts, to name a few.

The U.S. Society on Dams (USSD) is a professional organization "dedicated to advancing the technology of dam engineering, construction, operation, maintenance, and safety." The organization also works on endorsing "socially and environmentally responsible water resources projects" and promotes "awareness of the role of dams in the beneficial and sustainable development" of U.S. water resources.[43] Tables 5.13, 5.14, and 5.15 show the ten highest dams in the United States, the ten largest man-made reservoirs in the United States, and the ten largest hydroelectric projects in the United States, from the USSD Register of Dams; USSD's website contains more complete data.

The Bureau of Reclamation collects extensive basin and reservoir data for the seventeen western states for which it is responsible (Arizona, California, Colorado, Idaho, Kansas, Montana, Nebraska, Nevada, New Mexico, North Dakota, Oklahoma, Oregon, South Dakota, Texas, Utah, Washington, and Wyoming)

Table 5.16
Significant Twentieth-Century Studies on Water Policy

Name	Year	Description
Report of the Inland Waterways Commission	1908	Senate Document 325, 60th Congress, 1st Session
White House Conference of Governors	1908	Held at the White House; put conservation issues into the public consciousness and stimulated large number of private and state-level conservation initiatives.[a]
Joint Conservation Conference of National and State Officials	1908	Held at the end of the year to receive recommendations of the National Conservation Commission, which compiled an inventory of U.S. natural resources[b]
Report of the National Conservation Commission	1909	Senate Document 676, 60th Congress, 2nd Session
North American Conservation Conference	1909	Convened by President Theodore Roosevelt; held in Washington and attended by representatives of Canada, Newfoundland, Mexico, and the United States.[c]
Report of the National Waterways Commission	1912	Included recommendation for integrated watershed management; not accepted by the federal government[d]
Report of the President's Committee on Water Flow	1934	House Document 395, 73rd Congress, 2nd Session
U.S. Water Resources Committee	1936	Reported on drainage basin problems and programs
Report of the U.S. Commission on Organization of the Federal Government (first Hoover Commission)	1950	Reported on problems of overlapping and uncoordinated water agencies in the U.S. government. Recommended consolidation and an independent Board of Review for water projects.[e]
Report of the President's Water Resources Policy Commission (Cooke Commission)	1950	Highlighted four aspects of water policy: (1) extent of federal government participation; (2) appraisal of program priorities based on social needs; (3) criteria for evaluation of water project feasibility; (4) new legislation needed.[f]
House Committee on Public Works (Jones Subcommittee)	1952	Water resources policy; Committee Print Nos. 21, 22, 23, and 24. 82nd Congress, 2nd Session.
Report of the President's Advisory Committee on Water Resources Policy	1956	House Document 315, 84th Congress, 2nd Session
Report of the Senate Select Committee on National Water Resources (Kerr Committee)	1961	Senate Document 29, 87th Congress, 1st Session
Report of the National Water Commission	1973	Final report issued after five years of work; offered over 200 recommendations for improving national water policy.[g]
Report of the National Commission on Water Quality (NCWQ)	1976	One major conclusion was that, for many water bodies, because of toxic substances discharged from non-point sources such as urban and agricultural runoff, application of best available treatment (BAT) to point sources would not achieve the goals of the Clean Water Act.[h]
U.S. Water Resources Council	1978	Key finding was that maintaining urban domestic and commercial water supplies would be the premier challenge in the future, followed by the need to accommodate growing recreational and environmental demands.[i]

Table 5.16, *continued*

aLibrary of Congress Website, "Documentary Chronology of Selected Events in the Development of the American Conservation Movement, 1847–1920" (online; available: http://memory.loc.gov/ammem/amrvhtml/cnchron5.html; accessed July 11, 2002), 1.
bIbid.
cIbid.
dRobert W. Adler, "Addressing Barriers to Watershed Management," as cited on EPA Website (online; available: http://www.epa.gov/owow/watershed/Proceed/adler.html; accessed December 30, 2002).
ePeter Rogers, *America's Water: Federal Roles and Responsibilities* (Cambridge: MIT Press, 1996), 54.
fIbid., 55.
gIbid., 58.
hR. Dickinson Roop, "The Clean Water Act's First 20 Years: Progress toward Fishable, Swimmable Water" (online; available: http://www.bae.ncsu.edu/bae323/Supplements/CleanWaterAct.txt; accessed November 20, 2002).
iRogers, *America's Water,* 63.
Source: Based on Rogers, *America's Water,* Appendix 2, and sources cited in table.

and provides development technology information on their website. The Army Corps of Engineers also has information on their website on development projects in the rest of the nation.[44] The EPA provides additional data for water that is involved in development, but most of that is focused on water quality.

Policy References

U.S. Policy Information

Table 5.16 shows a summary of significant twentieth-century studies on water policy. For additional information on U.S. water policy, see Chapters 2, 3, and 4.

Table 5.17 lists some of the U.S. interstate agreements on freshwater issues. As noted many times in this text, it is the states that are primarily charged with water-policy decisions. The agreements in this table reflect negotiations and settlements between or among various states, localities, and regions. A full list of the interstate water agreements in effect can be found on the website of the Council of State Governments at their link to state water legislation.[45]

International Policy Information

Table 5.18 lists the international agreements, declarations, resolutions, and other documents available on the International Water

Table 5.17
U.S. Interstate Water-Policy Agreements

Apalachicola—Chattahoochee—Flint River Basin Compact

Chesapeake Bay Commission Agreement (Bi/Tri-State Agreement on the Chesapeake Bay)

Colorado River Compact

Columbia River Compact (Oregon-Washington Columbia River Fish Compact)

Delaware Valley Urban Area Compact—Delaware Valley Regional Planning Commission

Interstate Water Supply Compact (Vermont—New Hampshire)

Big Blue River Compact (Kansas-Nebraska)

Klamath River Compact

La Plata River Compact

Missouri River Toll Bridge Compact

New England Interstate Water Pollution Control Compact

Ohio River Valley Water Sanitation Compact

Potomac River Compact of 1958

Red River Compact

Snake River Compact

Susquehanna River Basin Compact Pennsylvania

Tennessee—Tombigbee Waterway Development Compact

Upper Colorado River Basin Compact

Wheeling Creek Watershed Protection And Flood Prevention Compact

Yellowstone River Compact

Source: From "Compacts Believed to Be in Effect in 2001," Council on State Governments Website (online; available: http:// ssl.csg.org/compactlaws/comlistlinks.html; accessed July 2, 2002), 1; the website includes links to descriptions of the agreements.

Table 5.18
International U.S. Water Agreements

Convention and Statute on the Regime of Navigable Waterways of International Concern. Barcelona, April 20, 1921

Ramsar Convention on Wetlands of International Importance Especially as Waterfowl Habitat. Ramsar, Iran, February 2, 1971

U.N. Convention to Combat Desertification. U.N. General Assembly, New York, NY, 1994

U.N. Convention on the Law of the Non-navigational Uses of International Watercourses. U.N. General Assembly, New York, NY, May 1997

International Declarations and Resolutions

Madrid Declaration on International Regulations Regarding the Use of International Watercourses for Purposes other than Navigation. Institute of International Law, 24 Annuaire de l'Institut de Droit International, 1911

Resolution Concerning the Utilization of Non-Maritime Waters for Purposes Other than Navigation, International Law Institute, 1961

Resolution 3129 (XXVIII) on Cooperation in the Field of the Environment Concerning Natural Resources Shared by Two or More States. New York, December 13, 1973

Helsinki Rules on the Uses of the Waters of International Rivers. International Law Association, 1966

Seoul Rules on International Groundwaters. International Law Association, 1986

International Law Commission Resolution on Confined Transboundary Groundwater. U.N. General Assembly, New York, NY, 1997

Other International Documents

Dublin Statement on the Water and Sustainable Development. Dublin, Ireland, 1992

Transboundary Groundwaters: The Bellagio Draft Treaty. Bellagio, Italy, 1987

UN Conference on Environment and Development. Rio de Janeiro, June 1992. Chapter 18: "Protection of the Quality and Supply of Freshwater Resources: Application of Integrated Approaches to the Development, Management and Use of Water Resources"

Second World Water Forum and Ministerial Conference. World Water Council, Dutch Government, The Hague/The Netherlands, March 2000. "Declaration of The Hague"

Source: International Water Law Project Website, documents link "International Documents" (online; available: http://www. internationalwaterlaw.org/; accessed July 20, 2002), 1. Most of the agreements listed on the website include links that provide additional, detailed descriptions of the agreements, declarations, resolutions, and documents.

Table 5.19

International Case Law on Water Issues

Permanent Court of International Justice

Jurisdiction of the European Commission of the Danube Between Galatz and Braila, Advisory Opinion, [1927], P.C.I.J. (Ser. B) No. 14

Territorial Jurisdiction of the International Commission of the Oder River [1929], P.C.I.J. (Ser.A) No. 23, (Sept. 10)

Oscar Chinn Case, [1934], P.C.I.J. (Ser. A/B) No. 63

Diversion of Water from the Meuse case (Netherlands v. Belgium) [1937], P.C.I.J. (Ser. A/B) No. 70

International Court of Justice

Case Concerning the Gabcikovo-Nagymaros Project (Hungary/Slovakia). September 1997

Case Concerning Kasikili/Sedudu Island (Botswana/Namibia). December 13, 1999

Notification of a Joint Request to the ICJ by Benin and Niger Regarding a Boundary Dispute on the River Niger. 2002

Other Tribunals

Helmand River Delta Case. Arbitral awards of August 19, 1872 and April 10, 1905

San Juan River Case. Arbitral award of March 22, 1888, rendered by Grover Cleveland

Kushk River Case. Award of August 22, 1893, rendered by an Anglo-Russian Commission

Faber Case. Award of 1903 rendered by the umpire, Henrey M. Duffield, appointed by a German-Venezuelan Mixed Claims Commission

Chamizal Arbitration. Argument and appendix to the case of the United States before the International Boundary Commission, United States–Mexico, Hon. Eugene Lafleur, presiding under the provisions of the Convention between the United States of America and the United States of Mexico, concluded June 24, 1910, by the United States (1911)

Tacna-Arica Case. Award of March 4, 1925, rendered by President Calvin Coolidge

Württemberg and Prussia v. Baden (The Donauversinkung Case), German Staatsgerichtshof. June 18, 1927

Zarumilla River Case. Arbitral award of July 14, 1945, rendered by the Chancellery of Brazil

Lake Lanoux Arbitration case (Spain v. France), 24 Int'l L. Rep. 101 (1957)

Gut Dam Case (Canada/United States of America). Decisions of January 15, 1968; February 12, 1968; and September 27, 1968, rendered by the Lake Ontario Claims Tribunal

Helmand River Case (Afghanistan/Persia)

San Juan River Case (Costa Rica/Nicaragua) (Costa Rica v. Nicaragua)

Source: International Water Law Project Website, link to "Case Law" (online; available: http://www.internationalwaterlaw.org/; accessed July 20, 2002), 1. Some of the case law listed on the website includes links that provide addi-

Law Project's website.[46] The website provides links that give full details for each agreement listed. As you can see, there are very few international agreements in effect on the topic of freshwater. Nevertheless, some have been in effect since the start of the twentieth century.

Table 5.19 lists the actual case law from various global justice venues available on the International Water Law Project's website.[47] There is no single justice institution with jurisdiction over international cases, and the lawsuits that involve environmental issues have been addressed in various tribunals. You can see, however, that international water case law dates back to 1872.

Notes

1. G. Tyler Miller Jr., *Living in the Environment*, 5th ed. (Belmont, CA: Wadsworth Publishing Co., 1988), 208–209; William Ashworth, *Nor Any Drop to Drink* (New York: Summit Books, 1982), 31.

2. Ashworth, *Nor Any Drop to Drink*, 30; Miller, *Living in the Environment*, 209.

3. Peter E. Black, *Watershed Hydrology* (Chelsea, MI: Ann Arbor Press, 1996), 47, 249.

4. Ibid., 87.

5. Peter Rogers, *America's Water: Federal Roles and Responsibilities* (Cambridge: MIT Press, 1996), 37–38.

6. USGS, "Earth's Water: How Much Water Is There on (and in) the Earth?" in USGS Website (online; available: http://ga.water.usgs.gov/edu/earthhowmuch.html; accessed June 26, 2002), 1.

7. USGS, "Earth's Water," 1.

8. Miller, *Living in the Environment*, 209.

9. USGS, "Earth's Water," 1.

10. Black, *Watershed Hydrology*, 88.

11. USGS, "USGS: Science for a Changing World—Water Resources: Hydrologic Unit Maps," on USGS Website (online; available: http://water.usgs.gov/GIS/huc.html; accessed June 30, 2002), 1.

12. Black, *Watershed Hydrology*, 88; Rogers, *America's Water*, 28–29.

13. Ralph A. Wurbs, "Managing Our Precious Liquid Asset," *World and I*, 15, no. 10 (October 2000): 133.

14. Rogers, *America's Water*, 27–28.

15. USGS, "Earth's Water," 1.

16. Rogers, *America's Water*, 27–28.

17. Miller, *Living in the Environment*, 209.

18. Rogers, *America's Water*, 31.

19. USGS, "Earth's water," 1.

20. USGS Website, "Groundwater Use in the United States" (online; available: http://ga.water.usgs.gov/edu/wugw.html; accessed July 17, 2002), 1.

21. USGS, "Ground-Water Data for the Nation," on USGS Website (online; available: http://waterdata.usgs.gov/nwis/gw; accessed July 10, 2002), 1.

22. Fred Powledge, *Water: The Nature, Uses, and Future of Our Most Precious and Abused Resource* (New York: Farrar Straus Giroux, 1982), 27–28.

23. USGS, "Earth's Water," 1.

24. Black, *Watershed Hydrology,* 210.

25. Powledge, *Water,* 29.

26. Rogers, *America's Water,* 28–29.

27. Powledge, *Water,* 30.

28. USGS, "Surface-Water Data for the Nation," on USGS Website (online; available: http://waterdata.usgs.gov/nwis/sw; accessed July 10, 2002), 1.

29. Miller, *Living in the Environment,* 214–218.

30. Ibid., 218–219.

31. Ibid., 219.

32. Peter H. Gleick, "Making Every Drop Count," *Scientific American,* February 2001: 42–43.

33. Miller, *Living in the Environment,* 213.

34. USGS, "The National Water-Use Information Program: Water-Use Information for Planners, Managers, Policy Makers, Educators, and the General Public," on USGS Website (online; available: http://water.usgs.gov/watuse/wufactsheet.html#HDR6; accessed July 25, 2002, 1 (Water Use in the United States).

35. Miller, *Living in the Environment,* 213.

36. Gleick, "Making Every Drop Count," 42–43.

37. Rogers, *America's Water,* 30–31.

38. Ibid.

39. Gleick, "Making Every Drop Count," 43.

40. Miller, *Living in the Environment,* 213.

41. Ibid.

42. "What Is a Dam?" on USSD Website (online; available: http://www.uscid.org/~uscold/whatsdam.html; accessed July 27, 2002), 1.

43. "United States Society on Dams," on USSD Website (online; available: http://www.uscid.org/~uscold/index.html; accessed July 25, 2002), 1.

44. "What Is the Bureau of Reclamation?" on U.S. Bureau of Reclamation Website (online; available: http://www.usbr.gov/main/what/who.html; accessed December 7, 2002), 1; "Services for the Public," on Army Corps of Engineers Website (online; available: http://www.usace.army.mil/public.html#Water; accessed July 21, 2002), 1.

45. "Suggested State Legislation," on Council on State Governments Website (online; available: http://ssl.csg.org/compactlaws/comlistlinks.html; accessed July 2, 2002), 1.

46. "International Documents," on International Water Law Project Website (online; available: http://www.internationalwaterlaw.org/; accessed July 20, 2002), 1.

47. "Case Law," on International Water Law Project Website (online; available: http://www.internationalwaterlaw.org/; accessed July 20, 2002), 1.

6

Directory of Government and International Agencies, Organizations, and Associations

This chapter provides the reader with several comprehensive directories. The first part of the chapter includes information about federal, state, and local government entities in the United States that are involved in freshwater management issues. The second part of the chapter offers a directory of nonprofit, professional, and international organizations and associations that are devoted to freshwater concerns.

U.S. Government Agencies

Federal Government Agencies

This section, devoted to federal institutions with a role in water policy, is intended to provide several things to the reader regarding freshwater issues. First, it gives a very good picture of the decentralization of water policy in the United States. Second, it gives the reader a glimpse of the scope of freshwater issues by including short descriptions of the agency's duties in reference to water policy. Third, it also presents the most current contact information, as of this writing, including the website addresses, which are the sources for the information included for each agency.

125

EXECUTIVE OFFICE OF THE PRESIDENT
Main Offices
Executive Office of the President
U.S. General Services Administration
1800 F St. NW
Washington, DC 20405
Phone: (800) FED-INFO (333-4636)
E-mail: president@whitehouse.gov or
vice.president@whitehouse.gov
Website: http://www.firstgov.gov/Agencies/Federal/
Executive/EOP.shtml

The Executive Office of the President is made up of White House offices and agencies that help form and implement the policy directions and programs of the president, which reflect the political will and culture of the time. The White House offices and agencies that most affect water policy are the Office of Management and Budget (OMB), the Domestic Policy Council (DPC), the Office of Science and Technology Policy (OSTP), and the Council on Environmental Quality (CEQ). If the reader is concerned about something happening at the federal level that concerns water, the president and vice president are among the national officials who can be contacted to voice those concerns.

Council on Environmental Quality (CEQ)
The White House
1600 Pennsylvania Ave. NW
Washington, DC 20500
Phone comments: (202) 456-1111
Switchboard: (202) 456-1414
Fax: (202) 456-246
Website: http://www.whitehouse.gov/ceq/

The CEQ coordinates federal environmental efforts and works with agencies and other White House offices to develop environmental policies and initiatives. The council's chair is appointed by the president, with the advice and consent of the Senate, and serves as the principal adviser to the president on environmental policy issues. The CEQ reports annually to the president on the state of the environment, oversees the implementation by federal agencies of the environmental impact assessment process, and acts as a referee when agencies disagree about such assessments.

Domestic Policy Council (DPC)
The White House
1600 Pennsylvania Ave. NW
Washington, DC 20500
Phone: (202) 456-1111
Switchboard: (202) 456-1414
Fax: (202) 456-246
Website: http://www.whitehouse.gov/dpc/index.html

The DPC coordinates the domestic policymaking process in the White House and offers policy advice to the president, working to ensure that domestic policy initiatives are coordinated and consistent throughout federal agencies. It also oversees the implementation of domestic policy and represents the president's priorities to other branches of government. The DPC's activities affect freshwater issues because it helps set priorities for the proposal, support, or opposition for water legislation and programs.

Office of Management and Budget (OMB)
725 17th St. NW
Washington, DC 20503
Phone: (202) 395-3080
Fax: (202) 395-3888
Website: http://www.whitehouse.gov/omb/

The OMB's mission is to assist the president in guiding the preparation of the federal budget and to supervise its administration by the agencies of the executive branch. It evaluates the effectiveness of the agencies' programs, policies, and procedures; assesses competing funding demands among various agencies; sets funding priorities; and ensures that agency reports, rules, testimony, and proposed legislation are consistent with the president's budget. The activities of the OMB have implications for water management because support or opposition for the funding of water proposals, programs, or legislation is based on the OMB's procedures.

Office of Science and Technology Policy (OSTP)
Executive Office of the President
Washington, DC 2050
Phone: (202) 395-7347
E-mail: ostpinfo@ostp.eop.gov
Website: http://www.ostp.gov/

The continuing mission of OSTP is spelled out in the National Science and Technology Policy, Organization, and Priorities Act of 1976 (PL 94-282). The act calls for OSTP to serve as a source of scientific and technological analysis and judgment for the president regarding major policies, plans, and programs of the federal government. Among other things, the act authorizes OSTP to work with the private sector to ensure that federal investments in science and technology contribute to environmental quality, including freshwater issues.

DEPARTMENT OF AGRICULTURE (USDA)
Main Offices
Secretary Ann M. Veneman
U.S. Department of Agriculture
Washington, DC 20250
Website: http://www.usda.gov/

The USDA is in the president's cabinet. Among its areas of concern are the maintenance of agriculture, so that the nation has a safe, affordable, nutritious, and accessible food supply, and the care of agricultural, forest, and range lands. The agencies within the USDA most concerned with water issues are the Economic Research Service (ERS), the Natural Resources Conservation Service, and the Farmers Home Administration.

Economic Research Service (ERS)
1800 M St. NW
Washington, DC 20036-5831
Phone: (202) 694-5050
Fax: (202) 694-5700
Website: http://www.ers.usda.gov/

Agriculture uses ground and surface water in the United States, accounting for 80 percent of the consumptive water use of the nation as a whole and over 90 percent of the consumptive water use in many western states. Among other things, the ERS investigates water allocation, water conservation, and water management issues facing irrigated agriculture. In addition, other sectors of agriculture than irrigation are examined for their competitive influence on the nation's water supplies. The ERS studies the impact of water reallocation among agricultural, environmental, and urban users.

Farmers Home Administration
Website: http://www.home-loans-directory.com/
glossary-terms/Farmers-Home-Administration-FmHA/

The Farmers Home Administration has grants available for water and sewer systems. It has the authority to make loans to public bodies and nonprofit corporations in rural areas to construct or improve community facilities. Projects such as water and sewer systems, fire and rescue vehicles, fire stations, hospital improvements, and other essential community facilities are eligible for loans. Applicants for these loans must be unable to get credit elsewhere at reasonable rates and terms.

The Natural Resources Conservation Service
Conservation Communications Staff
PO Box 2890
Washington, DC 20013
Website: http://www.nrcs.usda.gov/

The goal of the Natural Resources Conservation Service is to help people conserve, maintain, and improve natural resources and environment. Among its programs are the Watershed Rehabilitation Service, the Dam Safety Program, and the Wetlands Reserve Program.

DEPARTMENT OF COMMERCE
Main Offices
Secretary Donald L. Evans
U.S. Department of Commerce
1401 Constitution Ave. NW
Washington, DC 20230
E-mail: webmaster@doc.gov
Website: http://www.commerce.gov/

The Department of Commerce is part of the president's cabinet. It promotes job creation, economic growth, sustainable development, and improved living standards. It works in partnership with business, universities, communities, and workers. The Coastal and Marine Resources of the National Oceanic and Atmospheric Administration (NOAA) and the National Weather Service (NWS) are directly concerned with water issues.

Coastal and Marine Resources
NOAA Coastal Services Center
2234 South Hobson Ave.
Charleston, SC 29405-2413
Phone: (843) 740-1200
Fax: (843) 740-1224
Websites: NOAA Coastal Services Center:
http://www.csc.noaa.gov/techniques/volunteer/index.html
NWS: http://www.nws.noaa.gov/

NOAA's "Volunteering for the Coast" website is directed at those interested in environmental stewardship through personal action. It provides information provided on volunteer opportunities, coordinating volunteer efforts, and on ways to build successful volunteer programs.
The National Weather Service provides weather, hydrologic, and climate forecasts and warnings for the United States, its territories, adjacent waters, and ocean areas. NWS data and products form a national information database and infrastructure that can be used by other governmental agencies, the private sector, the public, and the global community.

DEPARTMENT OF DEFENSE (DOD)
Main Offices
Secretary Donald H. Rumsfeld
1000 Defense Pentagon
Washington, DC 20301
Directorate for Public Inquiry and Analysis
Office of the Secretary of Defense
(Public Affairs)
Room 3A750, The Pentagon
1400 Defense Pentagon
Washington, DC 20301-1400
Website: http://www.defenselink.mil/

The DOD is the U.S. government defense institution. Its U.S. Army Corps of Engineers have been involved in navigation, flood control, environmental protection, disaster response, and other water-related engineering projects.

U.S. Army Corps of Engineers
441 G St. NW

Washington, DC 20314
Phone: (202) 761-0008
Fax: (202) 761-1683
Website: http://www.usace.army.mil/

The Army Corps of Engineers provides responsive engineering services to the nation, including in the planning, design, building, and operation of water-resources and other civil works projects. These include Navigation, Flood Control, Environmental Protection, Disaster Response, etc.

DEPARTMENT OF ENERGY (DOE)
Main Offices
Secretary Spencer Abraham
U.S. Department of Energy
1000 Independence Ave. SW
Washington, DC 20585
Phone: toll free, (800) DIAL-DOE (342-5363)
Fax: (202) 586-4403
E-mail: the.secretary@hq.doe.gov
Website: http://www.energy.gov/

The Department of Energy is a cabinet-level agency. Its overarching mission is enhancing national security. Responsibility for accomplishing this mission is shared among four principle program lines: the department's national defense programs, its energy program, its environmental program, and its science program. The agencies within the department most concerned with water issues are the Office of Energy Efficiency and Renewable Energy (EERE), the Federal Energy Regulatory Commission (FERC), the Bonneville Power Administration (BPA), the Southwestern Power Administration, the Southeastern Power Administration, and the Western Area Power Administration.

Bonneville Power Administration (BPA)
PO Box 3621
Portland, OR 97208-3621
Phone: (503) 230-3000; toll free, (800) 282-3713
E-mail: comment@bpa.gov
Website: http://www.bpa.gov/indexmain.shtml

The BPA, under the U.S. Department of Energy, markets wholesale electrical power and operates transmission services in the Pacific Northwest. The power comes from thirty-one federal hydro-electric projects, one nonfederal nuclear plant, and several other nonfederal power plants. The hydroelectric projects and the electrical system are known as the Federal Columbia River Power System. About 45 percent of the electric power used in the Northwest comes from the BPA.

Federal Energy Regulatory Commission (FERC)
Division of Dam Safety and Inspections Headquarters
888 1st St. NE
Washington, DC 20426
Phone: (202) 502-6734
Fax: (202) 219-2731
Website: http://www.ferc.fed.us/

The FERC is an independent regulatory agency within the Department of Energy. Among other things, FERC licenses and inspects private, municipal, and state hydroelectric projects and oversees environmental matters related to natural gas, oil, electricity, and hydroelectric projects.

Southeastern Power Administration (Southeastern)
Phone: (706) 213-3864; (706) 213-3865
Fax: (706) 213-3819; (706) 283-1787
E-mail: ops@sepa.fed.us
Website: http://sepa.fed.us/

Southeastern markets federal hydroelectric power at the lowest possible cost to public entities and cooperatives in the southeastern United States. It is responsible for marketing electric power and energy generated at reservoirs operated by the U.S. Army Corps of Engineers in the states of West Virginia, Virginia, North Carolina, South Carolina, Georgia, Florida, Alabama, Mississippi, Tennessee, and Kentucky as well as in southern Illinois.

Southwestern Power Administration (Southwestern)
Phone: (918) 595-6600
Fax: (918) 595-6656
E-mail: info@swpa.gov
Website: http://www.swpa.gov/

Southwestern Power Administration is an agency of the U.S. Department of Energy that markets and delivers federal hydroelectric power. Southwestern attempts to make the best use of federal assets in order to repay the federal investment while balancing the power needs of the diverse interests of other water users. The agency is responsible for marketing hydroelectric power produced at twenty-three U.S. Army Corps of Engineers multipurpose dams. By law, publicly held entities, such as rural electric cooperatives and municipal utilities, are given preference in the marketing of this power and associated energy. Southwestern has over 100 such "preference" customers, which ultimately serve over 7 million consumers.

Western Area Power Administration
PO Box 281213
Lakewood, CO 80228-8213
Phone: (720) 962-7050; (720) 962-7059
Fax:(720) 962-7050
Website: http://www.wapa.gov/

The Western Area Power Administration, located within the U.S. Department of Energy, markets and delivers cost-based hydroelectric power and related services within a fifteen-state region of the central and western United States. It markets and conveys electricity from multi-use water projects. Its transmission system carries electricity from fifty-five hydropower plants operated by the Bureau of Reclamation, the U.S. Army Corps of Engineers, and the International Boundary and Water Commission. Together, these plants have a capacity of 10,600 megawatts

DEPARTMENT OF THE INTERIOR
Main Offices
Secretary Gale Norton
U.S. Department of the Interior
1849 C St. NW
Washington, DC 20240
Phone: (202) 208-3100
Website: http://www.doi.gov/

The Department of the Interior is in the president's cabinet. Since 1849, it has had a wide range of responsibilities entrusted to it, including, for example, the construction of the water system of the nation's capital, the exploration of the western wilderness, the regulation of territorial governments, the management of public parks, and the basic responsibilities for Indians, public lands, patents, and pensions—all of them in one way or another having to do with the internal development of the nation or the welfare of its people. Among its departments with an impact on water issues are the Bureau of Land Management (BLM), the Office of Surface Mining Reclamation and Enforcement, the Bureau of Reclamation, the Fish and Wildlife Service, the U.S. Geological Survey (USGS), the National Park Service (NPS).

Bureau of Land Management (BLM)
1849 C St. NW
Washington, DC 20240
Phone: (202) 208-6731
Website: http://www.blm.gov/nhp/

The mission of the Bureau of Land Management is to sustain the health, diversity, and productivity of public lands.

Bureau of Reclamation
1849 C St. NW
Washington, DC 20240-0001
Phone: (202) 513-0501
Fax: (202) 513-0314
Website: http://www.usbr.gov/main/what/index.html

The Bureau of Reclamation has constructed more than 600 dams and reservoirs. Water projects such as dams, power plants, and canals constructed by the bureau in the seventeen western states (Arizona, California, Colorado, Idaho, Kansas, Montana, Nebraska, Nevada, New Mexico, North Dakota, Oklahoma, Oregon, South Dakota, Texas, Utah, Washington, and Wyoming) encouraged homesteading and promoted the economic development of the West. The bureau strives to manage, develop, and protect water and related resources in an environmentally and economically sound manner. Reclamation seeks to protect local economies and preserve natural resources and ecosystems through the effective use of water.

Fish and Wildlife Service
Division of Information Technology Management
Information Quality Guidelines Coordinator
Room 340
4401 N. Fairfax Dr.
Arlington, VA 22203
Fax: (703) 358-2251
E-mail: InfoQuality@fws.gov

Website: http://www.fws.gov/
Habitat and Conservation Section
E-mail: refuges@fws.gov
Website: http://refuges.fws.gov/habitats/index.html

The Habitat and Conservation Section of the Fish and Wildlife Service addresses, among other concerns, bird habitat conservation, contaminants, ecosystem conservation, endangered species, invasive species, wetlands, and wilderness. Among its programs are comprehensive conservation plans, a contaminant information and analysis system for refuges, and habitat management plans.

National Park Service (NPS)
National Park Service Headquarters
1849 C St. NW
Washington, DC 20240
Phone: (202) 208-6843
Website: http://www.nps.gov/

The NPS, formed by the Organic Act of 1916, promotes and regulates the use of national parks, monuments, and reservations for the purpose of conserving the scenery, natural and historic objects, and wildlife. Its purpose is to allow these resources to be enjoyed in a way that will leave them unimpaired for the benefit of future generations. The NPS also strives to be a guardian of the nation's diverse cultural and recreational resources, an environmental advocate, a world leader in the parks and preservation community, and a pioneer in the drive to protect U.S. open space.

Office of Surface Mining Reclamation and Enforcement–Clean Streams Program
1951 Constitution Ave. NW
Washington, DC 20240
Phone: (202) 208-2719
Website: http://www.osmre.gov/acsihome.htm

The Office of Surface Mining Reclamation and Enforcement, in cooperation with the states and Native American tribes, carries out the requirements of the Surface Mining Control and Reclamation Act (SMCRA). Its Clean Streams Program is a broad-based program that involves citizens, industry, and government entities in cleaning up streams polluted by acid drainage and eliminating acid mine drainage from abandoned coal mines.

Begun as an initiative in 1994, this program has funded seventy-seven projects in ten states.

U.S. Geological Survey (USGS)
USGS National Center
12201 Sunrise Valley Dr.
Reston, VA 20192
Phone: (703) 648-4000
USGS Information Number: (888) ASK-USGS (275-8747)
Websites: http://www.usgs.gov/
Water Resources of the United States: http://water.usgs.gov/

Among its other activities, the USGS provides reliable scientific information to describe and understand the earth and manages water, biological, energy, and mineral resources. Its website "Water Resources of the United States" is the perfect starting point for a search for any water information in any state.

DEPARTMENT OF JUSTICE (DOJ)
Main Offices
950 Pennsylvania Ave. NW
Washington, DC 20530-0001
Phone: (202) 353-1555
E-mail: AskDOJ@usdoj.gov
Website: http://www.usdoj.gov/

The DOJ is a cabinet-level agency whose mission is to enforce the law, to defend the interests of the United States according to the law, and to provide federal leadership in preventing and controlling crime. It plays a role in the enforcement of environmental and freshwater protection and use laws, and this role can be crucial in the way water resources are managed.

DEPARTMENT OF STATE
Main Offices
Secretary Colin L. Powell
U.S. Department of State
2201 C St. NW
Washington, DC 20520
Phone: (202) 647-4000
Website: http://www.state.gov/

The Department of State is part of the president's cabinet. It is the lead U.S. foreign affairs agency, and the secretary of state, the ranking member of the cabinet and fourth in line of presidential succession, is the president's principal adviser on foreign policy and the person chiefly responsible for U.S. representation abroad. The Department of State's interest in water issues is focused on the relation between U.S. water interests and other nations' water interests.

Oceans, International Environment, and Scientific Affairs Office (OES)
U.S. Department of State
2201 C St. NW
Washington, DC 20520
Phone: (202) 647-4000
Website: http://www.state.gov/www/global/oes/

The OES is involved with and has access to international water issues and negotiations. It is key to the Department of State's foreign policy formulation and implementation regarding issues of global environment, science, and technology.

DEPARTMENT OF TRANSPORTATION
Main Offices
Secretary Norman Y. Mineta
U.S. Department of Transportation
400 7th St. SW
Washington, DC 20590
Phone: (202) 366-4000
Website: http://www.dot.gov/index.cfm

The Department of Transportation is a cabinet-level agency. Among its other responsibilities, it oversees the formulation of national transportation policy. Its sections most concerned with water issues are the Maritime Administration (MARAD), the St. Lawrence Seaway Development Corporation (SLSDC), and the Office of Pipeline Safety.

Maritime Administration (MARAD)
U.S. Department of Transportation
400 7th St. SW
Washington, DC 20590
Phone: toll free, (800) 99-MARAD (996-2723); (800) 996-2723
Website: http://www.marad.dot.gov/

The overall mission of the Maritime Administration is to promote the development and maintenance of an adequate, well-balanced U.S. merchant marine that is sufficient to carry the nation's domestic waterborne commerce. It also promotes waterborne foreign commerce that is capable of serving as a naval and military auxiliary in time of war or national emergency. MARAD seeks to ensure that the United States has adequate shipbuilding and repair services, efficient ports, effective water and land transportation systems, and reserve shipping capacity in time of national emergency.

Office of Pipeline Safety
U.S. Department of Transportation
Office of Pipeline Safety, Research and
  Special Programs Administration
400 Seventh St. SW
Room 7128
Washington DC 20590-0001
Phone: (202) 366-4595
Fax: (202) 366-4566
Website: http://ops.dot.gov/

The Office of Pipeline Safety is concerned to ensure the safe, reliable, and environmentally sound operation of the nation's pipeline transportation system, including water transportation.

St. Lawrence Seaway Development Corporation (SLSDC)
Policy Headquarters
400 Seventh St. SW
Suite 5424
Washington, DC 20590
Phone: (202) 366-0091; toll free, (800) 785-2779
Fax: (202) 366-7147
Websites: http://www.seaway.dot.gov/
http://www.greatlakes-seaway.com/en/aboutus/slsdc.html

SLSDC serves the U.S. transportation system by improving the operations and maintenance of the St. Lawrence Seaway to make it a safe, reliable, efficient, and competitive deep-draft international waterway. It works in cooperation with the Canadian St. Lawrence Seaway Management Corporation.

U.S. CONGRESS
Main Offices
U.S. House of Representatives
Washington, DC 20515
Phone: (202) 224-3121
TTY: (202) 225-1904
Website: http://www.house.gov/

U.S. Senate
Website (which provides contact for individual senators):
http://www.senate.gov/

The Congress is the legislative branch of the U.S. government. Its members are influential in making water policy, funding it, and providing statutes that mandate enforcement issues. Those who are concerned about water topics can contact their senators and congressional representatives to make their voices heard.

Congressional Budget Office (CBO)
The Congressional Budget Ford House Office Building
  (formerly House Annex II)
4th Floor
2nd and D Sts. SW
Washington, DC 20515-6925
Phone: (202) 226-2600
Fax: (202) 226-2714
Website: http://www.cbo.gov/

The CBO provides Congress with objective, timely, nonpartisan analyses, information, and estimates needed for economic and budgetary decisions. The CBO's mandate is relatively narrow, but its subject matter gives it a broad reach, reflecting the wide array of activities that the federal budget covers and the major role the budget plays in the U.S. economy. It thus influences decisions made regarding water legislation or programs, and funding issues can be crucial to water management.

Congressional Research Service (CRS)
Library of Congress
101 Independence Ave. SE
Washington, DC 20540-7500
Website: http://www.governmentguide.com/

Congress created the CRS in order to have its own source of non-partisan, objective analysis and research. Its sole mission is to provide the U.S. Congress, throughout the legislative process, with comprehensive and reliable analysis, research, and information that is timely, objective, nonpartisan, and confidential. This objective research is important to the formulation of water legislation.

INDEPENDENT AGENCIES
Appalachian Regional Commission
1666 Connecticut Ave. NW
Washington, DC 20235
Phone: (202) 884-7700
Fax: (202) 884-7691
E-mail: crea@arc.gov
Website: http://www.arc.gov

The Appalachian Regional Commission's mission is to be an advocate for and partner with the people of Appalachia to create opportunities for self-sustaining economic development and improved quality of life. Among its water-related activities is the creation of programs to develop tourism in Appalachia.

Environmental Protection Agency (EPA)
Office of Water (4101M)
1200 Pennsylvania Ave. NW
Washington, DC 20460
E-mail: See the website's "Contact Us" link for e-mail addresses for regional offices.
Website: http://www.epa.gov/ebtpages/water.html

The EPA is charged with the enforcement of federal clean water and safe drinking water laws. It provides support for municipal wastewater treatment plants, and takes part in pollution prevention efforts aimed at protecting watersheds and sources of drinking water. The agency carries out both regulatory and voluntary programs to fulfill its mission to protect the nation's waters.

Federal Maritime Commission
800 North Capitol St. NW
Room 900
Washington, DC 20573
Phone: (202) 523-5783; (202) 523-5860

Fax: (202) 523-5785; (202) 523-3725
Website: http://www.fmc.gov/

The Federal Maritime Commission regulates common carriers by water and others involved in the foreign and domestic offshore commerce of the United States. It was formed under provisions of the Shipping Act (1916), the Intercoastal Shipping Act (1933), the Shipping Act of 1984; section 19 of the Merchant Marine Act (1920); the Foreign Shipping Practices Act of 1988; statutes governing the financial responsibility for death or injury to passengers and for nonperformance of voyages, and other applicable statutes. Among the water-related issues it addresses are the responsibilities of those carrying cargo and passengers on the Great Lakes and other navigable waters.

General Accounting Office (GAO)
Office of Public Affairs
441 G St. NW
Washington, DC 20548
Phone: (202) 512-4800
Website: http://www.gao.gov/

The GAO is an agency that, at the request of Congress, studies the programs and expenditures of the federal government. It advises Congress and the heads of executive agencies, such as the Environmental Protection Agency, about ways to make government more effective and responsive. It evaluates federal programs, audits federal expenditures, and issues legal opinions, and its reports to Congress include recommendations for action. One example of water-related research carried out by the GAO is the report "Delaware River Deepening Project: Comprehensive Reanalysis Needed" (GAO-02-604, June 7, 2002).

Tennessee Valley Authority (TVA)
400 W. Summit Hill Dr.
Knoxville, TN 37902-1499
Phone: (865) 632-2101
Website: http://tva.gov/

The TVA operates a network of reservoirs and power plants that supply affordable, reliable power and manage a thriving, complex river system in the Tennessee Valley. It built dams to harness the region's rivers, control floods, improve navigation, and generate electricity.

BOARDS, COMMITTEES, AND COMMISSIONS
Delaware River Basin Commission
25 State Police Dr.
PO Box 7360
West Trenton, NJ 08628-0360
Phone: (609) 883-9500
Fax: (609) 883-9522
Website: http://www.state.nj.us/drbc/drbc.htm

The Delaware is the longest undammed river east of the Mississippi, extending 330 miles from the confluence of its east and west branches at Hancock, New York, to the mouth of the Delaware Bay. The river is fed by 216 tributaries, the largest being the Schuylkill and Lehigh Rivers in Pennsylvania. In all, the basin contains 13,539 square miles, draining parts of Pennsylvania (6,422 square miles, or 50.3 percent of the basin's total land area), New Jersey (2,969 square miles, 23.3 percent), New York (2,362 square miles, 18.5 percent), and Delaware (1,002 square miles, 7.9 percent). Over 17 million people rely on the waters of the Delaware River Basin for drinking and industrial use. New York City, which lies outside the watershed, gets roughly half its water from three reservoirs located on tributaries to the Delaware, and the Delaware Bay is within a day's drive for about 40 percent of the U.S. population, even though the basin drains only 0.4 percent of the total continental U.S. land area. The commission includes four basin-state governors and a federal representative who is a presidential appointee. It works to carry out river-basin planning and development, and it acts as the regulatory agency for the interstate partnership.

Mississippi River Commission (MRC)
Public Affairs
Phone: (601) 634-5760
Fax: (601) 634-7110
E-mail: webmaster@mvd02.usace.army.mil
Website: http://www.mvd.usace.army.mil/MRC/history.htm

The Mississippi River Commission was established in 1879 to facilitate the improvement of the Mississippi River from the Head of Passes near its mouth to its headwaters. Today, the MRC covers three areas: investigations to determine necessary improvements, construction of new facilities, and maintenance and operation of systems in place.

**Pacific Northwest Electric Power and Conservation
Planning Council (Northwest Power Planning Council)**
Northwest Power Planning Council
Public Affairs Division
851 SW 6th Ave.
Suite 1100
Portland, Oregon 97204
Phone: (503) 222-5161; (800) 452-5161
Fax: (503) 820-2370
E-mail: info@nwppc.org
Website: http://www.nwppc.org

Through the Northwest Power Act of 1980 (PL 96-502), the U.S. Congress authorized Idaho, Montana, Washington, and Oregon to create the Pacific Northwest Electric Power and Conservation Planning Council (commonly known as the Northwest Power Planning Council). The four state governors each appoint two members to this planning and policymaking body. Congress charged the council with developing a program to protect, mitigate, and enhance fish and wildlife affected by the development, operation, and management of hydroelectric facilities in the Columbia River Basin; to assure the Pacific Northwest an adequate, efficient, economical, and reliable power supply; to develop a power plan that included a twenty-year demand forecast, an energy conservation program, and the fish and wildlife program; and to involve the public extensively in the decisionmaking process.

Susquehanna River Basin Commission
1721 North Front St.
Harrisburg, PA 17102
Phone: (717) 238-0423
Fax: (717) 238-2438
E-mail: srbc@srbc.net
Website: http://www.srbc.net/

The Susquehanna River Basin Commission, an interstate watershed agency, applies comprehensive watershed management and planning principles to manage the water resources of the Susquehanna River Basin. The commission's sphere of influence is not determined by political boundaries. Rather, the Susquehanna River and its many tributaries form the 27,510-square-mile drainage area. Under the authority of the Susquehanna River Basin Compact, the commission can deal with water-resource problems occurring anywhere in this vast drainage area. It has adopted a comprehensive plan to guide not only its own policies but also those of its members—New York, Pennsylvania, Maryland, and the federal government. This plan is the official blueprint for the management and development of the basin's water resources.

BILATERAL ORGANIZATIONS
International Boundary and Water Commission (United States–Mexico)
U.S. Section offices:
4171 North Mesa
Suite C-310
El Paso, TX 79902-1441
Phone: toll free, (800) 262-8857

The International Boundary and Water Commission works to provide sensitive, timely, and fiscally responsible boundary-water and environmental services in the United States–Mexico border region. It provides these services to create an atmosphere of binational cooperation, in a manner responsive to the concerns of the public and other stakeholders in both nations. The region along the boundary is characterized by deserts, rugged mountains, abundant sunshine, and two major rivers—the Colorado River and the Rio Grande—which provide life-giving waters to the largely arid but fertile lands along the rivers in both countries. The international cooperation is vital to the management of these water resources.

International Joint Commission (United States–Canada)
U.S. Section offices:
1250 23rd St. NW
Suite 100
Washington, DC 20440
Phone: (202) 736-9000
Fax: (202) 735-9015
Canadian Section offices:
234 Laurier Ave. W
22nd Floor
Ottawa, ON K1P 6K6
Canada
Phone: (613) 995-2984

Fax: (613) 993-5583
Joint website: http://www.ijc.org/

Canada and the United States created the International Joint Commission because each country is affected by the other's actions in lake and river systems along the border. The two countries attempt to manage these waters for the benefit of both U.S. and Canadian citizens and to protect them for future generations. From time to time, differing needs conflict, and the commission may play the role of authorizing uses while protecting competing interests in accordance with rules set out by the two governments in the treaty establishing the committee. For example, the commission may be called upon to approve applications for dams or canals in these waters. If it approves such a project, it can set conditions limiting water levels and flows to protect shore properties and wetlands and the interests of farmers, shippers, and other interested parties. Once the structure is built, the commission may continue to play a role in its operations.

State Government Agencies

In this section, we present the key elements of water management in each of the U.S. states. The entries have been designed to give the reader an idea of what the different states consider to be priorities for water management in their jurisdiction. All the information in the entries comes from the website addresses listed for each state. The states' websites should be accessed to find additional, more in-depth information.

The entries give the most up-to-date contact information, as of this writing, for the primary state water agencies, divisions, or departments. They also outline the basic mission of each agency, division, or department or give information regarding the laws that created it. And last, each entry outlines the main duties of the agency, division, or department, or presents information about its key offices or programs, or lists its partner agencies in the state.

You will notice that the states are very different in their approaches to water management. For example, some states organize management around water quality. Others separate quality concerns from other water issues, making one division responsible for quality and creating other divisions to deal with irrigation, navigation, recreation, hydroelectric power, or other freshwater concerns. Also, some states are very descriptive about their duties in their website; others are very sparse in their explanations of what their water departments do. The list clearly demonstrates these differences.

Alabama
Alabama Department of Environmental Management
    (ADEM)—Water Division
PO Box 301463
Montgomery, AL 36130-1463
Phone: (334) 271-7823
Fax: (334) 279-3051
Website: http://www.adem.state.al.us/

ADEM administers all federal environmental laws, including the Clean Air, Clean Water, and Safe Drinking Water Acts and federal laws on solid and hazardous waste. ADEM assumed these responsibilities only after it was demonstrated that state laws and regulations are at least equivalent to federal standards and that the state has matching funds and personnel available to administer the programs.

Duties, key departments, or partner agencies: Industrial Water, Municipal Water, Water Quality, Drinking Water, State Revolving Fund, Operator Certification, and Groundwater.

Alaska
Alaska Department of Natural Resources:
Division of Mining, Land, and Water
550 West 7th Ave.
Anchorage, AK 99501
Phone: (907) 269-8600
Fax: (907) 269-8904
Website: http://www.dnr.state.ak.us/mlw/index.htm

Alaska's constitution declares water to be a public resource, and all surface and subsurface waters on all lands are reserved to the people for common use and are subject to appropriation in accordance with the Alaska Water Use Act.

Duties, key departments, or partner agencies: Water Resources Program (Water Management Unit, Hydrologic Survey Unit, Dam Safety and Construction Unit), Navigability Program, Aquatic Farming Program.

Arizona
Arizona Department of Water Resources
500 North 3rd St.
Phoenix, AZ 85004
Phone: (602) 417-2400; toll free (800) 352-8488
Website: http://water.az.gov/default.htm

The Arizona Department of Water Resources administers and enforces Arizona's groundwater code and surface water–rights laws except for those related to water quality. It negotiates with external political entities to protect Arizona's Colorado River water supply, oversees the use of groundwater and surface water under state jurisdiction, and represents Arizona in discussions of water rights with the federal government.

Duties, key departments, or partner agencies: Rural Arizona Watershed Alliance, Recharge: The Underground Water Storage Program, Governor's Water Management Commission, Arizona Water Protection Fund, Arizona Water Banking Authority.

Arkansas
Arkansas Department of Environmental Quality
Water Division
8001 National Dr.
Little Rock, AR 72209
Phone: (501) 682-0654
Fax: (501) 682-0910
Website: http://www.adeq.state.ar.us

The Arkansas Department of Environmental Quality was created to preserve and enhance the quality of the state's waters in accordance with environmental laws and regulations.

Duties, key departments, or partner agencies: Water Programs, Water Quality Standards, Water Samples, Wetlands, Groundwater, Extraordinary Resource Water, Fish Kills, Clean Lakes Program.

California
California Department of Water Resources
PO Box 942836
Room 1115-17
Sacramento, CA 94236-0001
Phone: (916) 653-0488
E-mail: chippl@water.ca.gov

Website: http://www.dwr.water.ca.gov/
dir-organizationsR2/ORG-Div_Executive_R2.html

The California Department of Water Resources manages the water resources of California, in cooperation with other agencies, to benefit the people of the state and to protect, restore, and enhance the natural and human environments.

Duties, key departments, or partner agencies: Reclamation Board, Water Transfers Office, Bay-Delta Office, Division of Flood Management, Division of Land and Right of Way, Division of Safety of Dams, Division of Planning and Local Assistance, Division of Operations and Maintenance, State Water Project Analysis Office, Division of Engineering, Division of Environmental Services, Office of Water Education, Division of Management Services, Office of the Chief Counsel, Division of Fiscal Services, Division of Technology Services, Equal Opportunity and Management Investigations Office, Internal Audit Office.

Colorado
Colorado Division of Water Resources
(Office of the State Engineer)
1313 Sherman St.
Room 818
Denver, CO 80203
Phone: (303) 866-3581
Fax: (303) 866-3589
E-mail: dwrweb@state.co.us
Website: http://www.water.state.co.us/

The Colorado Division of Water Resources attempts to take a leadership role in the Colorado water community and in water issues related to the western United States. This is accomplished by focusing on the following areas: people, water, and stewardship.

Duties, key departments, or partner agencies: Dam Safety, Ground Water, Surface Water, and Records.

Connecticut
Connecticut Department of Environmental Protection
Bureau of Water Management
79 Elm St.
Hartford, Connecticut 06106-5127
Phone: (860) 424-3704

Fax: (860) 424-4067
Website: http://www.dep.state.ct.us/wtr/index.htm

The Connecticut Department of Environmental Protection protects and restores the state's surface water, groundwater, and water-related resources to protect the public water supply, human health and safety, and the propagation of fish and aquatic life; to provide hazard mitigation and river restoration; and to preserve and enhance water-based recreation and the natural character and economic well-being of the state.

Duties, key departments, or partner agencies: Aquifer Protection, Floodplain Management, Dam Safety, Wetlands Protection, River Restoration.

Delaware
Delaware Department of Natural Resources and
  Environmental Control (DNREC)
89 Kings Highway
Dover, DE 19901
Phone: (302) 739-4764
Website: http://www.dnrec.state.de.us/

The home page of the Delaware Department of Natural Resources and Environmental Control proclaims "Protecting Delaware's Environment for Future Generations." The website provides a comprehensive listing of links to the many divisions covered by the DNREC.

Duties, key departments, or partner agencies: Water Resources, Watershed Management, Water Quality.

Florida
Florida Department of Environmental Protection
Water Resources Management
3900 Commonwealth Blvd.
Tallahassee, FL 32399
Phone: (850) 488-2976
Website: http://www.dep.state.fl.us/default.htm

The home page of the Florida Department of Environmental Protection proclaims "More Protection, Less Process." It manages water quality and quantity through the state's five water-management districts.

Duties, key departments, or partner agencies: Domestic and Industrial Wastewater Management, Everglades Technical Support, Dam Safety, Coastal and Aquatic Managed Areas.

Georgia
Georgia Department of Natural Resources
Georgia Environmental Protection Division
2 Martin Luther King Jr. Dr.
Suite 1152 East Tower
Atlanta, Georgia 30334
Phone: (404) 657-5947; toll free, (888) 373-5947
Fax: (404) 651-5778
Website: http://www.ganet.org/dnr/environ/

The Georgia Department of Natural Resources works to sustain, enhance, protect, and conserve Georgia's natural, historic, and cultural resources for present and future generations.

Duties, key departments, or partner agencies: Watershed Protection, Drinking Water, Fish Consumption Guidelines, Floodplain Management, Water Allocation and Resources, Water Use Restrictions, Establishment of a Joint Study Committee to Create a Comprehensive State Water Plan.

Hawaii
Department of Land and Natural Resources
Commission on Water Resource Management
PO Box 621
Honolulu, HI 96813
Phone: (808) 587-0214
Fax: (808) 587-0219
E-mail: dlnr_cwrm@exec.state.hi.us
Website: http://www.state.hi.us/dlnr/cwrm/index.html

Hawaii's Commission on Water Resource Management is required to implement and utilize comprehensive water-resources planning in its regulation and management of water resources.

Duties, key departments, or partner agencies: The Hawaii Water Plan (Water Resource Protection Plan, State Water Projects Plan, Water Quality Plan, Agricultural Water Use and Development Plan, County Water Use and Development Plans); the Hawaii Drought Plan.

Idaho
Idaho Department of Water Resources
1301 North Orchard St.
Boise, ID 83706
Phone: (208) 327-7900
Fax: (208) 327-7866
Website: http://www.idwr.state.id.us/

The Idaho Department of Water Resources was created in 1895 to ensure that water and energy are conserved and available to sustain Idaho's economy, ecosystems, and the resulting quality of life.

Duties, key departments, or partner agencies: Water Management Division, Resource Protection Bureau, Water Allocation Bureau, Adjudication Bureau, Water Planning Bureau, Technical Services Bureau, Energy Division.

Illinois
Illinois Environmental Protection Agency
Bureau of Water
1021 North Grand Ave. East
Springfield, IL 62702
Phone: (217) 782-3397
Website: http://www.epa.state.il.us/water/index.html

The Illinois Environmental Protection Agency works to ensure that the rivers, streams, and lakes of Illinois will support a variety of uses. These include the protection of aquatic life, recreation, and drinking water supplies and the protection of the groundwater in Illinois. It also ensures that every Illinois public water system provides consistently safe drinking water.

Duties, key departments, or partner agencies: Water Pollution Control, Public Water Supply, Financial Assistance.

Indiana
Indiana Natural Resources Commission
Indiana Government Center South
402 W. Washington St.
Room W272
Indianapolis, IN 46204
Phone: (317) 232-4699

Fax: (317) 233-2977
Website: http://www.IN.gov/nrc/

The Department of Natural Resources is the state agency primarily responsible by statute for regulating activities related to "water quantity."

Duties, key departments, or partner agencies: Lake Michigan and Other Navigable Waters, Dams and Dam Safety, Water Wells and Groundwater Rights, Water Well Drilling, Surface Water Rights, Water Withdrawal Facilities, Conservancy District, Wetlands and Habitat Mitigation.

Iowa
Iowa Environmental Protection Division
Water Quality Bureau
Henry A. Wallace Bldg.
502 E. 9th St.
Des Moines, IA 50319-0034
Phone: (515) 281-5817
Fax: (515) 281-8895
E-mail: epdweb@dnr.state.water.ia.us
Website: http://www.state.ia.us/epd/index.htm

The Water Supply Section of the Iowa Department of Natural Resources regulates public drinking water supplies in Iowa according to the federal Safe Drinking Water Act, under authority from the U.S. Environmental Protection Agency. It is responsible for water quality and water quantity programs. The Wastewater Section issues both construction and operation permits.

Duties, key departments, or partner agencies: Water Use, Public Water Supply, Operations Permits/Lab Information, Water Quality, Water Quantity, Floodplain Management, Dam Safety Inspections, Wastewater.

Kansas
Kansas Department of Health and Environment
Division of Environment
Bureau of Water
1000 S.W. Jackson St.
Suite 420
Topeka, KS 66612-1367
Phone: (785) 296-5500

Fax: (785) 296-5509
Website: http://www.kdhe.state.ks.us/water/index.html

The Bureau of Water administers programs related to public water supplies, wastewater treatment systems, the disposal of sewage, and non–point sources of pollution. Programs are intended to provide safe drinking water, prevent water pollution, and assure compliance with state and federal laws and regulations such as the Clean Water Act and Safe Drinking Water Act.

Duties, key departments, or partner agencies: Water Quality, Surface Water, Wastewater Treatment.

Kentucky
Kentucky Natural Resources and Environmental
  Protection Cabinet
Kentucky Division of Water
14 Reilly Rd.
Frankfort, KY 40601
Phone: (502) 564-3410
Website: http//water.nr.state.ky.us/dow/dwhome.htm

The Kentucky Division of Water is responsible for managing, protecting, and enhancing the water resources of the Commonwealth of Kentucky for present and future generations using voluntary, regulatory, and educational programs.

Duties, key departments, or partner agencies: Environmental Emergencies, News and Publications, Water Permits and Approvals, Public Hearings and Public Meetings, Watershed Management, Water Watch.

Louisiana
Louisiana Department of Environmental Quality
PO Box 82135
Baton Rouge, LA 70884-2135
Phone: (225) 765-0219
Fax: (225) 765-0222
E-mail: webmaster@deq.state.la.us
Website: http://www.deq.state.la.us/

The Louisiana Department of Environmental Quality (DEQ) was created by the Louisiana Legislature on February 1, 1984, by a statute known as the Louisiana Environmental Quality Act

(EQA). Its mission is to maintain a healthful and safe environment for the people of Louisiana. The department is staffed by biologists, chemists, physicists, geologists, engineers, lawyers, and other professionals dedicated to preserving and protecting Louisiana's environment.

Duties, key departments, or partner agencies: Water Quality, Water Cycle, Water Resources, Storm Water Discharge, Source Water Protection.

Maine
Maine Department of Environmental Protection (DEP)
Bureau of Land and Water Quality
17 State House Station
Augusta, ME 04333-0017
Phone: (207) 287-7688; toll free, (800) 452-1942
Fax: (207) 287-7191
E-mail: deplw@sstate.me.us
Website: http://www.state.me.us/dep/blwq/homepage.htm

Maine DEP works to achieve environmental protection and regulation in the state of Maine. The Bureau of Land and Water Quality administers land and water quality protection programs and includes five divisions: two regulatory divisions, a science division, a planning division, and a financial and technical assistance division.

Duties, key departments, or partner agencies: Coastal Waters, Lakes, Groundwater, Streams/Rivers, Grants and Loans, Treatment Facilities, Monitoring and Assessment, Toxic and Biological Monitoring, Permits and Standards, Wastewater Protection, Watershed Planning and Management.

Maryland
Maryland Department of the Environment
2500 Broening Highway
Baltimore, MD 21224
Phone: (410) 631-3000; toll free, 800-633-6101
E-mail: webmaster@mde.state.md.us
Website: http://www.mde.state.md.us/environment/index.html

The Maryland Department of the Environment strives to protect and restore the quality of Maryland's air, land, and water resources, while fostering economic development, healthy and safe communities, and quality environmental education for the benefit of the environment, public health, and future generations.

Duties, key departments, or partner agencies: Wetlands and Waterways, Stormwater Management Program, Source Water Assessment Plan, Water Quality and Drinking Water, State Flood Hazard Mitigation Program, Pfiesteria Fact Sheet, Wellhead Protection Program, Fish and Shellfish Tissue Contaminant Monitoring, Maryland's Surface Water Quality Standards.

Massachusetts
Massachusetts Water Resources Authority (MWRA)
Charlestown Navy Yard
100 First Ave.
Boston, MA 02129
Phone: toll free, (866) 888-2808
Fax: (617) 626-4516
Website: http://www.mwra.state.ma.us/

The MWRA is an independent authority that provides wholesale water and sewer services to its customer communities. It was created by the legislature in 1984 and inherited operations and facilities to promote water conservation. The overarching theme for all its water conservation activities has been the twofold mission of protecting water resources while helping consumers control their costs.

Duties, key departments, or partner agencies: Watershed Protection, Water Treatment, Water Delivery (Metro West Tunnel), Covered Water Storage, Distribution Pipeline Improvements.

Michigan
Department of Environmental Quality (DEQ)
Constitution Hall
PO Box 30473
Lansing, MI 48909
Phone: (517) 335-9218
E-mail: deq-webmaster@Michigan.gov
Website: http://www.MI.gov/deq/

Land and Water Management Division
Phone: (517) 373-1120

Surface Water Quality Division
Phone: (517) 373-1949

The Michigan DEQ regulates activities that may have potential impacts on the public trust or riparian rights or that may impair or destroy the waters or other natural resources of the state. These resources include inland lakes and streams, the Great Lakes, wetlands, and groundwater. The water quality programs establish water quality standards, assess water quality, provide regulatory oversight for all public water supplies, issue permits to regulate the discharge of industrial and municipal wastewaters, and monitor state water resources for water quality, the quantity and quality of aquatic habitat, the health of aquatic communities, and compliance with state laws.

Duties, key departments, or partner agencies: Drinking Water; Great Lakes; Groundwater; Inland Lakes, Streams, and Surface Water; Wastewater Treatment Systems and Water Management; Water Quality Monitoring and Wetlands Protection.

Minnesota
Minnesota Department of Agriculture (MDA)
90 West Plato Blvd.
St. Paul, MN 55107
Phone: (651) 297-2200; toll free, (800) 967-2474
Website: http://www.mda.state.mn.us

The Minnesota Department of Agriculture (MDA) works toward a diverse agricultural industry that is profitable and environmentally sound. It works to protect public health and safety regarding food and agricultural products and to ensure orderly commerce in agricultural and food products. To help maintain pure water and fertile soil, MDA assists farmers and homeowners by developing guidelines for soil amendments and nutrient management in order to prevent excessive applications. It samples well water to check for pesticides and contamination and tests soils to analyze their composition.

Duties, key departments, or partner agencies: Flood Information (provides flood-damage prevention, a financial assistance program, and flood-cleanup assistance), Free Water Testing for Nitrates (gives general guidance and detailed technical information to help with the cleanup of agricultural chemical environmental contamination and emergency incidents in Minnesota), Incident

Response Program (offers general guidance and detailed technical information to help with the cleanup of agricultural, chemical, environmental, contamination, and emergency incidents in Minnesota).

Mississippi
Department of Environmental Quality
Office of Land and Water Resources
PO Box 10631
Jackson, MS 39289-0631
Phone: (601) 961-5332
Website: http://www.deq.state.ms.us%2Fnewweb%
2Fhomepages.nsf

The Office of Land and Water Resources, as part of the Department of Environmental Quality, is the agency charged with the conservation, management, protection, and the encouragement of appropriate development of the water resources of Mississippi.

Duties, key departments, or partner agencies: Division of Permitting and Monitoring, Division of Water Resources, Division of Hydrologic Investigation and Reporting, Division of Dam Safety.

Missouri
Department of Natural Resources
PO Box 176
Jefferson City, MO 65102
Phone: (573) 751-3443; toll free, (800) 361-4827
E-mail: oac@mail.dnr.state.mo.us
Website: http://www.dnr.state.mo.us/water.htm

The website provides links to all divisions and programs dealing with water resources and issues.

Duties, key departments, or partner agencies: Dam and Reservoir Safety Program, Environmental Quality Issues, Geologic Survey and Resource Assessment, Public Drinking Water Program, Soil and Water Conservation Program, Water Pollution Control Program, Water Resources Program.

Montana
Montana Department of Natural Resources and Conservation, Water Resources Division
48 North Last Chance Gulch

PO Box 201601
Helena, MT 59620-1601
Phone: (406) 444-6601
Fax: (406) 444-5918
Website: http://www.dnrc.state.mt.us/

The Water Resources Division of the Montana Department of Natural Resources and Conservation works to provide for the best use of the state's water resources for the citizens of Montana.

Duties, key departments, or partner agencies: Water Well Contractors, Dams and Canals, Floodplain Management, Water Rights, Water Supply Management, Montana Watercourse, Drought.

Nebraska
Nebraska Department of Natural Resources
301 Centennial Mall South
Lincoln, NE 68509-4676
Phone: (402) 471-2363
Fax: (402) 471-2900
Website: http://www.nrc.state.ne.us/

The home page of the Nebraska Department of Natural Resources declares that the department is dedicated to the sustainable use and proper management of the state's natural resources.

Duties, key departments, or partner agencies: Administration, Surface Water (addresses water rights and stream measurement), Ground Water (addresses well registration and administers rules and uses), Floodplain and Dam Safety (concerned with floodplain management, flood mitigation, and dam safety), Resources Management Fund (concerned with the water quality fund, water well decommissioning, and soil and water conservation).

Nevada
State of Nevada
Department of Conservation and Natural Resources
Division of Water Resources
123 W. Nye Lane
Room 246
Carson City, NV 89706-0818
Phone: (775) 687-4380
Fax: (775) 687-6972
Website: http://ndwr.state.nv.us/

Nevada's Department of Conservation and Natural Resources conserves, protects, manages, and enhances the state's water resources for its citizens through the appropriation and reallocation of the public waters.

Duties, key departments, or partner agencies: Water Rights, Engineering, Information Services, Floodplain Information, Water Planning, Mapping.

New Hampshire
Department of Environmental Services
6 Hazen Dr.
PO Box 95
Concord, NH 03302-0095
Phone: (603) 271-3503
Fax: (603) 271-2867
Website: http://www.des.state.nh.us

The Department of Environmental Services protects, maintains, and enhances environmental quality and public health in New Hampshire. The website states that its goals are to ensure that all New Hampshire's lakes and ponds, rivers and streams, coastal waters, groundwater, and wetlands are clean and support healthy ecosystems, provide habitats for a diversity of plant and animal life, and support appropriate uses; that the long-term and cumulative impacts of development, land-use changes, and water activities are well understood and well managed to minimize the impacts of human activities on our waters; that all drinking water in New Hampshire, whether surface or groundwater, is safe, conservatively used, and available; that all dams in New Hampshire are constructed, maintained, and operated in a safe manner; and that lake, streamflow, and surface and groundwater resources are used efficiently and managed to protect environmental quality, to enhance public safety and flood protection, and to support and balance a variety of social and ecological water needs.

Duties, key departments, or partner agencies:
- Safe Drinking Water Division: Conducts engineering reviews of all proposals to develop or expand public water supplies; conducts regular water quality sampling, water facility inspections, and facility operator licensing educational programs and offers technical assistance; administers a source-water protection program that includes a grant program for protecting lands surrounding water supplies.

- Wastewater Division: Oversees an extensive loan and state grant program for wastewater treatment facilities, reviews the engineering designs for such facilities, and ensures their proper construction and operation.
- Surface Water Division: Maintains active lake- and river-monitoring programs and biological and chemical analyses of rivers and water bodies; conducts water analyses on state waters, including those involving drinking water and industrial and municipal wastewater effluents; oversees lake and river volunteer monitoring programs, a public beach and swimming pool inspection program, and an acid rain monitoring program.

New Jersey
Department of Environmental Protection
PO Box 402
Trenton, NJ 08625-0402
Phone: (609) 777-3373
Fax: (609) 292-7695
Website: http://www.NJ.gov/dep/index.html

New Jersey's Department of Environmental Protection works to preserve, sustain, protect, and enhance the environment to ensure the integration of high environmental quality, public health, and economic vitality. Among its other goals and activities are the following: It develops and integrates an environmental master plan to assist in decisionmaking by making resource data available on the Geographic Information System. It defines and publishes reasonable, clear, and predictable scientifically based standards. It provides residents and visitors with affordable access to safe and clean open space and to historic and natural resources. It assures that nontreatable wastes are isolated, managed, and controlled. It uses education and communication to enhance environmental awareness and stewardship.

Duties, key departments, or partner agencies: Division of Water Quality, Water Supply Administration, Engineering (Dam Safety Section), Division of Watershed Management, Water Monitoring Management, Bureau of Marine Water Monitoring, Bureau of Freshwater and Biological Monitoring.

New Mexico
New Mexico Environment Department

Drinking Water Bureau
Harold S. Runnels Building
1190 St. Francis Dr.
Santa Fe, NM 87502-2855
Phone: (505) 827-2855; toll free, (800) 219-6157
Fax: (505) 827-7545
Website: http://www.nmenv.state.nm.us/dwb/dwbtop.html

The Drinking Water Bureau preserves, protects, and improves New Mexico's drinking water quality. Emphasis is placed on upholding the federal Safe Drinking Water Act and providing technical assistance, system oversight, and community outreach about safe drinking water.

Duties, key departments, or partner agencies: The Water and Wastewater Bureaus are concerned with Drinking Water, Radiation Control, DOE Oversight, Ground Water Quality, Surface Water Quality, Hazardous Waste, and Well Water Permits.

New York
New York State Department of Environmental Conservation
Division of Water
625 Broadway
Albany, NY 12233
Phone: (518) 402-8559
E-mail: dowinfo@gw.dec.state.ny.us
Website: http://www.dec.state.ny.us/

The New York State Department of Environmental Conservation serves as a steward of New York's water resources, protects and conserves those resources, assures their equitable and public beneficial use, maintains reasonable standards of water purity and quality, and protects the life, welfare, and property of the people of the state from adverse impact from the waters.

Duties, key departments, or partner agencies:
- To protect water quality in lakes, rivers, aquifers, and coastal areas by regulating wastewater discharges, monitoring bodies of water, and controlling surface runoff
- To manage freshwater resources and help communities prevent flood damage and beach erosion
- To promote water stewardship and education
- To maintain water quality suitable for all human, fish, and wildlife use and to plan for water conservation

• To carry out drought monitoring and management, flood control, coastal resource protection, and inspection of dams and to ensure public participation in decisions about water.

North Carolina
North Carolina Department of Environment
    and Natural Resources
Division of Water Resources
1611 Mail Service Center
Raleigh, NC 27699-1611
Phone: (919) 733-4064
Fax: (919) 733-3558
Website: http://www.dwr.ehnr.state.nc.us/

The North Carolina Division of Water Resources is responsible for local water supply plans, the state water supply plan, the registration of water withdrawals and transfers, and the provision of technical assistance to system operators of the public water supply and their consultants. Services include analyses of existing water supply systems, recommendations on new sources of water supply, coordination of regional cooperation among local water supply systems, and evaluation of future water demands.

Duties, key departments, or partner agencies: Local Water Supply Plans, North Carolina Water Supply Plans, River Basin Water Quality Assessment and Plan, Drought Monitoring, Well Networks Monitoring, Water Quality Improvements.

North Dakota
North Dakota State Water Commission
900 East Blvd.
Bismarck, ND 58505-0850
Phone: (701) 328-2750
Fax: (701) 328-3696
E-mail: info@swc.state.nd.us
Website: http://www.swc.state.nd.us/

The North Dakota State Water Commission provides stewardship of North Dakota's water resources in order to guarantee that North Dakota will enjoy an adequate supply of high-quality water in the twenty-first century. Water resource management will balance the water needs for present and future generations. In order to do so, it will address several critical water development issues, including developing Missouri River water, developing adequate water supplies for eastern North Dakota, financing future water development, and balancing the public interest and the public trust. Water quality responsibilities are shared with the North Dakota Department of Health's Environmental Health Section.

Duties, key departments, or partner agencies: Water Commission (concerned with water laws and policies, and water supplies for irrigation and for recreation, fish, and wildlife), Department of Health Municipal Facilities (concerned with the Clean Water Drinking Water Program), Water Quality Issues (including surface water, waste water, the Groundwater Protection Program, and the Antifreeze Registration Program).

Ohio
Ohio Department of Natural Resources
Division of Water
1939 Fountain Square
Columbus, OH 43224-1385
Phone: (614) 265-6717
Fax: (614) 447-9503
E-mail: water@dnr.state.oh.us
Website: http://www.dnr.state.oh.us/water/

The mission of the Ohio Department of Natural Resources is to ensure the wise management of Ohio's water resources and to be a leader in water-resource management by providing the highest quality customer service.

Duties, key departments, or partner agencies: Canal Lands Program, Coastal Engineering Program, Dam Safety Program, Floodplain Management Program, Groundwater Mapping and Technical Services, Lake Erie Water Level Monitoring, Water Planning.

In partnership with the Ohio Environmental Protection Agency, the Ohio Department of Natural Resources implements laws and regulations regarding water quality standards, carries out water quality planning, and supervises public drinking water supplies and the cleanup of unregulated hazardous waste sites.

In partnership with the Ohio Water Development Authority, the Ohio Department of Natural Resources provides financing to local governments for drinking water, wastewater, and solid waste facilities and issues private activity bonds for sewage facilities, solid waste facilities, facilities that furnish potable water, and facilities for the disposal of hazardous waste.

Oklahoma
Oklahoma Water Resource Board (OWRB)
3800 N. Classen Blvd.
Oklahoma City, OK 73118
Phone: (405) 530-8800
Website: http://www.owrb.state.ok.us/

The Oklahoma Water Resource Board (OWRB) manages and protects the water resources of the state, plans for Oklahoma's long-range water needs, and ensures that all Oklahomans have adequate quantities of good water.

Duties, key departments, or partner agencies: Planning and Management, Water Quality, Financial Assistance, Administration.

Oregon
State of Oregon
Water Resources Department
158 12th St. NE
Salem, OR 97301-4172
Phone: (503) 378-8455
Fax: (503) 378-2496
Website: http://www.wrd.state.or.us/

The Oregon Water Resources Department practices and promotes wise long-term water management.

Duties, key departments, or partner agencies: Water Rights, Stream Flows and Lake Levels, Well Logs.

Pennsylvania
Pennsylvania Department of Environmental Protection
Office of Water Management
200 Main Capitol Building
Harrisburg, PA 17120
Phone: (717) 787-4686
Website: http://www.dep.state.pa.us/

The Office of Water Management plans, directs, and coordinates departmental programs associated with the management and protection of Pennsylvania's water resources. It administers and oversees departmental programs involving planning for surface and groundwater quantity and quality and for soil and water conservation. It coordinates policies, procedures, and regulations that influence the quality of the public water supply, withdrawals from the public water supply, planning for sewage facilities, point source municipal and industrial discharges, encroachments upon waterways and wetlands, dam safety, earth-disturbance activities, and the control of stormwater and non–point source pollution. It coordinates the planning, design, and construction of flood-protection and stream-improvement projects.

Duties, key departments, or partner agencies: Water Supply and Wastewater Management, Watershed Management.

Rhode Island
Rhode Island Water Resources Board
100 North Main St.
5th Floor
Providence, RI 02903
Phone: (401) 222-2217; (401) 222-2218
Fax: (401) 222-4707
Website: http://www.info.state.ri.us

The Rhode Island Water Resources Board and the Water Resources Board Corporate was established by chapter 46-15 of the Rhode Island General Laws. The General Assembly recognized that Rhode Island's water resources are among the state's most valuable—if not the most valuable—of all its natural resources. The Rhode Island Water Resources Board Corporate (the Board Corporate) is a separate legal entity. It has a distinct legal existence from the state and is not a department of state government. The Water Resources Board Corporate establishes water supply facilities; leases facilities to cities, towns, districts, and other municipal, quasi-municipal, or private corporations or companies; and engages in the water supply business in Rhode Island.

Duties, key departments, or partner agencies:
Rhode Island Water Resources Board: Development, Protection, Use of State Water Resources, Conservation.

South Carolina
South Carolina Department of Health and Environmental Control
Bureau of Water
2600 Bull St.
Columbia, SC 29201
Phone: (803) 898-4300
Fax: (803) 898-4315
Website: http://www.scdhec.net/water

The South Carolina Bureau of Water ensures high-quality waters fit for drinking, fishing, and swimming throughout South Carolina.

Duties, key departments, or partner agencies: Drinking Water, Ground Water, Water Monitoring, Pollution Control, Quality Reports.

South Dakota
Department of Environmental and Natural Resources (DENR)
Joe Foss Building
523 E. Capitol
Pierre, SD 57501
Phone: (605) 773-3754
Fax: (605) 773-6035
Website: http://www.state.sd.us/denr/denr_organization.htm
(provides links to all the programs described below)

South Dakota's Water Rights Program is primarily responsible for managing the appropriation and use of the state's water resources. South Dakota began primary enforcement of the federal Safe Drinking Water Act in 1983. The South Dakota Drinking Water Program, located in Pierre, is part of DENR. It develops and enforces the South Dakota Drinking Water Standards that apply to the approximately 720 public water systems that currently exist in South Dakota. The Groundwater Quality Program is responsible for managing South Dakota's groundwater resources. This includes directing the cleanup of all spills and Superfund projects, regulating above-ground and underground storage tanks, overseeing the Superfund Amendments and Reauthorization Act (SARA) Title III program, issuing groundwater discharge permits, implementing the Underground Injection Control program, and helping protect the groundwater resources through the Source-water Assessment and Protection program. The primary responsibilities of the Surface Water Program are to provide environmental regulation for wastewater dischargers, to establish surface water–quality standards, and to measure the ambient surface water to determine if the public health and uses of the state's natural resources are protected.

Duties, key departments, or partner agencies: Administration, Engineering, Drinking Water, Quality and Monitoring of Surface Water, Quality and Monitoring of Groundwater, Water Rights.

Tennessee
Tennessee Department of Environment and Conservation (TDEC)
Division of Water Supply
6th Floor, L&C Tower
401 Church St.
Nashville, TN 37243-1549
Phone: (615) 532-0191
E-mail: Water.Supply@state.tn.us
Website: http://www.state.tn.us/environment/

The Tennessee Department of Environment and Conservation protects Tennessee's rich and great diversity of natural and cultural resources and the quality of Tennessee's air, land, and water. It preserves, conserves, enhances, and promotes Tennessee's natural and cultural resources.

Duties, key departments, or partner agencies: Water Supply, Ground Water, Rivers Assessment, Streams and Lakes Water Quality, Drinking Water, Scenic Rivers Program.

Texas
Texas Water Development Board (TWDB)
PO Box 13231
Capitol Station
1700 N. Congress Ave.
Austin, TX 78711-3231
Phone: (512) 463-7847
Fax: (512) 475-2053
E-mail: info@twdb.state.tx.us
Website: http://www.twdb.state.tx.us/index.htm

The Texas Water Development Board (TWDB) provides leadership, technical services, and financial assistance in support of planning, conservation, and responsible development of water. The TWDB is charged with statewide water planning and the administration of low-cost financial programs for those plans, the design and construction of water supply systems, wastewater treatment, and projects for flood control and agricultural water conservation. The TWDB can also make financial assistance available to political subdivisions within Texas.

Duties, key departments, or partner agencies: Water Planning, Data Collection and Dissemination, Financial Assistance, Technical Assistance, Groundwater Management, Drought Management.

Utah
Utah Department of Natural Resources
Division of Water Rights
1594 W. North Temple
Suite 220
PO Box 146300
Salt Lake City, UT 84114-6300
Phone: (801) 538-7240
Website: http://www.waterrights.utah.gov/

Within the Utah Department of Natural Resources, the Division of Water Rights is the state agency that regulates appropriation and distribution of water in Utah. It is an office of public record. All water right records are available in the Salt Lake City office or from the website.

Duties, key departments, or partner agencies: Well Drilling, Dams and Stream Alteration, Geographic Information System (GIS) Data, Flow Records.

Division of Water Resources
1594 W. North Temple
PO Box 146201
Salt Lake City, Utah 84114-6201
Phone: (801) 538-7230 (division director)
Website: http://www.water.utah.gov/

The Division of Water Resources of the Utah Department of Natural Resources promotes the orderly and timely planning, conservation, development, utilization, and protection of Utah's water resources.

Duties, key departments, or partner agencies: Interstate Streams, Construction Program, Water Conservation.

Division of Water Quality
PO Box 144870
Salt Lake City, Utah 84114-4870
Phone: (801) 538-6146
Fax: (801) 538-6016
Website: http://www.waterquality.utah.gov

The Division of Water Quality's mission is to protect, maintain, and enhance the quality of Utah's water for appropriate beneficial uses.

Duties, key departments, or partner agencies: Water Quality Management, Construction Assistance, Groundwater Management, Watershed Management, Storm Water Program.

Vermont
Water Resources Board
National Life Records Center Building
Drawer 20
Montpelier, VT 05602
(802) 828-3309
Website: http://www.state.vt.us/wtrboard/

Vermont's Water Resources Board's mission is to ensure that a citizen board, which is independent of the Agency of Natural Resources (ANR), adopts and (on appeal) interprets the rules guiding the management of Vermont's water resources and wetlands. The board provides meaningful citizen involvement and oversight in the adoption and implementation of Vermont's policies for water resources management and wetland protection, and it provides for an administrative appeal from related regulatory decisions of the ANR. The board's activities are directed primarily toward the protection of water quality, the resolution of conflicting uses of public waters, the designation and protection of significant wetlands, and the designation of outstanding resource waters in a manner consistent with the public interest.

Duties, key departments, or partner agencies: Interaction with the Environmental Board and the ANR, Water Quality Standards, Wetland Resources.

Virginia
Virginia Department of Environmental Quality
629 East Main St.
PO Box 10009
Richmond, VA 23240-0009
Phone: (804) 698-4000
Website: http://www.deq.state.va.us/

The Virginia Department of Environmental Quality is dedicated to protecting Virginia's environment and promoting the health and well-being of its citizens by planning and implementing environmental programs.

Duties, key departments, or partner agencies: Water Quality Monitoring, Impaired Water Monitoring, Water Resources, Ground Water, Surface Water, Storm Water, Wastewater Treatment Plants, Water Reports, Water Permits, Chesapeake Bay Program, Clean Marina Program, Coastal Program.

Washington
Washington State Department of Ecology
Headquarters
PO Box 47600
Olympia, WA 98504-7600
Phone: (360) 407-6000
Website: http://www.ecy.wa.gov/

The Washington State Department of Ecology protects, preserves, and enhances Washington's environment and promotes the wise management of air, land, and water for the benefit of current and future generations. Its goals are to prevent pollution, clean up pollution, and support sustainable communities and natural resources.

Duties, key departments, or partner agencies: Watershed Planning, Water Quality Management, Water Resources Management.

West Virginia
West Virginia Bureau of Commerce
Water Development Authority
90 MacCorkle Ave. SW
Charleston, WV 25303
Phone: (304) 558-2200
Website: http://www.wvwda.org/index1.cfm

West Virginia's Water Development Authority seeks to provide communities in West Virginia with financial assistance for the development of wastewater, water, and economic infrastructures, to protect the state's streams, to improve the drinking water quality, to protect public health, and to encourage economic growth.

Duties, key departments, or partner agencies: Concerned with Wastewater Facilities Funding, Public Water Facilities, Stream Protection, and Improvement of Drinking Water Quality. Maintains a Hearing Board and interacts with the Office of Water Resources.

Wisconsin
Department of Natural Resources
Division of Water

101 S. Webster St.
Madison WI 53703
Phone: (608) 266-2621
Fax: (608) 261-4380
Website: http://www.dnr.state.wi.us/

The Division of Water protects and enhances Wisconsin's natural resources: air, land, and water; wildlife, fish, and forests; and the ecosystems that sustain all life. It provides a healthy, sustainable environment and a full range of outdoor opportunities and ensures the right of all people to use and enjoy these resources in their work and leisure. And in doing so, it strives to consider the future and generations to follow.

Duties, key departments, or partner agencies: Concerned with Drinking Water, Groundwater, Fisheries Management and Habitat Problems, Watershed and Great Lakes Basins Management. Interacts with the Ground Water Co-ordination Council in groundwater projects, data management, public information and education, laboratory analysis and facilities, and allocation of state funds for research.

Wyoming
Department of Environmental Quality
122 W. 25th St.
Herschler Building 4-W
Cheyenne, WY 82002
Phone: (307) 332-3144
Fax: (307) 332-3183
Website: http://deq.state.wy.us/

The Wyoming Department of Environmental Quality, recognizing that pollution to the air, land, and water of the state will imperil public health and welfare, works to prevent, reduce, and eliminate pollution; preserve and enhance the air and water; reclaim the land of the state; work with Wyoming citizens to plan the development, use, reclamation, preservation, and enhancement of the state's air, land, and water resources; and retain for the state of Wyoming control of its air, land, and water resources.

Duties, key departments, or partner agencies: Groundwater Management, Watershed Management, Source Water Protection, Wastewater Protection.

Local Government Agencies

Villages, towns, cities, and metropolitan areas usually have some management structure in place to provide and protect local water supplies for their citizens. Municipalities become especially important, in terms of freshwater management, if they are large population centers like Boston, Chicago, Los Angeles, or New York. This is because large population centers often rely on water supplies that lie outside the urban area and must be delivered or diverted from some other region of the state, from a neighboring state, or from Canada or Mexico. On the other hand, if urban areas include a major source of freshwater for the region, they are responsible for more than their own urban concerns: They have an influence and impact over the freshwater issues of other areas. Therefore, it is vital for local governments to maintain some political connections with outside entities in order to quench the thirst of their residents or to live up to their responsibilities for the resource they control. If they can supply their own water and are rather self-contained, they still must be concerned with pollution issues from dense populations as well as with allocation, distribution, conservation, and recreational efforts. Cities need institutions in place to handle these kinds of duties.

The following list of examples of metropolitan water-management institutions gives the reader a good idea of the various water-management structures that exist in several large urban metropolitan areas in the United States. All of the information in the entries comes from the website addresses listed for each city.

Anchorage
Anchorage Water and Wastewater Utility (AWWU)
3000 Arctic Blvd.
Anchorage, AK 99503-3898
Phone: (907) 564-2700; toll free, (866) 650-2700
E-mail: awwu@ci.anchorage.ak.us
Website: http://www.awwu.ci.anchorage.ak.us/website/default.htm

The Anchorage Water and Wastewater Utility provides water production and distribution and wastewater treatment.

Atlanta
United Water Services Atlanta
Phone: (404) 221-0995

United Water Services Atlanta also operates in public-private partnership with:
Big Canoe Water and Wastewater Facilities
Big Canoe, GA 30143
Phone: (706) 268-3400
and
City of Atlanta Bureau of Wastewater Services
Website: http://www.ci.atlanta.ga.us/citydir/Dpw/wws/Server_Copy/WWS_Website/WWSWP.html

Atlanta's water system is privatized. The United Water Services Atlanta (whose parent company is Ondeo [Suez]) operates and maintains Atlanta's water-treatment plants, Hemphill and Chattahoochee. It operates twelve water-system storage tanks, seven zone-transfer pumping stations, 25,000 fire hydrants, and a 2,400-mile network of water-distribution mains.

Boston
City of Boston Water Quality Programs
Environment Department
Room 805
1 City Hall Plaza
Boston, MA 02201
Phone: (617) 635-3850
Fax: (617) 635-3435
E-mail: Environment@ci.boston.ma.us
Website: http://www.cityofboston.gov/environment/waterquality.asp

City of Boston Water Quality Programs also works with:
Boston Water and Sewer Commission
Website: http://www.bwsc.org/mainpage.html

The City of Boston Water Quality Programs are concerned with stormwater monitoring, the stenciling of catchbasins with the message "Don't dump drains to Boston Harbor," a Land and Water Conservation Fund, and a Seaport Plan.

Chicago
City of Chicago Department of Water
Phone: (312) 744-7001
Fax: (312) 744-7119
E-mail: water@ci.chi.il.us
Website: http://www.ci.chi.il.us/Water/

The City of Chicago Department of Water includes the following bureaus: Administrative Services, Distribution, Treatment, Pumping, Quality, Engineering, Services.

Dallas
Dallas Water Utilities Department
Dallas City Hall
1500 Marilla St.
Room 4A North
Dallas, TX 75201
Phone: (214) 670-3144
Fax: (214) 670-3154
Website: http://www.dallascityhall.com/dallas/eng/html/water_utilities.html

The Dallas Water Utilities Department deals with water supplies and wastewater services.

Denver
Denver Water Department
1600 W. 12th Ave.
Denver CO 80204
Phone: (303) 628-6000
Fax: (303) 628-6199
TDDY: (303) 534-4116
Website: http://www.water.denver.co.gov/indexmain.html

The Denver Water Department is responsible for the collection, storage, quality control, and distribution of drinking water.

District of Columbia
Water and Sewer Authority (DCWASA)
5000 Overlook Ave. SW
Washington, DC 20032
Phone: (202) 787-2000
Fax: (202) 787-2210
Website: http://www.dcwasa.com/education/css/publicinformation.cfm

The mission of the DCWASA is to provide high-quality water to customers and efficient wastewater collection and treatment services, while protecting D.C. waterways and the environment. *Duties, key departments, or partner agencies:* Drinking Water, Wastewater Treatment and Maintenance, Sewer Systems Management, Storm Water Flow Control.

Honolulu
Honolulu Board of Water Supply
630 S. Beretania St.
Honolulu, HI 96843
Phone: (808) 532-6500
E-mail: ContactUs@hbws.org
Website: http://www.lava.net/bws/mm01_ct01_mainpage.htm

The Honolulu Board of Water Supply provides municipal water supply to meet the domestic needs and fire protection for the island of Oahu. It also addresses water quality issues.

Houston
City of Houston Public Works and Engineering Department
Water Conservation Branch
PO Box 1562
Houston, TX 77251
Phone: (713) 837-0473
Website: http://www.ci.houston.tx.us/pwe/utilities/
conservation/

The Water Conservation Branch produces and distributes over 145 billion gallons of water per year and treats over 90 billion gallons per year of wastewater.

Kansas City, Missouri
Kansas City Water Services Department
414 E. 12th St.
Kansas City, MO 64106
Phone: (816) 513-1400
Fax: (816) 513-2085
E-mail: water@kcmo.org
Website: http://www.kcmo.org/water.nsf/web/
home?opendocument

The Kansas City Water Services Department is responsible for water, wastewater (sewer), industrial waste, and stormwater.

Los Angeles
Los Angeles Department of Water and Power

PO Box 51111
Los Angeles, CA 90051-0100
Phone: (213) 481-5411; toll free, (800) DIAL-DWP (342-5397)
E-mail: ccenter@ladwp.com
Website: http://www.ladwp.com/home.htm

The Los Angeles Department of Water and Power is concerned with water supply, water quality, water conservation, water projects, and research and development.

Miami
Miami–Dade County Water and Sewer Department
3575 S. Lejeune Rd.
Coral Gables, FL 33146
Phone: (305) 665-7471
Website: http://www.co.miami-dade.fl.us/wasd/

The Miami–Dade County Water and Sewer Department concerns itself with water production and distribution and with wastewater.

Minneapolis
Minneapolis Public Works Department
Water Treatment and Distribution Services
Public Service Center
250 S. 4th St.
Room 206
Minneapolis, MN 55415
Phone: (612) 673-2418
Fax: (612) 673-3723
Website: http://www.ci.minneapolis.mn.us/citywork/
public-works/water/

Water supply, water treatment, and water distribution for Minneapolis are provided by its Public Works Department.

New York City
City of New York Department of Environmental Protection
Customer Service Center
59-17 Junction Boulevard
10th Floor
Flushing, NY 11373
Phone: (718) DEP-HELP (337-4357); toll free,

(888) H2O-SHED (426-7433)
Website: http://www.nyc.gov/html/dep/html/about.html

The City of New York Department of Environmental Protection is concerned with watershed protection, water quality, the status and history of New York City's water supply system, and wastewater treatment.

Phoenix
Phoenix Water Services Department
Phoenix City Hall
200 W. Washington St.
Phoenix, AZ 85003
Phone: (602) 262-6011
E-mail: water.customer.service@phoenix.go
Website: http://phoenix.gov/WATERSERVICES/index.html

The Phoenix Water Services Department aims to provide high-quality, reliable, and cost-effective water services that meet public needs and maintain public support.

Pittsburgh
Pittsburgh Water and Sewer Authority (PWSA)
Phone: (412) 255-2423
E-mail: info@pgh2o.com
Website: http://www.pgh2o.com/

The Pittsburgh Water and Sewer Authority seeks to provide a safe and ample supply of water. It is also concerned with water conservation and water waste prevention.

St. Louis
City of St. Louis Water Division
Department of Public Utilities
1640 S. Kings Highway
St. Louis, MO 63110
Phone: (314) 868-5640, ext. 221
E-mail: water_questions@stlwater.com
Website: http://www.stlwater.com/

The City of St. Louis Water Division is dedicated to supplying the highest-quality water to its customers and has provided the City of St. Louis with fresh, clean drinking water since 1831.

San Francisco
San Francisco Water Department
SF Public Utilities Commission
1155 Market St.
4th Floor
San Francisco, CA 94103
Phone: (415) 554-3155
E-mail: info@sfwater.org
Website: http://sfwater.org/main.cfm

The San Francisco Water Department provides water to 2.4 million people in San Francisco, Santa Clara, Alameda, and San Mateo counties. The regional system consists of over 280 miles of pipelines, over sixty miles of tunnels, eleven reservoirs, five pump stations, and two water-treatment plants.

Seattle
Seattle Public Utilities (SPU)
Dexter Horton Building
710 2nd Ave.
10th Floor
Seattle, WA 98104-1717
Phone: (206) 684-3000
E-mail: Respond.SPU@ci.seattle.wa.us
Website: http://www.cityofseattle.net/util/

Seattle Public Utilities supplies drinking water to more than 1.3 million people in the Seattle–King County area. It also provides essential sewer and drainage services.

U.S. and International Organizations and Associations

This section covers U.S. and international nonprofit organizations and professional associations concerned with freshwater issues.

Nonprofit Organizations

A nonprofit organization is one that does not make a profit on the money it collects. This means the money cannot be used to the advantage of any private shareholder or individual. Rather, the money is used to further the goals of the organization, which gives some kind of service to the public. The Internal Revenue Service recognizes nonprofit organizations under the categories of "charitable, religious, educational, scientific, literary, testing for public safety, fostering national or international amateur sports competition, or the prevention of cruelty to children or animals."[1] The organizations listed below are nonprofit and are dedicated to U.S. freshwater issues. All the information in the entries was obtained from the website listed under the title of the organization. These websites should be accessed to get further information, or the reader can write or call them using the contact information.

The Alabama Rivers Alliance
2027 2nd Ave. N
Suite A
Birmingham, AL 35203
Phone: (205) 322-6395; toll free, (877) 862-5260
Fax: (205) 322-6397
E-mail: alabamariv@alabamarivers.org
Website: http://www.alabamarivers.org/

The mission of the Alabama Rivers Alliance is to unite the citizens of Alabama to protect clean, healthy waters.

Alleghenies Watershed Network
Pennsylvania Environmental Council
64 S. 14th St.
Pittsburgh, PA 15203
Phone (412) 481-9400
Fax (412) 481-9401
E-mail: jmnovak@stargate.net
Website: http://www.alleghenywatershed.org/
html/awnhme.htm

The Alleghenies Watershed Network is a forum for education about watershed issues and networking among the many entities working on watershed projects in Pennsylvania. Originally focused on the Allegheny River Watershed, the network expanded in 1999 to include the entire Monongahela River Watershed, thus covering the entire Upper Ohio River Watershed and most of western Pennsylvania. It is part of the Pennsylvania Environmental Council.

American Rivers
1025 Vermont Ave. NW
Suite 720
Washington, DC 20005
Phone: (202) 347-7550
Fax: (202) 347-9240
E-mail: amrivers@amrivers.org
Website: http://www.amrivers.org/
American Rivers is a national nonprofit organization dedicated to the restoration and protection of rivers. The group works to improve river health, to raise awareness among decisionmakers, to serve and mobilize the river conservation movement, and to collaborate with partners to develop a national "river agenda" to create a unified vision for improving river health across the United States.

Amigos Bravos
PO Box 238
Taos, NM 87571
Phone: (505) 758-3874
Fax: (505) 758-7345
E-mail: bravos@amigosbravos.org
Website: http://www.amigosbravos.org/

Amigos Bravos is the only nonprofit river advocacy group in New Mexico dedicated to preserving both the ecological and cultural richness of the Rio Grande watershed. Its mission is to return New Mexico's rivers and the Rio Grande watershed to drinkable quality wherever possible and to safe for nondrinking uses, fishing, and so on everywhere else. It works to see that natural flows are maintained and, if those flows have been disrupted by human intervention, to see that they are regulated to protect and reclaim the river ecosystem.

Anchorage Waterways Council (AWC)
PO Box 241774
Anchorage, AK 99524-1774
Phone: (907) 277-9287
E-mail: awc@alaska.net
Website: http://www.anchwaterwayscouncil.org/

AWC is a nonprofit organization dedicated to the protection, restoration, and enhancement of Anchorage's waterways.

Bluegrass Wildwater Association (BWA)
PO Box 4231
Lexington, KY 40544
Website: http://www.surfbwa.org/

The objectives of the BWA organization are to encourage the enjoyment, preservation, and exploration of U.S. waterways for self-powered watercraft (such as canoes and kayaks). The group strives to protect the wilderness character of these waterways through conservation of water, wildlife, and parks. BWA promotes safety and proficiency in all aspects of wildwater activities as well as appreciation for the recreational value of wilderness waterways and wildwater sports.

California Tahoe Conservancy
2161 Lake Tahoe Blvd.
Suite 2
South Lake Tahoe, CA 96150
Phone: (530) 542-5580
Fax: (530) 542-5591
Website: http://www.tahoecons.ca.gov/

The California Tahoe Conservancy's mission is to reserve, protect, restore, enhance, and sustain the unique and significant natural resources and opportunities of the Lake Tahoe Basin.

Cape Fear River Watch, Inc.
617 Surry St.
Wilmington, NC 28401
Phone: (910) 762 5606; toll free, (800) 380-3485
Fax: (910) 772-9381
E-mail: cfrw@wilmington.net
Website: http://capefearriverwatch.wilmington.org

The mission of Cape Fear River Watch is to protect and improve the water quality of the Lower Cape Fear River Basin through education, advocacy, and action.

Colorado Rivers Alliance (CRA)
PO Box 1056
Fort Collins, CO 80522-1056
E-mail: info@coloradorivers.org
Website: http://www.coloradorivers.org/

The mission of the CRA is to protect the rivers in Colorado through the integration, cohesion, expansion, and advancement of the diverse community of those concerned with river protection. It is made up of organizations that are either focused on or contribute substantially to river conservation and which have a significant presence in Colorado.

Flathead Lakers
PO Box 70
Polson, MT 59860
Phone: (406) 883-1346
E-mail: lakers@cyberport.net
Website: http://www.flatheadlakers.org/

Flathead Lakers work for clean water, healthy ecosystems, and lasting quality of life in the Flathead watershed in northwest Montana.

For the Sake of the Salmon
319 S.W. Washington
Suite 706
Portland, OR 97204
Phone: (503) 223-8511
Fax: (503) 223-8544
E-mail: info@4sos.org
Website: http://www.4sos.org/

For the Sake of the Salmon seeks to improve and strengthen existing watershed group efforts. It supports new initiatives to protect existing healthy habitats and to restore productivity in areas where habitats have been degraded. The organization is a good source of information on watershed groups in the Northwest as well as on funding sources for watershed restoration.

Friends of the River (FOR)
915 20th St.
Sacramento, Ca 95814
Phone: (916) 442-3155
Fax: (916) 442-3396
E-mail: jmitchell@friendsoftheriver.org
Website: http://www.friendsoftheriver.org/

FOR educates, organizes, and advocates for the protection and restoration of California rivers, streams, and watersheds.

Georgia River Network
1090 South Milledge Ave.
Athens, GA 30605
Phone: (706) 549-4508
Fax: (706) 549-7791
E-mail: info@garivers.org
Website: http://www.garivers.org/

The Georgia River Network is the only nonprofit environmental organization solely dedicated to the conservation of Georgia's waters. The group helps people organize and advocate for the protection and restoration of rivers and watersheds. It builds local watershed group capacity and provides statewide policy analysis.

Great Lakes Commission
400 4th St.
Ann Arbor, MI 48103-4816
Phone: (734) 665-9135
Fax: (734) 665-4370
E-mail: glc@glc.org
Website: http://www.glc.org/

The Great Lakes Commission is a binational agency that promotes the orderly, integrated, and comprehensive development, use, and conservation of the water and related natural resources of the Great Lakes Basin and the St. Lawrence River.

Great Lakes Environmental Research Laboratory (GLERL)
2205 Commonwealth Blvd.
Ann Arbor, MI 48105-2945
Phone: (734) 741-2235
Lake Michigan Field Station
1431 Beach St.
Muskegon, MI 49441-1098
Phone: (231) 759-7824
Website: http://www.glerl.noaa.gov

GLERL conducts high-quality research and provides scientific research on important issues in both Great Lakes and marine coastal environments.

Idaho Rivers United (IRU)
PO Box 633
Boise, ID 83701
Phone: (208) 343-9376
E-mail: iru@idahorivers.org
Website: http://www.idahorivers.org/

The mission of the IRU is to protect, restore, and improve the rivers of Idaho and the communities that depend on them. The group is focused on the ecological integrity of Idaho's rivers and works to accomplish it through citizen involvement.

Know Your Watershed (KYW)
Conservation Technology Information Center (CTIC)
1220 Potter Dr.
Suite 170 W
Lafayette, IN 47906
Phone: (765) 494-9555
Fax: (765) 494-5969
Website: http://www.ctic.purdue.edu/KYW/

Know Your Watershed (KYW) is a national effort coordinated by the Conservation Technology Information Center (CTIC), a nonprofit data and technology information transfer center. KYW encourages the formation of local, voluntary watershed partnerships and helps assure that these partnerships accomplish their goals. It is sponsored by more than seventy national partners, which may be private or public corporations, government agencies, or nonprofit organizations. Each national partner provides financial or in-kind support. The KYW website is very informative.

Lake Michigan Federation
220 South State St.
Suite 1900
Chicago, IL 60604
Phone: (312) 939-0838
Fax: (312) 939-2708
Website: www.lakemichigan.org

The Lake Michigan Federation works to restore fish and wildlife habitat, to conserve land and water, and to eliminate toxics in the watershed of the largest lake in the United States.

Maine Rivers
3 Wade St.
Augusta, ME 04330
Phone: toll free, (800) 287-2345
Website: http://www.mainerivers.org/maine_rivers_home.htm

The mission of Maine Rivers is to unite, promote, and strengthen the efforts of citizens and watershed organizations to restore and protect Maine's river systems.

The National Organization for Rivers (NORS)
Membership Offices
212 W. Cheyenne Mountain Blvd.
Colorado Springs, CO 80906
Phone: (719) 579-8759
Fax: (719) 576-6238
E-mail: nationalrivers@email.msn.com
Website: http://www.nationalrivers.org

The mission of NORS is to confirm public-trust ownership of thousands of miles of rivers by getting river navigability law applied in actual practice on rivers throughout the United States. NORS works to conserve natural rivers and to confirm citizens' legal rights to visit and use rivers in nonconsumptive ways, such as canoeing, kayaking, rafting, fishing, or walking along.

New York Rivers United
PO Box 1460
Rome, NY 13442
Phone: (315) 339-2907
Fax: (315) 339-6082
E-mail: nyruorg@aol.com
Website: http://www.newyorkriversunited.org/

New York Rivers United is a nonprofit, statewide river conservation organization created in 1992 by a regional coalition of river groups. It was created in response to the pressing need for one organization to coordinate and promote an effective river-management strategy statewide.

River Alliance of Wisconsin
306 E. Wilson St.
2W

Madison, WI 53703
Phone: (608) 257-2424
Fax: (608) 260-9799
E-mail: wisrivers@wisconsinrivers.org
Website: http://wisconsinrivers.org/

The River Alliance of Wisconsin is a nonprofit, nonpartisan group of citizens, organizations, and businesses dedicated to the protection and restoration of Wisconsin rivers and watersheds.

River Management Society (RMS)
PO Box 9048
Missoula, MT 59807-9048
Phone: (406) 549-0514
Fax: (406) 542-6208
E-mail: rms@river-management.org
Website: http://www.river-management.org

The RMS is a national, nonprofit, professional society dedicated to the protection and management of North America's river resources. Members include federal, state, and local agency employees; educators; researchers; consultants; and all others dedicated to sound management of our rivers. Its objective is to advance the profession of river management by providing members with a forum to share information about the appropriate use and management of river resources.

River Network
520 S.W. 6th Ave.
1130
Portland, OR 97204
Phone: (800) 423-6747
Fax: (503) 241-9256
E-mail: info@rivernetwork.org
Website: http://www.rivernetwork.org/aboutrn/
abocontact.cfm

River Network helps people understand, protect, and restore their watersheds. The group considers itself to be the nation's leader in supporting grassroots river and watershed conservation groups, providing activists with the information and services they need.

Rivers Council of Minnesota
100 Second Ave. S
Suite 101
Sauk Rapids, MN 56379-1409
Phone: (320) 259-6800
Fax: (320) 259-6678
E-mail: bjohnson@riversmn.org
Website: http://www.riversmn.org/

The Rivers Council of Minnesota is a nonprofit organization dedicated to keeping the streams and rivers of Minnesota healthy.

Save Our Streams (SOS)
791 Aquahart Rd.
Suite 100
Glen Burnie, MD 21061
Phone: (410) 766-9443; toll free, (800) 448-5826
Fax: (410) 766-3932
E-mail: info@saveourstreams.org
Website: http://www.saveourstreams.org/SOS-main.htm

SOS has been recognized as the leading advocate for protecting and restoring Maryland's 17,000 miles of streams since 1970. The group educates citizens on a variety of issues, including water quality monitoring, watershed restoration, and the importance of wetland protection. Its work is respected and award winning, and the group produces handbooks, videos, and workshops that present scientific concepts in a way that lay people can easily relate to and understand.

Tennessee Clean Water Network (TCWN)
706 Walnut
Suite 200
Knoxville, TN 37902
Phone: (865) 522-7007
E-mail: info@tcwn.org
Website: http://www.tcwn.org/

The mission of the TCWN is to protect, restore, and enhance Tennessee's waters and the communities that depend on them.

Tip of the Mitt Watershed Council
426 Bay St.

Petoskey, MI 49770
Phone: (231) 347-1181
Fax: (231) 347-5928
E-mail: info@watershedcouncil.org
Website: http://watershedcouncil.org/

The Tip of the Mitt Watershed Council works to protect the future of the rich character of northern Michigan, which contains magnificent waters. It is a coalition of citizens, lake associations, businesses, and recreation enthusiasts working to maintain the environmental integrity and economic and aesthetic values of lakes, streams, wetlands, and groundwater.

Trout Unlimited
1500 Wilson Blvd.
310
Arlington, VA 22209-2404
Phone: toll free, (800) 834-2419
Fax: (703) 284-9400
E-mail: trout@tu.org
Website: http://www.tu.org/index.asp

The mission of Trout Unlimited is to conserve, protect, and restore North America's trout and salmon fisheries and their watersheds. The group works with an extensive volunteer network at local, state, and national levels to accomplish this mission.

Utah Rivers Council
1473 S. 1100 E
Suite H
Salt Lake City, UT 84105
Phone: (801) 486-4776
E-mail: urc@wasatch.com
Website: http://www.wasatch.com/~urc/

The Utah Rivers Council is a community-based, grassroots, nonprofit organization dedicated to the conservation and stewardship of Utah's rivers. It works to ensure sustainable clean water supplies for Utah's citizens and wildlife for generations to come.

The Watershed Management Council
PO Box 1090
Mammoth Lakes, CA 93546
E-mail: rick@watershed.org

Website: http://www.watershed.org/

The Watershed Management Council is a nonprofit educational organization dedicated to the advancement of the art and science of watershed management. Membership includes professionals, students, teachers, and individuals with an interest in promoting proper watershed management.

WaterWatch of Oregon
213 S.W. Ash
Suite 208
Portland, OR 97204
Phone: (503) 295-4039
Fax: (503) 295-2791
E-mail: info@waterwatch.org
Website: http://www.waterwatch.org/

WaterWatch of Oregon is the only conservation group devoted exclusively to restoring healthy flows to Oregon's rivers. Thousands of acre-feet of water remain in Oregon rivers and streams because of its work. It has prevented water removal and succeeded in getting laws passed and policies implemented that return water to streams.

Professional Organizations

Professional organizations are devoted to serving professionals in a specific field and to providing opportunities to share and gather new ideas in research and technologies. Below is a list of organizations devoted to freshwater management and science issues. Entries include the website address, which is the source of all the information included regarding these organizations, as well as current contact information.

American Filtration and Separations Society
252 North Washington St.
Suite A
Falls Church, VA 22046
Phone: (703) 538-1000
Fax: (703) 538-6305
E-mail: afssociety@aol.com
Website: http://www.afssociety.org

This group is a technical educational organization for engineers, scientists, and technologists in all areas of the fluid/particle separation field.

The American Ground Water Trust
16 Centre St.
Concord, NH 03301
Phone: (603) 228-5444
Fax: (603) 228-6557
E-mail: TrustInfo@agwt.org
Website: http://www.agwt.org

The American Ground Water Trust is a nonprofit educational organization headquartered in Concord, New Hampshire. The trust is an independent authority on the hydrologic, economic, and environmental significance of groundwater.

American Water Resources Association (AWRA)
4 West Federal St.
PO Box 1626
Middleburg, VA 20118-16126
Phone: (540) 687-8390
Fax: (540) 687-8395
E-mail: info@awra.org
Website: http://www.awra.org/

The mission of AWRA is to advance multidisciplinary water-resources management and research in order to foster a program of information exchange between professionals in water-related disciplines.

American Water Works Association (AWWA)
6666 W. Quincy Ave.
Denver, CO 80235
Phone: (303) 794-7711
Fax: (303) 794-3951.
Website: http://www.awwa.org/

The American Water Works Association (AWWA) is an international scientific and educational society dedicated to the improvement of drinking water quality and supply. Founded in 1881, AWWA is the largest organization of water supply professionals in the world. Its more than 50,000 members represent the full spectrum of the drinking water community: treatment plant operators and managers, scientists, environmentalists, manufacturers, academicians, regulators, and others who hold genuine interest in water supply and public health.

Association of Metropolitan Sewerage Agencies (AMSA)
1816 Jefferson Pl. NW
Washington, DC 20036-2505
Phone: (202) 833-AMSA (2672)
Fax: (202) 833-4657
E-mail: info@amsa-cleanwater.org
Website: http://www.amsa-cleanwater.org/

AMSA's mission is to lead the nation's publicly owned wastewater management agencies in the development and implementation of scientifically based, technically sound, and cost-effective environmental programs for protecting public and ecosystem health. It represents the interests of over 300 public agencies. AMSA members serve the majority of the population using sewer systems in the United States and collectively treat and reclaim more than 18 billion gallons of wastewater daily. The group maintains a key role in the development of environmental legislation and works with federal regulatory agencies to implement environmental programs.

Association of State Dam Safety Officials (ASDSO)
450 Old Vine St.
2nd Floor
Lexington, KY 40507-1544
Phone: (859) 257-5140
Fax: (859) 323-1958
E-mail: info@damsafety.org
Website: http://www.damsafety.org

Founded in 1984, the ASDSO has served as one of the premier professional organizations for individuals committed to ensuring the safety of dams in the United States. The safe design, operation, and repair of all dams, privately and publicly owned, is the responsibility of engineers, dam owners, and dam operators. ASDSO opens its membership to government officials, engineering consultants, contractors, manufacturers and suppliers, researchers, teachers, dam owners and operators, and university students.

The Irrigation Association
6540 Arlington Blvd.
Falls Church, VA, 22042-6638
Phone: (703) 536-7080
Fax: (703) 536-7019
Website: http://www.irrigation.org/

The Irrigation Association is a nonprofit organization. Its mission is to improve products and practices used to manage water resources and to help shape the global business environment of the irrigation industry. The Irrigation Association's interest in water resources ranges from the application of water for economic and environmental enhancement to conservation, drainage, improvement and recovery in agriculture, turf grass, landscape, and forestry.

National Ground Water Association (NGWA)
601 Dempsey Rd.
Westerville, OH 43081-8978
Phone: (614) 898-7791; toll free, (800) 551-7379
Fax: (614) 898-7786
E-mail: ngwa@ngwa.org
Website: http://www.ngwa.org/index.html

The mission of NGWA is to enhance the skills and credibility of all groundwater professionals, to develop and exchange industry knowledge, and to promote the groundwater industry and understanding of groundwater resources.

The Society of Wetland Scientists (SWS)
SWS Secretariat
1313 Dolly Madison Blvd.
Suite 402
McLean, VA 22101 USA
Phone: (703) 790-1745
Fax: (703) 790-2672
E-mail: SWS@BurkInc.com
Website: http://www.sws.org/index.html

SWS produces *Wetlands,* an international journal concerned with all aspects of wetlands biology, ecology, hydrology, water chemistry, soil and sediment characteristics, management, and laws and regulations. *Wetlands* is published quarterly and seeks to bring attention to pioneering wetlands work, work that is usually spread among a myriad of journals. SWS was formed in 1980 to promote the exchange of information related to wetland science.

The Water Environment Federation (WEF)
601 Wythe St.
Alexandria, VA 22314-1994
Phone: (703) 684-2400
Fax: (703) 684-2492
Website: http://www.wef.org/index.jhtml

The mission of the WEF is to deliver high-quality products and services to members and other interested parties, as well as to promote and advance the water quality industry, in order to benefit society through the protection and enhancement of the global water environment.

International Freshwater Organizations

The following list includes international organizations dedicated to global water issues. It is, of course, only a partial listing. All the descriptive information comes from the website addresses listed for each entry.

Global Rivers Environmental Education Network (GREEN)
Earth Force GREEN
1908 Mount Vernon Ave.
2nd Floor
Alexandria, VA 22301
Phone: (703) 299-9400
Fax: (703) 299-9485
E-mail: green@earthforce.org
Website: http://www.green.org/

GREEN provides educational opportunities for middle school– and high school–aged students. The students are shown how to understand, improve, and sustain the water resources in their communities. This program teaches essential academic skills, and educators are provided with various resources, such as an online watershed exploratory tool, water-monitoring equipment, technical manuals, and action guides.

Global Water Partnership
E-mail to: gwp@sida.se
Website: http://www.gwpforum.org/servlet/PSP

The mission of the Global Water Partnership is to "support countries in the sustainable management of their water resources." It is a working partnership among all those involved in water management: government agencies, public institutions, private companies, professional organizations, multilateral development agencies and others committed to the Dublin-Rio principles (in the Dublin statement on water and sustainable development, from the UN Conference on Environment and Development; see Chapter 5, "International Policy Information").

International Rivers Network (IRN)
1847 Berkeley Way
Berkeley, CA 94703
Phone: (510) 848-1155
Fax: (510) 848-1008
E-mail: info@irn.org
Website: http://www.irn.org/index.html

IRN supports local communities around the world working to protect rivers and watersheds. The group works to halt destructive river-development projects and to encourage equitable and sustainable methods of meeting needs for water, energy, and flood management.

International Water Law Project
E-mail: gabriel13@worldnet.att.net
Website: http://www.internationalwaterlaw.org/

The International Water Law Project website was created to provide pertinent information on international water law and policy and related topics. Specifically, it offers treaties, articles, news stories, case law, Internet links, and other relevant information. Many of the materials, such as treaties and articles, are offered in full text.

The International Water Management Institute (IWMI)
Private Bag X813
Silverton 0127
Pretoria, South Africa

Phone: (27-12) 845 9100
Fax: (27-12) 845 9110
E-mail: d.merrey@cgiar
Website: http://www.cgiar.org/iwmi/index.htm

The IWMI is a nonprofit scientific research organization focusing on the sustainable use of water and land resources in agriculture and on the water needs of developing countries.

LakeNet
LakeNet Secretariat
C/o Monitor International
300 State St.
Annapolis, MD 21403
E-mail: info@worldlakes.org
Website: http://www.worldlakes.org/

LakeNet is a global network of more than 800 people and organizations in ninety countries working for the conservation and sustainable management of lakes.

Wetlands International
Wetlands International Headquarters
PO Box 471
6700 AL Wageningen
The Netherlands
Phone: (international access code) 31 317 478854
Fax: (international access code) 31 317 478850
E-mail: post@wetlands.agro.nl
Website: http://www.wetlands.org/

The mission of Wetlands International is to sustain and restore wetlands, their resources, and biodiversity for future generations using research, information exchange, and conservation activities worldwide. It is a global, nonprofit organization dedicated to the work of wetland conservation and sustainable management. It has been active in over 120 countries.

The World Commission on Dams (WCD)
Website: http://www.dams.org/default.php

The WCD was created by consensus of thirty-nine participants from governments, the private sector, international financial institutions, organizations dedicated to fostering a civil society, and affected people. All parties worked together to establish the WCD, which had a mandate to review the development effectiveness of large dams and to develop internationally acceptable guidelines and standards for large dams. With the launch of its final report, the WCD completed its mandate, and after a one-year dissemination phase, it disbanded in October 2001. The Dams and Development Project (DDP) is a two-year follow-up to the work of the WCD. It is hosted by the U.N. Environment Program (UNEP) and was established on November 1, 2001. UNEP's website (www.unep-dams.org) provides information about follow-up initiatives around the world, reactions to the report, and submissions on good practices being followed globally. The DDP also distributes copies of the report overview and WCD CD-ROM.

The World Water Council
World Water Council Headquarters
Les Docks de la Joliette
Atrium 10.3
10 place de la Joliette
13002 Marseille
France
Phone: (international access code) 33 (4) 91 99 41 00
Fax: (international access code) 33 (4) 91 99 41 01
E-mail: wwc@worldwatercouncil.org
Website: http://www.worldwatercouncil.org/

The World Water Council is an international water policy think tank dedicated to strengthening the world water movement for improved management of the world's water resources. The mission of the World Water Council is to promote awareness and to build political commitment on critical water issues at all levels.

Notes

1. "Charities and Non-Profits," Internal Revenue Service Website (online; available: http://www.irs.gov/charities/index.html; accessed July 10, 2002), 1.

7

Selected Print and Nonprint Resources

This chapter is devoted to presenting various print and non-print resources for information about freshwater issues. The bibliography in the first part includes all print references cited in this book, as well as other works of interest. The second part, nonprint resources, is divided into films and videos, including videotaped lectures, software, CD-ROMs and database resources, and Internet sites that provide comprehensive information and data, using extensive links to other relevant sites.

Print Resources

Suggested Biographical Readings

This section suggests readings for more information about the key people mentioned in Chapter 3.

Bill Clinton

Babington, Charles. *"Clinton Sets New Efforts To Improve Water Quality."* Washington Post, May 30, 1999.

Campbell, Colin, and Bert A. Rockman, eds. *The Clinton Legacy.* New York: Chatham House, 2000.

Hohenberg, John. *The Bill Clinton Story: Winning the Presi-dency.* Syracuse, NY: Syracuse University Press, 1994.

Soden, Dennis L. *The Environmental Presidency.* Albany: State
University of New York Press, 1999.

James Madison
Hamilton, Alexander, James Madison, and John Jay. *The Federalist Papers.* New York: Penguin Books, 1961.
Ketcham, Ralph Louis. *James Madison: A Biography.* Char-
lottesville: University Press of Virginia, 1990.

Chief Justice John Marshall
Hobson, Charles F. *The Great Chief Justice: John Marshall and
the Rule of Law.* Lawrence: University Press of Kansas, 2000.
Silberdick-Feinberg, Barbara. *John Marshall.* Berkeley Heights,
NJ: Enslow Publishers, 1995.

John Muir
Fox, Stephen. *John Muir and His Legacy: The American Conser-
vation Movement.* Boston: Little and Brown, 1981.
Jones, Holway R. *John Muir and the Sierra Club: The Battle for
Yosemite.* San Francisco: Sierra Club, 1965.
Kines, William F., and Maymie B. Kimes. *John Muir: A Reading
Bibliography.* Fresno: Panorama West Books, 1986.
Lyon, Thomas J. *John Muir.* Ed. Wayne Chatterton and James H.
Maguire. Boise, ID: Boise State College, 1972.

Gale Norton
*"U.S. Department of the Interior Secretary Gale A. Norton
Speeches."* Online: U.S. Department of Interior Website. Avail-
able: http://www.doi.gov/secretary/speeches/index.html.
Access date: January 28, 2002.

Gifford Pinchot
Miller, Char. *Gifford Pinchot: The Evolution of an American Con-
servationist. Two Essays.* Milford, PA: Grey Towers Press,
1992.
———. *Gifford Pinchot and the Making of Modern Environmen-
talism.* Washington, DC: Island Press, 2001.
Pinchot, Gifford. *Breaking New Ground.* Washington, DC: Island
Press, 1987.
———. *The Fight for Conservation* (1910). Introduction by Gerald
D. Nash. Seattle: University of Washington Press, 1967.

Major John Wesley Powell

"Major John Wesley Powell." Online: John Wesley Powell Memorial Museum Website. Available: http://www.powellmuseum. org/MajorPowell.html. Access date: January 28, 2002.

Powell, John Wesley. *The Cañons of the Colorado.* Compiled from the records of J. W. Powell. New Orleans, LA: Historical Publications, 1993.

———. *The Exploration of the Colorado River.* Abridged from the 1st edition of 1875 with an introduction by Wallace Stegner. Chicago: University of Chicago Press, 1957.

Stegner, Wallace. *Beyond the Hundredth Meridian.* Boston, MA: Houghton Mifflin, 1953.

Theodore Roosevelt

Gable, John Allen. *The Bull Moose Years: Theodore Roosevelt and the Progressive Party.* Port Washington, NY: Kennikat Press, 1978.

King, Judson. *The Conservation Fight, from Theodore Roosevelt to the Tennessee Valley Authority.* Introduction by Clyde Ellis; foreword by Benton J. Stong. Washington, DC: Public Affairs Press, 1959.

Mowry, George Edwin. *The Era of Theodore Roosevelt, 1900–1912.* New York: Harper, 1958.

Roosevelt, Theodore. *The Autobiography of Theodore Roosevelt.* Condensed from the original edition, supplemented by letters, speeches, and other writings, and edited with an introduction by Wayne Andrews. New York: Octagon Books, 1958, 1975.

George Washington

Clark, E. Harrison. *All Cloudless Glory: The Life of George Washington.* Washington, DC: Regnery Publishing Co., 1996.

Irving, Washington. *George Washington: A Biography.* Ed. Charles Neider. Garden City, NY: Doubleday, 1976.

Books and Articles

Considering the scope of the topic of freshwater issues, the following bibliography can only be considered a partial list of relevant books and articles. All references cited in this publication are included, as well as several that were not. Most of the entries stand alone; however, some, which may seem to be out of place, have additional information to explain why they are included in the list.

Adler, Robert W. **"Addressing Barriers to Watershed Protection."** *Environmental Law* 25, no. 4 (Fall 1995): 973.

Anderson, Terry. *Water Crisis: Ending the Policy Drought.* Baltimore: The Johns Hopkins University Press, 1983.

Ashley, Jeffrey S., and Zachary A. Smith. *Groundwater Management in the West.* Lincoln: University of Nebraska Press, 1999.

Ashworth, William. *The Late Great Lakes: An Environmental History.* New York: Summit Books, 1982.

———. *Nor Any Drop to Drink.* New York: Summit Books, 1982.

Bain, Joseph S., Richard E. Caves, and Julius Margolis. *Northern California's Water Industry.* Baltimore: The Johns Hopkins University Press, 1966.

Barlow, Maude. **"Water Privatization and the Threat to the World's Most Precious Resource: Is Water a Commodity or a Human Right?"** *IFG Bulletin: Special Water Issue,* Summer 2001: 2.

Beard, Daniel P. **"Water Policy for the Next Generation."** *World Rivers Review* 11, no. 3 (July 1996): 1.

Black, Peter E. *Watershed Hydrology.* Chelsea, MI: Ann Arbor Press, 1996.

Blake, N. M. *Land into Water—Water into Land: A History of Water Management in Florida.* Tallahassee: University Presses of Florida, 1980.

———. *Water for the Cities: A History of the Urban Water Supply Problem in the United States.* Syracuse, NY: Syracuse University Press, 1956.

Boyle, Robert, John Graves, and T. H. Watkins. *The Water Hustlers.* San Francisco: Sierra Club Books, 1971.

Burton, Lloyd. **"Negotiating the Clean Up of Toxic Groundwater Contamination."** *Natural Resources Journal* 28, no. 1 (Winter 1988): 105–144.

Chasan, Daniel Jack. *The Water Link.* Seattle: University of Washington Press, 1981.

Ciriacy-Wantrup, S. V. *Resource Conservation: Economics and Policies.* Berkeley and Los Angeles: University of California Press, 1952.
This is a classic economics text that helps the researcher understand some of the foundations of natural resource economic approaches and subsequent policy decisions.

Council of State Governments. *State Water Quality Planning Issues.* Lexington, KY: Council of State Governments, 1982.

Davidson, B. R. *Australia, Wet or Dry? The Physical and Economic Limits to the Expansion of Irrigation.* Kingsgrove, NSW: Melbourne University Press, 1969.

DuMars, Charles T. **"New Challenges to Western Water Law."** In the symposium (of twelve articles) in *Natural Resources Journal* 29, no. 2 (Spring 1989).

———. **"Public Policy Considerations in State Water Allocations and Management."** *Rocky Mountain Mineral Law Institute Proceedings,* no. 42 (1996): 24.

DuMars, Charles T., M. O'Leary, and A. E. Ulton. *Pueblo Indian Water Rights: Struggle for a Precious Resource.* Tucson: University of Arizona Press, 1984.

Engelbert, Ernest A., and Ann Foley Scheuring, eds. *Competition for California Water.* Berkeley and Los Angeles: University of California Press, 1982.

Feldman, David Lewis. *Water Resources Management: In Search of an Environmental Ethic.* Baltimore: The Johns Hopkins University Press, 1991.

Frederick, Kenneth D., and James C. Hanson. *Water for Western Agriculture.* Washington, DC: Resources for the Future, 1982.

Getches, David H. *Water Law in a Nutshell.* St. Paul, MN: West Publishing Co., 1997.

Gleick, Peter H. **"Making Every Drop Count."** *Scientific American* 284, no. 2 (February 2001): 42.

———. *The World's Water, 2000–2001: The Biennial Report on Freshwater Resources.* Washington, DC: Island Press, 2000.

Gorbachev, Mikhail. **"Out of Water: The Distant Alarm Comes Closer."** *Civilization: The Magazine of the Library of Congress,* October/November 2000: 82.

Gordon, Wendy. *A Citizens' Handbook on Groundwater Protection.* New York: Natural Resources Defense Council, 1984.

Gottlieb, Robert. *A Life of Its Own.* Orlando, FL: Harcourt Brace Jovanovich, 1988.

Gottlieb, Robert, and Margaret FitzSimmons. *Thirst for Growth: Water Agencies as Hidden Government in California.* Tucson: University of Arizona Press, 1991.

Green, D. *Land of the Under-Ground Rain: Irrigation of the Texas High Plains, 1910–1970.* Austin: University of Texas Press, 1973.

Hartman, L. M., and Don Seastone. *Water Transfers: Economic*

Efficiency and Alternative Institutions. Baltimore: The Johns Hopkins University Press, 1970.

Hollon, W. E. *The Great American Desert Then and Now.* Lincoln: University of Nebraska Press, 1966.

Howe, Charles W. *Natural Resource Economics: Issues, Analysis, and Policy.* New York: John Wiley, 1979.
As earlier chapters have indicated, economics is vital to water management. The concepts in this text apply to water as well as other natural resources.

Hundley, Norris. *Dividing the Waters: A Century of Controversy between the United States and Mexico.* Berkeley and Los Angeles: University of California Press, 1966.

———. *Water and the West: The Colorado River Compact and the Politics of Water in the American West.* Berkeley and Los Angeles: University of California Press, 1975.

Hunter, Susan, and Richard W. Waterman. *Enforcing the Law: The Case of the Clean Water Acts.* Armonk, NY: M. E. Sharpe, 1996.

Johnson, Barbara Rose, and John M. Donahue, eds. *Water, Culture, and Power: Local Struggles in a Global Context.* Washington, DC: Island Press, 1998.

Kahrl, W. L. *Water and Power: The Conflict over Los Angeles' Water Supply in the Owens Valley.* Berkeley and Los Angeles: University of California Press, 1981.

Kelso, Maurice, William E. Martin, and Lawrence E. Mack. *Water Supplies and Economic Growth in an Arid Environment: An Arizona Case Study.* Tucson: University of Arizona Press, 1973.

Kneese, Allen V. *Measuring the Benefits of Clean Air and Water.* Washington, DC: Resources for the Future, 1984.

Kroeber, C. B. *Man, Land, and Water: Mexico's Farmlands Irrigation Policies, 1885–1911.* Berkeley and Los Angeles: University of California Press, 1983.

Krutilla, John V. *The Columbia River Treaty: The Economics of an International River Basin Development.* Baltimore: The Johns Hopkins University Press, 1967.

Liu, Sylvia. **"American Indian Reserved Water Rights: The Federal Obligation to Protect Tribal Water Resources and Tribal Autonomy."** *Environmental Law* 25, no. 2 (Spring 1995): 425.

Maass, Arthur. *Muddy Waters.* Cambridge, MA: Harvard University Press, 1951.

MacDonald, Douglas B. **"The Water Bill: We Pay It; the Question**

Is, Who Writes It?" *Civilization: The Magazine of the Library of Congress,* October/November 2000: 92.

Martin, R. *A Story That Stands Like a Dam: Glen Canyon and the Struggle for the Soul of the West.* New York: Henry Holt, 1989.

Martin, William E., and Nancy K. Lancy (photographer). *Saving Water in a Desert City.* Washington, DC: Resources for the Future, 1984.

McCool, Daniel. *Command of the Waters.* Berkeley and Los Angeles: University of California Press, 1987.

Meyer, M. C. *Water in the Hispanic Southwest: A Social and Legal History, 1550–1850.* Tucson: University of Arizona Press, 1984.

Miller, G. Tyler Jr. *Living in the Environment.* Fifth ed. Belmont, CA: Wadsworth Publishing Co., 1988.
This textbook is an introduction to environmental science, with an entire chapter devoted to water resources.

Napier, Ted L., Donald Scott, K. William Easter, and Raymond Supalla, eds. *Water Resources Research: Problems and Potentials for Agriculture and Rural Communities.* Ankeny, IA: Soil Conservation Society of America, 1983.

Pierce, John C., and Nicholas P. Loverich Jr. *Water Resources, Democracy, and the Technical Information Quandary.* Millwood, NY: Associated Faculty Press, 1986.

Pisani, Donald J. *From the Family Farm to Agribusiness: The Irrigation Crusade in California and the West, 1850–1931.* Berkeley and Los Angeles: University of California Press, 1984.

———. *Water, Land, and Law in the West: The Limits of Public Policy, 1850–1920.* Lawrence: University Press of Kansas, 1996.

Postel, Sandra. *Last Oasis: Facing Water Scarcity.* New York: W. W. Norton, 1992.

Powledge, Fred. *Water: The Nature, Uses, and Future of Our Most Precious and Abused Resource.* New York: Farrar, Straus, and Giroux, 1982.

Pye, Veronica, Ruth Patrick, and John Quarles. *Groundwater Contamination in the US.* Philadelphia: University of Pennsylvania Press, 1983.

Reisner, Marc. *Cadillac Desert: The American West and Its Disappearing Water.* New York: Viking Press, 1986.

Rogers, Peter. *America's Water: Federal Roles and Responsibilities.* Cambridge: The MIT Press, 1996.

Saliba, B. C., David B. Bush, William E. Martin, and Thomas C. Brown. **"Do Water Market Prices Appropriately Measure**

Water Values?" *Natural Resources Journal* 27, no. 3 (Summer 1987): 617–652.

Saunders, Margot. **"The Safe Drinking Water Act: Dilemmas for the Poor."** *Clearinghouse Review* 26, no. 12 (April 1, 1993): 1587.

Scarpino, P. V. *Great River: An Environmental History of the Upper Mississippi, 1890–1950.* Columbia: University of Missouri Press, 1985.

Sierra Club. *Poisons in the Water.* Natural Heritage Report no. 5. San Francisco: Sierra Club Books, 1982.

Simon, Paul. *Tapped Out: The Coming World Crisis in Water and What We Can Do About It.* New York: Welcome Rain, 1998.

Smith, Karen L. *The Magnificent Experiment: Building the Salt River Reclamation Project, 1890–1917.* Tucson: University of Arizona Press, 1986.

Smith, Zachary A. **"Centralized Decisionmaking in the Administration of Groundwater Rights: The Experience of Arizona, California, and New Mexico and Suggestions for the Future."** *Natural Resources Journal* 24 (July 1984): 641.

———. **"Competition for Water Resources: Issues in Federalism."** *Journal of Land Use and Environmental Law* 2, no. 2 (Spring 1987).

———. *The Environmental Policy Paradox.* 3rd ed. Upper Saddle River, NJ: Prentice Hall, 1995.

———. **"Federal Intervention in the Management of Groundwater Resources."** *Publius: The Journal of Federalism* 15, no. 1 (Winter 1985): 145.

———. *Groundwater in the West.* San Diego, CA: Academic Press, 1989.

———. *Groundwater Policy in the Southwest.* El Paso, TX: Western Press, 1985.

———. *Interest Group Interaction and Groundwater Policy Formation in the Southwest.* Lanham, MD: University Press of America, 1985.

———. **"Interstate and International Competition for Water Resources."** *Water Resources Bulletin* 23, no. 5 (October 1987).

———. **"Rewriting California Groundwater Law: Past Attempts and Prerequisites to Reform."** *California Western Law Review* 20, no. 2 (1984): 223.

———. **"Stability amid Change in Federal-State Water Relations."** *Capital University Law Review* 15, no. 32 (Spring 1986).

———, ed. *Water and the Future of the Southwest.* Albuquerque: University of New Mexico Press, 1989.

Thomassey Fink, Grenetta, and Zachary Smith. **"Arizona Government and Politics."** In *Uniting a Diverse Arizona: Background Report Prepared by Northern Arizona University,* ed. Kathryn Cruz Uribe, Margot Nason, and Frances Julia Riemer. Flagstaff: Seventy-Fifth Arizona Town Hall, October 31–November 3, 1999.
The chapter cited in this report includes a case study of groundwater law in Arizona.

Trelease, Frank J. *Water Law: Cases and Materials.* 3rd ed. St. Paul, MN: West Publishing, 1979.

Vickers, Amy. *Handbook of Water Use and Conservation.* Amherst, MA: WaterPlow Press, 2001.

Waggoner, Paul, ed. *Climate Change and U.S. Water Resources.* New York: John Wiley, 1990.

Walton, John. *Western Times and Water Wars: State Culture and Rebellion in California.* Berkeley and Los Angeles: University of California Press, 1992.

Warne, William. *The Bureau of Reclamation.* New York: Praeger, 1973.

Warriner, G. Keith, James J. Madden, Lynda Lukasik, and Kathleen McSpurren. **"Public Participation in Watershed Management: A Comparative Analysis."** *Canadian Water Resources Journal* 21, no. 3 (October 1, 1996): 253.

Wilkinson, Charles F. *Crossing the Next Meridian: Land, Water, and the Future of the West.* Washington, DC: Island Press, 1992.

Worster, Donald. *Rivers of Empire: Water, Aridity, and the Growth of the American West.* New York: Pantheon Books, 1985.

Wurbs, Ralph A. **"Managing Our Precious Liquid Asset."** *World and I* 15, no. 10 (October 2000): 133.

Yeager, Peter. *The Limits of Law: The Public Regulation of Private Pollution.* Cambridge: Cambridge University Press, 1991.

Nonprint Resources

Selected Films, Videos, Software, CD-ROMs, Databases

Films and Videos
In this section the reader will find selected films and videos on the subject of freshwater. The list includes the film's name and distributor, and a brief description provided by the distributor. All the information in each entry comes from the website listed.

Beneath Our Feet: Groundwater, Hidden Treasure
Distributor: Water Resources Education Network (WREN)
                 Resource Center
                 LWVPA-CEF
                 226 Forster St.
                 Harrisburg, PA 17102-3220
                 Phone: toll free, (800) 692-7281
                 E-mail: lwvpa@epix.net
                 Website: http://pa.lwv.org/wren/video.html
Produced by the Washington County Groundwater Coalition, a coalition of local groups in Washington County, Pennsylvania, this video shows many of the threats to the county's groundwater resources and encourages citizens and their local officials to take steps to protect their groundwater. Length: 16 minutes; date: 1992.

Beneath the Surface: Groundwater Education in Michigan
Distributor: Water Resources Education Network (WREN)
                 Resource Center
                 LWVPA-CEF
                 226 Forster Street
                 Harrisburg, PA 17102-3220
                 Phone: toll free, (800) 692-7281
                 E-mail: lwvpa@epix.net
                 Website: http://pa.lwv.org/wren/video.html
This film, produced by the W. K. Kellogg Foundation, gives an overview of the Groundwater Education in Michigan project and highlights successful local groundwater education projects in Michigan. Length: 10.5 minutes; date: 1993.

Black Sea: Voyage of Healing

Distributor: Bullfrog Films
                 Box 149
                 Oley, PA 19547
                 Phone: (610) 779-8226; toll free, (800) 543-FROG (3764)
                 Fax: (610) 370-1978
                 E-mail: bullfrog@igc.org
                 Website: http://www.bullfrogfilms.com/ ecologywater.html

In this color film, scientists and religious leaders meet to find the solution to the Black Sea in crisis. Directed by Peter Davis and produced by Harvey McKinnon and Peter Davis, the film is suitable for grades 10–12 through adult. Length: 54 minutes; date: copyright date: 1998; U.S. release date: 1999; ISBN: 1-56029-789-1.

Borderline Cases: Environmental Matters at the United States–Mexico Border

Distributor: Bullfrog Films
                 Box 149
                 Oley, PA 19547
                 Phone: (610) 779-8226; toll free, (800) 543-FROG (3764)
                 Fax: (610) 370-1978
                 E-mail: bullfrog@igc.org
                 Website: http://www.bullfrogfilms.com/ ecologywater.html

This film, produced by Lynn Corcoran, addresses the environmental impact of the two thousand factories *(maquiladoras)* on the United States–Mexico border. The film is suitable for grades 10–12 through adult. Length: 65 minutes; date: 1996; ISBN: 1-56029-681-X.

Cadillac Desert

Episode One: **Mulholland's Dream**
Episode Two: **An American Nile**
Episode Three: **The Mercy of Nature**
Episode Four: **Last Oasis**

Distributor: PBS
                 Website: http://www.pbs.org/kteh/ adillacdesert/home.html

Cadillac Desert, a PBS production of Trans Pacific Television and KTEH/San Jose Public Television, presented in association with KCET/Los Angeles, is a four-part documentary series about water, money, politics, and the transformation of nature. Winner of the duPont-Columbia Journalism Award, the series tells how Americans have used, abused, protected, controlled, fought over, and died for water.

The first three episodes of the series are based on Marc Reisner's book *Cadillac Desert*. They delve into the history of water use and misuse in the U.S. West. The final episode is based on Sandra Postel's book *Last Oasis* and examines the global impact of technologies and policies that came out of the U.S. manipulation of water. It demonstrates how they have created the need for conservation methods that will protect earth's water for the next century.

Common Ground: The Battle for Barton Springs
Distributors: The Video Project
                Phone: (800) 4-PLANET (475-2638)
                E-mail: video@videoproject.net
Canadian   McNabb and Connolly
distributor: 60 Briarwood Ave.
                Port Credit, Ont. L5G 3N6
                Canada
                Phone: (905) 278-0566
                Fax: (905) 278-2801
                E-mail: mcnabbconnolly@homeroom.ca
                Website: http://www.videoproject.org/subject_areas/subject_water.html

The citizens of Austin use the democratic process to save its spring. Length: 28 minutes; suitable for viewers from ninth grade to adult.

Cryptosporidium and USDA
Distributor: Water Resources Education Network (WREN)
                Resource Center
                LWVPA-CEF
                226 Forster St.
                Harrisburg, PA 17102-3220
                Phone: toll free, (800) 692-7281
                E-mail: lwvpa@epix.net
                Website: http://pa.lwv.org/wren/video.html

This is a technical discussion of the pathogen *Cryptosporidium*. It is suitable for training purposes but not for general audiences. Length: 25 minutes; date: 1996.

Cryptosporidium Parvum
Distributor: Water Resources Education Network (WREN)
Resource Center
LWVPA-CEF
226 Forster St.
Harrisburg, PA 17102-3220
Phone: toll free, (800) 692-7281
E-mail: lwvpa@epix.net
Website: http://pa.lwv.org/wren/video.html

This comprehensive video by the U.S. Department of Agriculture presents recent information on *Cryptosporidium* and cryptosporidiosis, both the parasite and the disease. Length: 28 minutes; date: 1998.

Downwind/Downstream: Threats to the Mountains and Waters of the American West
Distributor: Bullfrog Films
Box 149
Oley, PA 19547
Phone: (610) 779-8226; toll free, (800) 543-FROG (3764)
Fax: (610) 370-1978
E-mail: bullfrog@igc.org
Website: http://www.bullfrogfilms.com/ecologywater.html

Downwind/Downstream documents the serious threat to water quality, subalpine ecosystems, and public health in the Colorado Rockies from mining operations, acid rain, and urbanization. Ten thousand abandoned mines in the high country, plus thousands of acres covered with wastes from such huge operations as the Climax molybdenum mine, release a steady stream of toxic heavy metals into the headwaters of the western water supply—water on which cities as far apart as El Paso, Phoenix, Denver, and Los Angeles depend. The film, by Christopher McLeod, narrated by Peter Coyote, and produced by Robert Lewis and Christopher McLeod in association with the Environmental Research Group of Aspen, Colorado, is suitable for viewers from ninth grade to adult. It is available on 2 reels for schools. Length: 58 minutes.

Drinking Water: Quality on Tap
Distributors: The Video Project
Phone: (800) 4-PLANET (475-2638)
E-mail: video@videoproject.net
Canadian   McNabb and Connolly
distributor: 60 Briarwood Ave.
Port Credit, Ont. L5G 3N6
Canada
Phone: (905) 278-0566
Fax: (905) 278-2801
E-mail: mcnabbconnolly@homeroom.ca
Website: http://www.videoproject.org/subject_
areas/subject_water.html

This video is part of a complete educational program on community drinking water quality. It covers sources of drinking water (groundwater, surface water, watersheds), types of drinking water supply systems, treatment methods, delivery, private systems, drinking water regulations, home water treatment (testing, filtering devices, types of treatment), and bottled water. It was produced by the League of Women Voters of Michigan. Length: 25 minutes; date: 1991; ages sixteen to adult.

End of Eden
Distributor: People and the Planet
Suite 112
Spitfire Studios
63-71 Collier St.
London N1 9BE
England
Phone: (international access code) 44 (0)20 7713 8108
Fax: (international access code) 44 (0)20 7713 8109
E-mail: planet21@totalise.co.uk
Website: http://www.peopleandplanet.net/
section.php?section=14&topic=4

This film chronicles Iraq's ruthless destruction, since the end of the Gulf War in 1991, of one of the oldest civilizations on earth and their ecologically unique homeland.

EPA Training Program for Wellhead Protection (slide set)
Distributor: Water Resources Education Network (WREN)

Resource Center
LWVPA-CEF
226 Forster St.
Harrisburg, PA 17102-3220
Phone: toll free, (800) 692-7281
E-mail: lwvpa@epix.net
Website: http://pa.lwv.org/wren/video.html

This is a nine-module slide set for training in wellhead protection presented by the U.S. EPA Office of Water. Each module comes with extensive notes and background information as well as a list of key points to cover for each slide. The modules are Overview, Delineation, Identifying Contaminant Sources, Management Approaches, Financing Wellhead Protection, Contingency Planning, Tools for Indian Tribes, Compendium of Local Ordinances, and Summary of EPA Publications. With these materials a program of any length can be developed, ranging from a brief overview of groundwater to a full workshop on wellhead protection implementation. The materials are presented in such a way that they can be used by nonexperts familiar with the subject of wellhead protection. The kit may be borrowed for one month (a refundable deposit is required). Date: 1992.

Equatorial River: The Amazon
Distributor: Bullfrog Films
Box 149
Oley, PA 19547
Phone: (610) 779-8226; toll free, (800) 543-FROG
(3764)
Fax: (610) 370-1978
E-mail: bullfrog@igc.org
Website: http://www.bullfrogfilms.com/
ecologywater.html

Equatorial River shows how the water and nutrient cycles work in the Amazon basin. It provides a fundamental understanding of the interrelation of elements in this enormous and threatened ecosystem, now seen to be so vital to our planet. The film, by Bruce Mackay and William Hansen and produced by the National Film Board of Canada, is suitable for grade 7 through adult, and includes a teacher's guide. Length: 23 minutes; ISBN: 0-7722-0360-1.

Estuary
Distributor: Bullfrog Films
Box 149
Oley, PA 19547
Phone: (610) 779-8226; toll free, (800) 543-FROG
(3764)
Fax: (610) 370-1978
E-mail: bullfrog@igc.org
Website: http://www.bullfrogfilms.com/
subjects/water.html

Using exquisite underwater microphotography, this award-winning production provides a close-up look at an estuary. The film, by Don White and produced by the National Film Board of Canada, is suitable for grade 7 through adult. Length: 12 minutes; ISBN: 0-7722-0356-3.

Fight for Croton Watershed: Protection versus Filtration
Distributors: The Video Project
Phone: (800) 4-PLANET (475-2638)
E-mail: video@videoproject.net
Canadian McNabb and Connolly
distributor: 60 Briarwood Ave.
Port Credit, Ont. L5G 3N6
Canada
Phone: (905) 278-0566
Fax: (905) 278-2801
E-mail: mcnabbconnolly@homeroom.ca
Website: http://www.videoproject.org/subject_
areas/subject_water.html

This film covers what a watershed is, how development adversely affects it, and what citizens can do to protect it.

The Florida Water Story
Distributor: Courter Films and Associates
121 N.W. Crystal St.
Crystal River, FL 34428
Phone: (352) 795-2156
Fax: (352) 795-6144
E-mail: cfa@xtalwind.net
Website: http://www.xtalwind.net/~cfa/
8addinfo.htm

This is an award-winning two-hour PBS special program about the critical role water plays in all of Florida's environments. The program is divided into three parts: *Embrace of the Sea: Florida's Coastal Waters,* a one-hour program that takes the viewer on an eco-tour of Florida's famous coastline; *Florida's Fragile Fountain: Origins and Threats to Our Drinking Water,* a thirty-minute program that looks deep into Florida's fresh water drinking supplies; and *Golden Coins and Silver Ribbons: Florida's Treasured Lakes and Rivers,* a thirty-minute program on the health of inland lakes and rivers.

Flush Toilet, Goodbye
Distributor: Bullfrog Films
                 Box 149
                 Oley, PA 19547
                 Phone: (610) 779-8226; toll free, (800) 543-FROG
                 (3764)
                 Fax: (610) 370-1978
                 E-mail: bullfrog@igc.org
                 Website: http://www.bullfrogfilms.com/
                 subjects/water.html

The film presents the design of a composting toilet. Length: 29 minutes.

Green Works for Pennsylvania: **Watersheds I.**
Know Your Watershed
Distributor: Water Resources Education Network (WREN)
                 Resource Center
                 LWVPA-CEF
                 226 Forster St.
                 Harrisburg, PA 17102-3220
                 Phone: toll free, (800) 692-7281
                 E-mail: lwvpa@epix.net
                 Website: http://pa.lwv.org/wren/video.html

This film explains what Pennsylvanians are doing to protect their watersheds. The viewer will learn about "Environmental Ed's" seventh-grade watershed curriculum; volunteers involved with Pennsylvania's Water Snapshot; the Stream Relief program, and more.

Green Works for Pennsylvania: Watersheds II.
Protecting Our Watersheds
Distributor: Water Resources Education Network (WREN)

Resource Center
LWVPA-CEF
226 Forster St.
Harrisburg, PA 17102-3220
Phone: toll free, (800) 692-7281
E-mail: lwvpa@epix.net
Website: http://pa.lwv.org/wren/video.html

The film presents information on the concept of "knowing your watershed address" and a variety of programs to introduce people to their watersheds.

The Green Zone
Distributor: Bullfrog Films
Box 149
Oley, PA 19547
Phone: (610) 779-8226; toll free, (800) 543-FROG (3764)
Fax: (610) 370-1978
E-mail: bullfrog@igc.org
Website: http://www.bullfrogfilms.com/ecologywater.html

This film presents the argument that the riparian zone is as important to the river as the water itself. Length: 47 minutes; grades 7–12 through adult; ISBN: 1-56029-776-X.

Groundwater: Out of Sight, Out of Mind
Distributors: Water Resources Education Network (WREN)
Resource Center
LWVPA-CEF
226 Forster St.
Harrisburg, PA 17102-3220
Phone: toll free, (800) 692-7281
E-mail: lwvpa@epix.net
Website: http://pa.lwv.org/wren/video.html
PSU
Agricultural and Biological Engineering Dept.
246 Ag Engineering Bldg.
University Park, PA 16802
Website: http://pa.lwv.org/wren/video.html

Produced by the Adams County Groundwater Coalition, this video highlights localized issues related to groundwater management and protection and focuses on actions that government and citizens can take to protect the resource. Date: 1993.

Groundwater Video Series: The Case of the Mysterious Groundwater
Distributors: Water Resources Education Network (WREN)
Resource Center
LWVPA-CEF
226 Forster St.
Harrisburg, PA 17102-3220
Phone: toll free, (800) 692-7281
E-mail: lwvpa@epix.net
Website: http://pa.lwv.org/wren/video.html
PSU
Agricultural and Biological Engineering Dept.
246 Ag Engineering Bldg.
University Park, PA 16802
Website: http://pa.lwv.org/wren/video.html

This educational video uses animated graphics and creative video techniques to communicate technical concepts about groundwater. Length: 16 minutes; date: 1996.

Groundwater Video Series: Groundwater Protection. Blazing a Healthy Trail
Distributors: Water Resources Education Network (WREN)
Resource Center
LWVPA-CEF
226 Forster St.
Harrisburg, PA 17102-3220
Phone: toll free, (800) 692-7281
E-mail: lwvpa@epix.net
Website: http://pa.lwv.org/wren/video.html
PSU
Agricultural and Biological Engineering Dept.
246 Ag Engineering Bldg.
University Park, PA 16802
Website: http://pa.lwv.org/wren/video.html

A tale of the Old West that creatively defines Pennsylvania aquifers, relates land uses to contamination, and describes how to develop a community-based protection group. Length: 22 minutes.

**Groundwater Video Series: Groundwater Protection.
A Road Trip to Success**
Distributor: Water Resources Education Network (WREN)
Resource Center
LWVPA-CEF
226 Forster St.
Harrisburg, PA 17102-3220
Phone: toll free, (800) 692-7281
E-mail: lwvpa@epix.net
Website: http://pa.lwv.org/wren/video.html

Using creative techniques, this film describes the four goals for groundwater protection: developing good maps, creating inventories, choosing protection strategies, and monitoring the program. Length: 23 minutes.

A Guide to Water Testing
Distributor: Water Resources Education Network (WREN)
Resource Center
LWVPA-CEF
226 Forster St.
Harrisburg, PA 17102-3220
Phone: toll free, (800) 692-7281
E-mail: lwvpa@epix.net
Website: http://pa.lwv.org/wren/video.html

Trained volunteers demonstrate two forms of equipment, the Kick-Net and the D-Frame Net, used to collect biological material from both rocky-bottom and muddy-bottom streams. In addition to illustrating the collection of microorganisms, the video gives a brief description on the process of testing for various chemicals in a stream. This step-by-step video is a great aid to train new volunteers and refresh previous volunteers' skills. Produced by the Washington County Watershed Alliance. Length: 10 minutes.

In Our Water
Distributor: New Day Films
22-D Hollywood Ave.
Ho-ho-kus, NJ 07423
Phone: (201) 652.6590
Fax: (201) 652.1973
E-mail: curator@newday.com

Website: http://www.newday.com/films/In_
Our_Water.html

This film by Meg Switzgable defines the terrifying chemical
waste problems in the United States. It is available in both VHS
and 16mm formats. The film is available for rental as well as for
purchase. Length: 60 minutes.

The Intertidal Zone
Distributor: Bullfrog Films
                 Box 149
                 Oley, PA 19547
                 Phone: (610) 779-8226; toll free, (800) 543-FROG
                 (3764)
                 Fax: (610) 370-1978
                 E-mail: bullfrog@igc.org
                 Website: http://www.bullfrogfilms.com/s
                 ubjects/water.html

The Intertidal Zone provides a unique glimpse at the food chains,
interactive life cycles, and many special adaptations to this difficult environment. Through the eyes of a patient and observant
marine biologist, the audience explores the ecology of the intertidal zone, an area covered by the highest tides and exposed during the lowest. Produced by the National Film Board of Canada,
it is suitable for grades 5 through adult, and includes a teacher's
guide. Length: 17 minutes.

Into Deep Water
Distributor: Bullfrog Films
                 Box 149
                 Oley, PA 19547
                 Phone: (610) 779-8226; toll free, (800) 543-FROG
                 (3764)
                 Fax: (610) 370-1978
                 E-mail: bullfrog@igc.org
                 Website: http://www.bullfrogfilms.com/
                 subjects/water.html

The film addresses the problem of cleaning up our rivers, using
the Thames River watershed in Britain. Narrated by David Bel-
lamy; produced by George Courtice for TyneTees Television.
Grades 7–12 through adult; length: 28 minutes; date: 1986.

The Janorina Pipeline: A Joint Effort to Provide Water
Distributor: The International Committee of the Red Cross
(ICRC):
Production-Marketing-Distribution Unit
19 avenue de la Paix
CH 1202 Geneva
Switzerland
Fax: (international access code) 41 22 730 27 68
E-mail: dc_com_pmd.gva@icrc.org
Website: http://www.icrc.org/icrceng.nsf/
5cacfdf48ca698b641256242003b3295/9faf55c1189bf2
eb4125620e00357c2a?OpenDocument

This film, in English, shows large-scale work to repair a water-supply system, dating from the Austro-Hungarian Empire, that channels water from springs in the mountains down through a twenty-six-kilometer pipeline to Serb villages and the old town of Sarajevo. The ICRC carried out the first phase of the project, supervised the project, and served as a link between the two public authorities concerned and the local contractor. Length: 7 minutes; date: 1997.

Journey of the Blob
Distributor: Bullfrog Films
Box 149
Oley, PA 19547
Phone: (610) 779-8226; toll free, (800) 543-FROG
(3764)
Fax: (610) 370-1978
E-mail: bullfrog@igc.org
Website: http://www.bullfrogfilms.com/subjects/
water.html

This cautionary tale about pollution illustrates the water cycle. Length: 10 minutes; date: 1998.

Large Dams, False Promises
Distributors: The Video Project
Phone: (800) 4-PLANET (475-2638)
E-mail: video@videoproject.net
Canadian   McNabb and Connolly
distributor: 60 Briarwood Ave.
Port Credit, Ont. L5G 3N6
Canada

Phone: (905) 278-0566
Fax: (905) 278-2801
E-mail: mcnabbconnolly@homeroom.ca
Website: http://www.videoproject.org/
subject_areas/subject_water.html

This film addresses the impact of the more than two hundred dams built annually.

Life in a Watershed
Distributor: Water Resources Education Network (WREN)
Resource Center
WVPA-CEF
26 Forster St.
Harrisburg, PA 17102-3220
Phone: toll free, (800) 692-7281
E-mail: lwvpa@epix.net
Website: http://pa.lwv.org/wren/video.html

Adams County Conservation District. Length: 16 minutes.

Managing Lakes through Community Participation
Distributor: Water Resources Education Network (WREN)
Resource Center
LWVPA-CEF
226 Forster St.
Harrisburg, PA 17102-3220
Phone: toll free, (800) 692-7281
E-mail: lwvpa@epix.net
Website: http://pa.lwv.org/wren/video.html

This film, produced by the Federation of Lake Associations of New York and the New York Department of Environmental Conservation, describes how to organize community efforts to solve environmental problems. It shows useful techniques for community groups in a variety of situations. Length: 26 minutes; date: 1996.

Mother Earth
Distributor: National Film Board of Canada
350 Fifth Ave.
Suite 4820
New York, NY 10118
Phone: (212) 629-8890

Fax: (212) 629-8502
E-mail: NewYork@nfb.ca
Website: http://www.nfb.ca/international/
e/ny.html

Kathryn Dunlop, in her June 1991 review of *Mother Earth* for *Peace and Environment News* (http://perc.ca/PEN/1991-06/dunlop. html), wrote that *Mother Earth* "vividly juxtaposes images demonstrating the beauty and fragility of our natural environment and the intense and the intimate connection between Mother Earth and her inhabitants. This non-verbal, hauntingly scored film moves from harmony to destruction to hope."

The Murky Water Caper
Distributors: The Video Project
Phone: toll free, (800) 4-PLANET (475-2638)
E-mail: video@videoproject.net
Canadian McNabb and Connolly
distributor: 60 Briarwood Ave.
Port Credit, Ont. L5G 3N6
Phone: (905) 278-0566
Fax: (905) 278-2801
E-mail: mcnabbconnolly@homeroom.ca
Website: http://www.videoproject.org/subject_
areas/subject_water.html

This film presents a humorous play about water pollution. Ages 6–10; length: 30 minutes.

A Narmada Diary
Distributor: People and the Planet
Suite 112
Spitfire Studios
63-71 Collier St.
London N1 9BE
England
Phone: (international access code) 44 (0)20 7713 8108
Fax: (international access code) 44 (0)20 7713 8109
E-mail: planet21@totalise.co.uk
Website: http://www.peopleandplanet.net/
section.php?section=14&topic=4

The Adivasi, original inhabitants of the area under threat of submergence by this massive dam project, are fighting. The film documents their struggle to save their area from the construction of the Narmada Sardar Dam in India.

National Town Meeting on Groundwater Protection: Groundwater Protection. Looking at Solutions
Distributor: Water Resources Education Network (WREN)
                 Resource Center
                 LWVPA-CEF
                 226 Forster St.
                 Harrisburg, PA 17102-3220
                 Phone: toll free, (800) 692-7281
                 E-mail: lwvpa@epix.net
                 Website: http://pa.lwv.org/wren/video.html

This nationwide videoconference, televised in May 1994, discusses community programs to protect groundwater. It provides suggestions for other local activities and gives updates on groundwater provisions in proposals for renewing the Safe Drinking Water Act and the Clean Water Act. It was funded by the League of Women Voters Education Fund. Length: 120 minutes; date: 1994.

Natural Wastewater Treatment
Distributor: Bullfrog Films
                 Box 149
                 Oley, PA 19547
                 Phone: (610) 779-8226; toll free, (800) 543-FROG
                 (3764)
                 Fax: (610) 370-1978
                 E-mail: bullfrog@igc.org
                 Website: http://www.bullfrogfilms.com/
                 subjects/water.html

This film discusses the natural purification of wastewater by marsh plants. Length: 29 minutes; ISBN: 1-56029-574-0.

No Dam Good
Distributor: Bullfrog Films
                 Box 149
                 Oley, PA 19547
                 Phone: (610) 779-8226; toll free, (800) 543-FROG
                 (3764)

Fax: (610) 370-1978
E-mail: bullfrog@igc.org
Website: http://www.bullfrogfilms.com/
ecologywater.html

The film asks the question Will dams solve our economic problems? Produced by George Courtice for TyneTees Television. Grades 7 through adult. Length: 26 minutes.

Partnerships for Watersheds
Distributor: Water Resources Education Network (WREN)
                 Resource Center
                 LWVPA-CEF
                 226 Forster St.
                 Harrisburg, PA 17102-3220
                 Phone: toll free, (800) 692-7281
                 E-mail: lwvpa@epix.net
                 Website: http://pa.lwv.org/wren/video.html

Produced by the Conservation Technology Information Center, this film describes how various groups can work together to protect their watershed. Length: 12 minutes; date: 1994.

**People: A Solution to Waterway Pollution. Ten Steps
to Organizing a Waterway Cleanup**
Distributor: Water Resources Education Network (WREN)
                 Resource Center
                 LWVPA-CEF
                 226 Forster St.
                 Harrisburg, PA 17102-3220
                 Phone: toll free, (800) 692-7281
                 E-mail: lwvpa@epix.net
                 Website: http://pa.lwv.org/wren/video.html

Produced by Pennsylvania Clean Ways, the film provides information from successful cleanup programs. Length: 30 minutes; date: 1998.

Pointless Pollution: America's Water Crisis
Distributor: Bullfrog Films
                 Box 149
                 Oley, PA 19547
                 Phone: (610) 779-8226; toll free, (800) 543-FROG
                 (3764)

Fax: (610) 370-1978
E-mail: bullfrog@igc.org
Website: http://www.bullfrogfilms.com/
subjects/water.html

This film contains a vital message about non–point source pollution, an underrecognized cause of water pollution that encompasses all runoff pollution that does not come from a single
source, such as the pollution on our streets that flows into the
drains during a downpour or the runoff of fertilizers and pesticides from farmland, golf courses, and lawns. Presented and narrated by Walter Cronkite and produced by Wayne Ewing for the
Lower Colorado River Authority, the film is suitable for grades 7
through adult. Length: 28 minutes; ISBN: 1-56029-212-1.

Poison in the Rockies
Distributor: Bullfrog Films
             Box 149
             Oley, PA 19547
             Phone: (610) 779-8226; toll free, (800) 543-FROG
             (3764)
             Fax: (610) 370-1978
             E-mail: bullfrog@igc.org
             Website: http://www.bullfrogfilms.com/
             subjects/water.html

This film addresses threats to water quality in the Colorado Rockies. Grades 9–12 through adult; length: 56 minutes; ISBN: 1-56029-
065-X.

The Power to Protect: Three Stories about Groundwater
Distributor: Water Resources Education Network (WREN)
             Resource Center
             LWVPA-CEF
             226 Forster St.
             Harrisburg, PA 17102-3220
             Phone: toll free, (800) 692-7281
             E-mail: lwvpa@epix.net
             Website: http://pa.lwv.org/wren/video.html

This film, produced by Pennsylvania, the U.S. Environmental
Protection Agency, and others, documents case studies in three
New England communities and discusses how citizens, public in-
terest groups, farmers, businesses, and local governments

worked together to solve groundwater problems and to set up wellhead protection areas for their groundwater supplies. It comes with a workbook specific to Pennsylvania. Length: 32 minutes; date: 1989.

Protecting Our Water: Who's Got the Power?
Distributor: Water Resources Education Network (WREN)
                 Resource Center
                 LWVPA-CEF
                 226 Forster St.
                 Harrisburg, PA 17102-3220
                 Phone: toll free, (800) 692-7281
                 E-mail: lwvpa@epix.net
                 Website: http://pa.lwv.org/wren/video.html

Produced by the Stroud Water Research Center and the Delaware Nature Society, this film shows how our water resources are suffering due to changes in the land and how we can help alleviate the problem. Date: 1999.

Riparian Forest Buffers
Distributor: Water Resources Education Network (WREN)
                 Resource Center
                 LWVPA-CEF
                 226 Forster St.
                 Harrisburg, PA 17102-3220
                 Phone: toll free, (800) 692-7281
                 E-mail: lwvpa@epix.net
                 Website: http://pa.lwv.org/wren/video.html

This film illustrates the functions and values of the riparian forest habitat. It provides information on the "three-one riparian management system" and visits both urban and rural buffer projects. It was produced by the University of Maryland's Cooperative Extension Office. Length: 21 minutes.

River Spirits
Distributor: Bullfrog Films
                 Box 149
                 Oley, PA 19547
                 Phone: (610) 779-8226; toll free, (800) 543-FROG
                 (3764)

Fax: (610) 370-1978
E-mail: bullfrog@igc.org
Website: http://www.bullfrogfilms.com/
subjects/water.html

Two kayakers making the first descent of Carney Creek provide a lesson in conservation biology. Grade 7 through adult; length: 28 minutes.

Secrets of the Bay
Distributors: The Video Project
Phone: toll free, (800) 4-PLANET (475-2638)
E-mail: video@videoproject.net
Canadian McNabb and Connolly
distributor: 60 Briarwood Ave.
Port Credit, Ont. L5G 3N6
Canada
Phone: (905) 278-0566
Fax: (905) 278-2801
E-mail: mcnabbconnolly@homeroom.ca
Website: http://www.videoproject.org/subject_
areas/subject_water.html

This film describes the wildlife around San Francisco Bay. All ages; length: 28 minutes; date: 1990.

Secrets of the Salt Marsh
Distributor: Bullfrog Films
Box 149
Oley, PA 19547
Phone: (610) 779-8226; toll free, (800) 543-FROG
(3764)
Fax: (610) 370-1978
E-mail: bullfrog@igc.org
Website: http://www.bullfrogfilms.com/
subjects/water.html

A general overview of salt marsh ecology is beautifully captured here with crisp aerial, underwater, and time-lapse photography. Produced by Natural Arts Films for the Wetlands Institute, the film is suitable for grade 7 through adult and has a study guide. Length: 20 minutes; date: 1994.

Somalia: Bio, That's Life
Distributor: The International Committee of the Red Cross
(ICRC):
Production-Marketing-Distribution Unit
19 avenue de la Paix
CH 1202 Geneva
Switzerland
Fax: (international access code) 41 22 730 27 68
E-mail: dc_com_pmd.gva@icrc.org
Website: http://www.icrc.org/icrceng.nsf/
5cacfdf48ca698b641256242003b3295/9faf55c1189bf2
eb4125620e00357c2a?OpenDocument

Following a war that has left Somalia devastated and divided by
never-ending clan struggle, an almost-forgotten profession has
made a comeback in Mogadishu: the water vendor. The city's entire water-distribution system has been destroyed in the fighting
and the ICRC has therefore sunk many wells in an attempt to supply water to Mogadishu's population. The film is available in
French, English, and Spanish. Length: 9 minutes; date: 1998.

Splash
Distributor: National Film Board of Canada
350 Fifth Ave.
Suite 4820
New York, NY 10118
Phone: (212) 629-8890
Fax: (212) 629-8502
E-mail: NewYork@nfb.ca
Website: http://www.nfb.ca/international/
e/ny.html

Kathryn Dunlop, in her June 1991 review of *Splash*, an animated
short film, for *Peace and Environment News* (http://perc.ca/PEN/
1991-06/dunlop.html), described it as a lighthearted story of an
army of rain droplets attempting to make their way through a
natural watershed. The droplets have a tough journey, faced with
a host of human-produced "enemies" as they make their way
down from the sky and back up again.

Stormwater Management: Municipal Version
Distributor: Water Resources Education Network (WREN)

Resource Center
LWVPA-CEF
226 Forster St.
Harrisburg, PA 17102-3220
Phone: toll free, (800) 692-7281
E-mail: lwvpa@epix.net
Website: http://pa.lwv.org/wren/video.html

This training tool on stormwater management is produced by the Delaware County, Pennsylvania, Conservation District. Length: 20 minutes; date: 1997.

Stormwater Management: Public Version
Distributor: Water Resources Education Network (WREN)
Resource Center
LWVPA-CEF
226 Forster St.
Harrisburg, PA 17102-3220
Phone: toll free, (800) 692-7281
E-mail: lwvpa@epix.net
Website: http://pa.lwv.org/wren/video.html

This training tool on stormwater management is produced by the Delaware County, Pennsylvania, Conservation District. Length: 20 minutes; date: 1997.

Testing the Waters
Distributor: Bullfrog Films
Box 149
Oley, PA 19547
Phone: (610) 779-8226; toll free, (800) 543-FROG
(3764)
Fax: (610) 370-1978
E-mail: bullfrog@igc.org
Website: http://www.bullfrogfilms.com/
subjects/water.html

This film, produced by Lynn Corcoran, addresses toxic waste in our water, specifically, the attempted cleanup of the Niagara River. It is suitable for grades 9 through adult. Length: 57 minutes; in three parts for schools: part 1, 22 minutes; part 2, 21 minutes; part 3, 15 minutes.

Thinking Like a Watershed
Distributors: The Video Project
Phone: toll free, (800) 4-PLANET (475-2638)
E-mail: video@videoproject.net
Canadian McNabb and Connolly
distributor: 60 Briarwood Ave.
Port Credit, Ont. L5G 3N6
Canada
Phone: (905) 278-0566
Fax: (905) 278-2801
E-mail: mcnabbconnolly@homeroom.ca
Website: http://www.videoproject.org/subject_
areas/subject_water.html

This film describes a community's restoration of a salmon habitat. Grade 7 through adult; close captioned; length: 27 minutes; date: 1998.

Tools for Drinking Water Protection
Distributors: LWV Education Fund
LWV Publication Sales
1730 M St. NW
Washington, DC 20036
Phone: (202) 429-1965

Water Resources Education Network (WREN)
Resource Center
LWVPA-CEF
226 Forster St.
Harrisburg, PA 17102-3220
Phone: toll free, (800) 692-7281
E-mail: lwvpa@epix.net
Website: http://pa.lwv.org/wren/video.html

This program, a television videoconference, was aired on March 19, 1997. It presents regulatory and nonregulatory tools for preventing pollution of drinking water sources. Case studies of successful water programs are presented, and experts with experience in developing such programs share practical tips for communities interested in protecting their drinking water. Length: 120 minutes; date: 1997.

The Trouble with Manatees
Distributor: Courter Films and Associates
121 N.W. Crystal St.
Crystal River, FL 34428
Phone: (352) 795-2156
Fax: (352) 795-6144
E-mail: cfa@xtalwind.net
Website: http://www.xtalwind.net/
~cfa/8addinfo.htm

This is a high-quality documentary on manatees. Much of the program was made around the headwaters of the Crystal River, called Kings Bay. Located approximately sixty-five miles north of Tampa on Florida's Gulf Coast, Crystal River is the wintering ground of the largest and only increasing herd of manatees (now about three hundred) in the United States. The video contains footage obtained over a period of twenty years and illustrates some of the many environmental changes that have taken place during this time.

Turning the Toxic Tide
Distributor: Bullfrog Films
Box 149
Oley, PA 19547
Phone: (610) 779-8226; toll free, (800) 543-FROG (3764)
Fax: (610) 370-1978
E-mail: bullfrog@igc.org
Website: http://www.bullfrogfilms.com/
subjects/water.html

This film about conflict at a Canadian paper mill demonstrates the complexities of potential conflicts between jobs and environmental concerns. Produced by Bill Weaver and Shivon Robinsong for Across Borders Video, it is suitable for grade 7 through adult and has a study guide. Length: 27 minutes; date: 1994; ISBN: 1-56029-562-7.

Unconquering the Last Frontier
Distributor: Bullfrog Films
Box 149
Oley, PA 19547

Phone: (610) 779-8226; toll free, (800) 543-FROG
(3764)
Fax: (610) 370-1978
E-mail: bullfrog@igc.org
Website: http://www.bullfrogfilms.com/
ecologywater.html

This film chronicles Native Americans' struggle to survive in the midst of hydroelectric development.

The Underlying Threat
Distributor: Bullfrog Films
Box 149
Oley, PA 19547
Phone: (610) 779-8226; toll free, (800) 543-FROG
(3764)
Fax: (610) 370-1978
E-mail: bullfrog@igc.org
Website: http://www.bullfrogfilms.com/
ecologywater.html

Groundwater is the earth's largest supply of clean water, but it is fast becoming the catchall for much of our pollution. As Kathryn Dunlop points out in her June 1991 review of *The Underlying Threat* for *Peace and Environment News* (http://perc.ca/PEN/1991-06/dunlop.html), to appreciate the impact of this film, one must realize that 95 percent of the world's freshwater is underground. This film by Kevin Matthews produced by the National Film Board of Canada offers a look at the poisoning of underground water supplies and the devastating consequences for people whose drinking water comes from beneath the earth, focusing on two communities faced with a polluted water supply. The film's underlying message is that prevention is the only practical approach to groundwater contamination. It is suitable for grade 7 through adult. Length: 48 minutes.

Using Physical Groundwater Flow Models for Demonstration
Distributor: Water Resources Education Network (WREN)
Resource Center
LWVPA-CEF
226 Forster St.
Harrisburg, PA 17102-3220
Phone: toll free, (800) 692-7281

E-mail: lwvpa@epix.net
Website: http://pa.lwv.org/wren/video.html

This film, from the Penn State College of Agricultural Sciences, presents an overview of several table-size physical groundwater flow models and describes various programs developed by Cooperative Extension for use with adult and youth audiences. Length: 42 minutes; date: 1992.

The Wasting of a Wetland
Distributor: Bullfrog Films
Box 149
Oley, PA 19547
Phone: (610) 779-8226; toll free, (800) 543-FROG (3764)
Fax: (610) 370-1978
E-mail: bullfrog@igc.org
Website: http://www.bullfrogfilms.com/ecologywater.html

This award-winning film highlights the Everglades, one of the most critically endangered of all U.S. national parks. This prodigious wetland is being threatened by modern industrial pollution, agriculture, and development for a burgeoning human population. Produced by Daniel Elias, it is suitable for grades 7 through adult. Length: 23 minutes.

Water
Distributor: Bullfrog Films
Box 149
Oley, PA 19547
Phone: (610) 779-8226; toll free, (800) 543-FROG (3764)
Fax: (610) 370-1978
E-mail: bullfrog@igc.org
Website: http://www.bullfrogfilms.com/subjects/water.html

This program examines freshwater ecosystems, the effects of damming and diversion, a tool used to establish limits for phosphorus loaded into water, and scientific responsibilities for maintaining healthy ecosystems. Students also learn what dams are for and how they are built and what responsibility engineers have in resolving environmental problems. Produced by the National Film Board of Canada, it is suitable for grades 7 through 12 and has a guide. Length: 59 minutes.

Water after War
Distributor: The International Committee of the Red Cross (ICRC)
Production-Marketing-Distribution Unit
19 avenue de la Paix
CH 1202 Geneva
Switzerland
Fax: (international access code) 41 22 730 27 68
E-mail: dc_com_pmd.gva@icrc.org
Website: http://www.icrc.org/icrceng.nsf/
5cacfdf48ca698b641256242003b3295/9faf55c1189bf2
eb4125620e00357c2a?OpenDocument

This film, available in French, English, and Spanish, features three different types of water programs carried out by the ICRC in cooperation with local bodies. These three examples are set in different environments and use different approaches. They demonstrate that access to safe water is an essential component of any public health program. Length: 18 minutes; date: 1998.

Water and the Human Spirit
Distributor: Bullfrog Films
Box 149
Oley, PA 19547
Phone: (610) 779-8226; toll free, (800) 543-FROG (3764)
Fax: (610) 370-1978
E-mail: bullfrog@igc.org
Website: http://www.bullfrogfilms.com/
subjects/water.html

People from all walks of life demonstrate determination to improve water in their communities. Produced by Robert Peace. Grade 7 through adult. Length: 27 minutes.

The Water Cycle
Distributors: The Video Project
Phone: toll free, (800) 4-PLANET (475-2638)

Canadian
distributor:

E-mail: video@videoproject.net
McNabb and Connolly
60 Briarwood Ave.
Port Credit, Ont. L5G 3N6
Canada
Phone: (905) 278-0566
Fax: (905) 278-2801
E-mail: mcnabbconnolly@homeroom.ca
Website: http://www.videoproject.org/subject_
areas/subject_water.html

This film discusses Mono Lake and water-resource use. Ages 13 to adult; length: 28 minutes.

Water in Armed Conflicts
Distributor: The International Committee of the Red Cross
(ICRC)
Production-Marketing-Distribution Unit
19 avenue de la Paix
CH 1202 Geneva
Switzerland
Fax: (international access code) 41 22 730 27 68
E-mail: dc_com_pmd.gva@icrc.org
Website: http://www.icrc.org/icrceng.nsf/
5cacfdf48ca698b641256242003b3295/9faf55c1189bf2
eb4125620e00357c2a?OpenDocument

In times of conflict the destruction of water-supply systems frequently claims more victims than the fighting itself. This film, in English and Arabic, discusses how humanitarian organizations like the ICRC attempt to deal with shortages of drinking water, both in cities where the infrastructure has been damaged and in camps for refugees or displaced persons. Date: 1994.

Water in Iraq
Distributor: The International Committee of the Red Cross
(ICRC)
Production-Marketing-Distribution Unit
19 avenue de la Paix
CH 1202 Geneva
Switzerland
Fax: (international access code) 41 22 730 27 68

E-mail: dc_com_pmd.gva@icrc.org
Website: http://www.icrc.org/icrceng.nsf/
5cacfdf48ca698b641256242003b3295/9faf55c1189bf2
eb4125620e00357c2a?OpenDocument

The 1991 Gulf War and its immediate aftermath caused severe damage to much of Iraq's infrastructure. In addition, the sanctions imposed on Iraq since 1990 have made it difficult to repair water-treatment and pumping facilities, which largely depend on imported technology. This film, in English and Arabic, shows the ICRC helping throughout Iraq to maintain a system that could otherwise quickly collapse, with potentially devastating consequences for the civilian population. The film also gives a detailed account of the ICRC's ongoing water and sanitation program. Length: 11 minutes; date: 1996.

Water Sampling in Lakes and Their Tributaries

Distributor: Water Resources Education Network (WREN)
Resource Center
LWVPA-CEF
226 Forster St.
Harrisburg, PA 17102-3220
Phone: toll free, (800) 692-7281
E-mail: lwvpa@epix.net
Website: http://pa.lwv.org/wren/video.html

This clear and detailed explanation, from the Federation of Lake Associations of New York, shows nonprofessionals how to collect accurate water samples from lakes and streams and how to prepare them for shipment to a water test laboratory. Length: 20 minutes; date: 1996.

Water, Water Everywhere

Distributor: Water Resources Education Network (WREN)
Resource Center
LWVPA-CEF
226 Forster St.
Harrisburg, PA 17102-3220
Phone: toll free, (800) 692-7281
E-mail: lwvpa@epix.net
Website: http://pa.lwv.org/wren/video.html

This film follows "Flo," a water drop, through the water cycle. Flo visits the Delaware River and Lake Erie to highlight water pollution and what students can do to clean up water. Length: 24 minutes; date: 1995.

We All Live Downstream

Distributors:	The Video Project
	Phone: toll free, (800) 4-PLANET (475-2638)
	E-mail: video@videoproject.net
Canadian distributor:	McNabb and Connolly
	60 Briarwood Ave.
	Port Credit, Ont. L5G 3N6
	Canada
	Phone: (905) 278-0566
	Fax: (905) 278-2801
	E-mail: mcnabbconnolly@homeroom.ca
	Website: http://www.videoproject.org/subject_ areas/subject_water.html

This film addresses the pollution of the Mississippi River. High school to adult; length: 30 minutes.

Witness to the Future: The Legacy of *Silent Spring* and Call to Environmental Action

Distributors:	The Video Project
	Phone: toll free, (800) 4-PLANET (475-2638)
	E-mail: video@videoproject.net
Canadian distributor:	McNabb and Connolly
	60 Briarwood Ave.
	Port Credit, Ont. L5G 3N6
	Canada
	Phone: (905) 278-0566
	Fax: (905) 278-2801
	E-mail: mcnabbconnolly@homeroom.ca
	Website: http://www.videoproject.org/subject_ areas/subject_water.html

This film is an inspirational call to action. Length: 50 minutes.

Videotaped Lectures

All the videotaped lectures in this section are available from the following distributor:

Distributor: Water Resources Data System Library (WRDS)

PO Box 3943
University of Wyoming
Laramie, WY 82071
Phone: (307) 766-6661; WRDS Main Office phone:
(307) 766-6651
Fax: (307) 766-3785
E-mail: library@wrds.uwyo.edu
Website: http://www.wrds.uwyo.edu/
library/videos/videos.html

Adams, John C. **Direct Viable Count: New Methodology for Determining Bacteria in Drinking Water**
Date: May 5, 1989

Adler, L. **An Economic Analysis of Water Resource Development in Wyoming**
Date: May 4, 1990

Bozek, M. **Variability in Habitat Use by Young Trout**
Date: October 27, 1989

Carron, Keith. **Fiber Optic Detection of Water Pollutants**
Date: April 27, 1990

Case, Jim. **Geologic Hazards in Wyoming: Planning for Future Water Projects**
Date: September 8, 1989 (1 hour, 2 minutes)

DeBrey, Larry. **Impact of Sediment on the Aquatic Insects of High Mountain Streams: Much Ado about Nothing?**
Date: March 23, 1990

Fassett, Gordon. **Allocation and Management of Water Resources in Wyoming**
Date: March 31, 1989

Grigg, Neil. **Western Water Issues for the 1990s**
Date: March 2, 1990

Guenther, P. **Effects of Minimum Pool Levels on Trout in Small Wyoming Reservoirs**
Date: December 1, 1989

Henszey, Bob. **The Hydrology of Wet Meadows along the Platte River in Central Nebraska**
Date: March 9, 1990

Hubert, Wayne. **Populations and Habitat Changes Associated with an Increase in Maximum Flows of Douglas Creek, Wyoming**
Date: January 27, 1989

Huntoon, Peter. **Transient Storages in Uplift Sedimentary Sections in Wyoming and Its Role in Recharge to Major Aquifers**

Date: April 28, 1989

Lowry, Sue. **Economic Evaluation of Riparian Reclamation at Muddy Creek, Wyoming**
Date: September 15, 1989 (58 minutes)

Michelsen, Ari. **Potential Role of Option Contracts for Solving Urban-Agricultural Drought Water Supply Problems**
Date: February 2, 1990

Middleton, M. **Soluble Salts and Sediments along Degraded and Improving Riparian Zones in Southwest Wyoming**
Date: March 30, 1990

Ostresh, Larry. **Computer Generated Wyoming Water Atlas**
Date: October 20, 1989 (51 minutes)

Parker, M. **Streams, Riparian Zones, and Water Quality**
Date: September 29, 1989 (1 hour)

Pratt, Beth. **Wyoming's Non–Point Source Management Plan**
Date: November 3, 1989 (54 minutes)

Reddy, Katta. **Measurement of Calcite Ion Activity Products in Soils as Related to the Quality of Water**
Date: January 26, 1990

Schmal, N. **Historical Impacts of Railroad Tie Drive on Stream and Riparian Habitats**
Date: April 21, 1989

Seytoux, M. **Water Rights and the Conjunctive Management of Surface and Ground Waters**
Date: September 22, 1989

Snider, J. **Chemical Composition of Snow and Cloud Water at Elk Mountain Observatory**
Date: November 17, 1989

Sturges, D. **Snow Fencing to Increase Water Yield**
Date: December 8, 1989 (50 minutes)

Wesche, Tom. **Sediment Transport in High Mountain Streams**
Date: November 10, 1989 (56 minutes)

Wiley, R. **Riparian (Streamside) Habitat Fisheries Concerns**
Date: October 6, 1989

Software

It is very easy to find resources for freshwater-related software on the Internet. Below is a sample listing of suppliers of software applications. Each entry includes a website address and a short description of the types of software program(s) available from the supplier, based on the information provided on the website.

Freshwater Software, Inc.
U.S. Headquarters
5603 Arapahoe Ave.
Boulder, CO 80303
Phone: (303) 443-2266
Fax: (303) 545-9533
Website: http://www.freshwater.com/index.htm

Freshwater Software provides software solutions to help water industry professionals with real-time applications available on the web, around the clock, seven days a week.

The Scientific Software Group (SSG)
PO Box 708188
Sandy, Utah 84070
Phone: (801) 208-3011; toll free, (866) 620-9214
Fax: (801) 302-1160
E-mail: info@scisoftware.com or webmstr@scisoftware.com
Website: http://www.scisoftware.com/

SSG is the world's largest distributor of software for groundwater modeling. Software is available to model flow, contaminant transport, and finite difference and finite element models, among other things.

Water Resources Applications Software
U.S. Geological Survey
Hydrologic Analysis Software Support Program
437 National Center
Reston, VA 20192
E-mail: h2osoft@usgs.gov
Website: http://water.usgs.gov/software/

The U.S. Geological Survey (USGS) makes software and related material (data or documentation) available to be used in the public interest and in the advancement of science.

Water Resources Consulting Services (WRCS) Hydrology and Hydraulics Software Shop
Water Resources Consulting Services
16355 Fourth St.
PO Box 19
Guerneville, CA 95446
Phone: (707) 869-9727; toll free, (800) 776-3070

Fax: (707) 869-9727
E-mail: wrcs@waterengr.com
Website: http://www.waterengr.com/

Water Resources Consulting Services (WRCS) is a civil engineering consulting firm in the field of surface water resources, hydrology, and hydraulics. They are an authorized vendor of surface water hydrology and hydraulics computer programs, both commercial and from the U.S. Army Corps of Engineers.

CD-ROMs and Databases

An Internet search for CD-ROMs and databases will present the researcher with immediate options to explore. Below is a sample list of the variety of resources available.

University of Wisconsin Aquatic Sciences Center
Water Resources Institute
Wisconsin-Water Resources Institute
Phone: (608) 262-3577
Fax: (608) 262-0591
Website: http://wri.wisc.edu/library/subject.
html_water databases

This website is a good link to relevant databases. It also has links to the University of Wisconsin's Aquatic Sciences Center Water Resources Institute home page, which is very comprehensive. The Water Resources Institute coordinates research programs that are applicable to the solution of present and emerging water-resource problems. To do so, it has developed a broadly based research, training, information transfer, and public service program involving personnel from many academic disciplines in the University of Wisconsin System.

U.S. Department of Agriculture Agricultural
Research Service (ARS) Water Database
ARS
14th and Independence Ave. SW
Washington, DC 20250
Phone: (202) 720-3656
Fax: (202) 720-5427
E-mail: eknipling@ars.usda.gov
Website: http://hydrolab.arsusda.gov/arswater.html

The U.S. Department of Agriculture's Agricultural Research Service (ARS) Water Database is a collection of precipitation and stream-flow data from small agricultural watersheds in the United States.

U.S. Department of Agriculture Water Quality Information Center Water-Related Databases
Phone: (301) 504-5755
E-mail: agref@nal.usda.gov
Website: http://www.nal.usda.gov/wqic/dbases.html

This website, maintained by the Water Quality Information Center at the National Agricultural Library Agricultural Research Service, located at the U.S. Department of Agriculture, gives both links to and descriptions of several relevant databases.

U.S. EPA Databases and Software
U.S. Environmental Protection Agency
Office of Water (4101M)
1200 Pennsylvania Ave., NW
Washington, DC 20460
E-mail: OW-GENERAL@epa.gov
Website: http://www.epa.gov/water/soft.html

Published by the Environmental Information Management System of the EPA Office of Water, this site contains descriptions of more than seventy Office of Water databases, models, and other information resources.

U.S. Geological Survey (USGS) National Stream Water-Quality Monitoring Networks (WQN) Database
USGS National Center
12201 Sunrise Valley Dr.
Reston, VA 20192
Phone: (703) 648-4000
Website: http://water.usgs.gov/pubs/dds/wqn96cd/

The WQN database contains water quality and streamflow data collected at 679 stations in the United States. The water quality data include a set of sixty-three physical, chemical, and biological properties analyzed during more than 60,000 stream visits. The water quality data reflect sampling using relatively consistent sampling and analytical methods over a wide range of stream-flow conditions.

Internet Sites and References

The following Internet sites have one thing in common: All include links to or are themselves sites that provide additional links to water-resources information or water-related bibliographies. The sites included in this section are particularly helpful for researchers because they provide efficient links that help you limit the time spent searching for relevant pages. The descriptive information about each website is based on the site itself.

The Edwards Aquifer Home Page
E-mail: eckhardt@txdirect.net
Website: http://www.edwardsaquifer.net/

The Edwards Aquifer is a unique groundwater system containing one of the most prolific artesian aquifers in the world. Gregg A. Eckhardt, an environmental scientist who is an expert on the Edwards Aquifer, maintains this site. It is written in nontechnical language and is intended to help the general public become better informed about the aquifer and issues surrounding it.

Environmental Health Center
1025 Connecticut Ave. NW
Suite 1200
Washington, DC 20036
Phone: (202) 293-2270
Fax: (202) 293-0032
Website: http://www.nsc.org/ehc/nlic/waterbib.htm

The Environmental Health Center is a division of the National Safety Council. This website is devoted to the subject of lead in drinking water. It provides a bibliography of printed resources on the subject.

Great Lakes Information Network (GLIN)
Great Lakes Commission
400 Fourth St.
Argus II Building
Ann Arbor, MI 48103-4816
Phone: (734) 665-9135
Fax: (734) 665-4370
E-mail: manninen@glc.org
Website: http://www.great-lakes.net/

GLIN is a partnership that brings together, in one place online, information about the environment, economy, tourism, and education in the Great Lakes–St. Lawrence region of North America. Its network includes state, Canadian provincial, federal, and regional partner agencies and organizations.

Groundwater.com
E-mail: mhaines@groundwater.com.
Website: http://www.groundwater.com/

This site was set up in 1995 to serve as a directory of online groundwater resources. The site's mission is "to ensure that groundwater plays its full part in meeting the needs of society and the environment and to promote a common understanding of groundwater issues." It covers groundwater published papers, other relevant publications, groundwater news items, groundwater consultants, groundwater equipment, groundwater software, a groundwater job-search page, and groundwater links, among other categories. It has a very comprehensive links page.

The Hydrogeologist's Home Page
E-mail: diodato@thehydrogeologist.com
Website: http://www.thehydrogeologist.com/index.htm

This site was established in 1995 to provide access to hundreds of links to hydrogeological organizations, software and data repositories, jobs, and other information. The organization and institutes link is especially good for researchers, and the earth sciences link lists good technical resources.

Inter Africa Group: Bibliography of Water-Related Documents
Inter Africa Group
PO Box 1631
Addis Ababa
Ethiopia
Phone: 251 1 518790
Fax: 251 1 517554
E-mail: iag@telecom.net.et
Website: http://www.interafrica.org/vrc/water.html

The Inter Africa Group built this bibliography as a tool for policymakers, students, academics, and others interested in researching contemporary water issues.

**The National Council for Science and the Environment
(NCSE) Clean Water Bibliography**
1725 K St. NW
Suite 212
Washington, DC 20006
Phone: (202) 530-5810
E-mail: cnie@cnie.org
Websites: Clean Water Bibliography: http://www.csa.com/
routenet/cnie/dec97/absforu.html
Fresh Water bibliography: http://www.csa.com/
routenet/cnie/pop/fw/fwbib.html

The National Council for Science and the Environment (NCSE)
works to improve the scientific basis for environmental decisionmaking. The Council, supported by nearly five hundred academic, scientific, environmental, and business organizations, promotes an approach to environmental science that integrates
interdisciplinary research.

Native Americans and the Environment
American Indian Heritage Foundation
Washington, DC, Headquarters
6051 Arlington Blvd.
Falls Church, VA 22044
Phone: (202) INDIANS (463-4267); (703) 237-7500
Fax: (703) 532-1921
E-mail: aihf@dgsys.com
Website: http://www.indians.org/library/bibl.html

This site provides a bibliography on Native American water
rights, including information on dams, as well as a very comprehensive look at Native American environmentalism and its key
issues.

**Northwest Territories Action on Water Component of the Arctic
Environmental Strategy**
Water Resources Division
Indian and Northern Affairs Canada
Yellowknife, NT, X1A 2R3
Canada
Phone: (867) 669-2661
Fax: (867) 669-2716
E-mail: lathamb@inac.gc.ca

Website: http://www.aina.ucalgary.ca/aes/

This bibliography was prepared for the Water Resources Division of Indian and Northern Affairs Canada by the Arctic Science and Technology Information System (ASTIS) at the Arctic Institute of North America, University of Calgary, Canada. The publications cited report the results of research carried out between 1991 and 1997 under the Arctic Environmental Strategy on all aspects of freshwater in the Northwest Territories and Nunavut.

River Alliance of Wisconsin
River Alliance of Wisconsin
306 East Wilson St.
No. 2W
Madison, WI 53703
Phone: (608) 257-2424
Fax: (608) 260-9799
E-mail: wisrivers@wisconsinrivers.org
Website: http://www.wisconsinrivers.org/links.html

The River Alliance of Wisconsin is a nonprofit, nonpartisan group of citizens, organizations, and businesses dedicated to the protection and restoration of Wisconsin rivers and watersheds. Their links page, at the website listed here, is very comprehensive.

RiverResource
E-mail RiverResource@highlands.com
Website: http://www.riverresource.com/default.html

Students can use the RiverResource website as a gateway to productive Internet exploration for information on valuable river resources. RiverResource provides connections to facts, books, and people studying rivers. Classrooms can also share information they are gathering about rivers. The links page is extensive.

Robert Teeter's Home Page—Water Librarians' Home Page
Website: http://www.interleaves.org/~rteeter/index.html

This page contains links to resources compiled by Robert Teeter, a librarian in a California water agency. It is comprehensive with useful links. There is no formal contact information listed; however, the website does have a comment form that can be submitted online if you have questions.

U.N. Department of Public Information
Dag Hammarskjöld Library
U.N. Headquarters
Department of Public Information
First Ave. at 46th St.
New York, NY 10017
Phone: help line for non–United Nations users (U.N.-related queries only): (212) 963-1457
E-mail: www_dhl@un.org
Website: http://www.un.org/Depts/dhl/me_water.htm

This bibliography lists books and journal articles focused on the issue of water resources in the Middle East. It covers works published from 1993 to the present and contains only materials in the two working languages of the United Nations, English and French.

University of Arizona Department of
Hydrology and Water Resources
Building 11, Room 122
PO Box 210011
Tucson AZ 85721-0011
Phone: (520) 621-7120
Fax: (520) 621-1422
E-mail: genine@hwr.arizona.edu
Website: http://www.hwr.arizona.edu/globe/h2oissues.html

The University of Arizona publishes this page, "Links to Western Water Resources Issues." It is extensive, well organized, and helpful. It covers issues, states, regions, and organizations.

U.S. Bureau of Reclamation River Systems
and Meteorology Group
Technical Service Center
Denver Federal Center
Building 67, Room 550
Mail Code D-8510
Denver, CO 80225-0001
E-mail: waterspots <vleverson@do.usbr.gov>
Website: http://www.usbr.gov/rsmg/links/waterspots.html

The River Systems and Meteorology Group of the U.S. Bureau of Reclamation works to provide water-management, hydrological, and meteorological services for better water management through science. Their website, called the Waterspots Page, is intended to assist researchers in locating information on the web about the topic of water.

U.S. Department of Agriculture (USDA)
Water Quality Information Center
National Agricultural Library
10301 Baltimore Ave.
Beltsville, MD 20705
Phone: (301) 504-5755
E-mail: wqic@nal.usda.gov.
Websites: Source Water Management Page:
http://www.nal.usda.gov/wqic/; Water Quality Information
Center Home page: http://www.nal.usda.gov/wqic/

The National Agricultural Library of the U.S. Department of Agriculture produces this site, which provides comprehensive electronic access to information about water and agriculture.

U.S. Environmental Protection Agency (EPA) Office of Water
U.S. Environmental Protection Agency, Office of Water (4101M)
1200 Pennsylvania Ave. NW
Washington, DC 20460
E-mail: OW-GENERAL@epa.gov
Website: http://www.epa.gov/OW/index.html

The EPA maintains excellent websites. The one listed above will give you an index to the Office of Water pages. The following is a good entry site that links to all the EPA offices having to do with water: Website: http://www.epa.gov/ebtpages/water.html

U.S. Government Printing Office Water
Management Bibliography
Superintendent of Documents
U.S. Government Printing Office
Mail stop SDE
732 North Capitol St., NW
Washington, DC 20401
Phone: toll free, (888) 293-6498; (202) 512-1530
Fax: (202) 512-1262
E-mail: gpoaccess@gpo.gov
Website: http://bookstore.gpo.gov/sb/sb-050.html

This site, called GPO Access, is a service of the U.S. Government

Printing Office. It provides free electronic access to a huge variety of informational products produced by the federal government. This page provides a bibliography on water management, pricing for the books listed, and the opportunity to purchase the books.

U.S. Society on Dams
1616 Seventeenth St.
Suite 483
Denver, CO 80202
Phone: (303) 628-5430
Fax: (303) 628-5431
E-mail: stephens@ussdams.org
Website: http://www.uscid.org/~uscold/index.html

The U.S. Society on Dams (USSD) is a nationwide professional organization dedicated to advancing dam safety and the technology of dam engineering, construction, operation, and maintenance. Their website is extremely comprehensive and gives a tremendous amount of information regarding water resources and dams.

Water Quality Materials Bibliography
Phone: (888) EXT-INFO (398-4636)
E-mail: extension@aes.purdue.edu
Website: http://hermes.ecn.purdue.edu:8001/
server/water/bib/wq.html

Purdue University publishes this site for its Cooperative Extension System, a distance-learning department of the university. The site provides educational materials to help staff specialists and others find valuable resources. Entries are arranged according to categories and subcategories related to freshwater issues.

Water Resources Data System: The Wyoming
Water Bibliography
The Water Resources Data System
PO Box 3943
Laramie, WY 82071-3943
Phone: (307) 766-6651
Fax: (307) 766-3785
E-mail: wrds@uwyo.edu

Websites: Wyoming Water Bibliography: http://www.wrds.
uwyo.edu/wrds/dbms/waterbib/sel.html

Water Resources Data System: http://www.wrds.uwyo.edu/

The Water Resources Data System, which is operated by the Department of Civil and Architectural Engineering at the University
of Wyoming, is a clearinghouse of hydrological and climatologi-
cal data for the State of Wyoming. The Wyoming Water Bibliography was created to provide a comprehensive storage and re-
trieval system dealing with the development, management, and
use of Wyoming's water resources. It is meant to be a tool to be
used in planning, policymaking, and management of Wyoming's
water resources.

Water Resources of Washington State
Phone: (888) ASK-USGS (275-8747)
Website: http://wwwdwatcm.wr.usgs.gov/outreach.html

This page, "Outreach and Education," is a U.S. Geological Survey
link to the Water Resources of Washington State. It has both very
basic links and links that lead to more extensive listings. It is excellent for use in educational settings.

The World Meteorological Organization
Information and Public Affairs Office
7 bis, avenue de la Paix
CH 1211 Geneva 2
Switzerland
Phone: (41 22) 730-8315
Fax: (41 22) 733-2829 or 730-8027
E-mail: ipa@gateway.wmo.ch
Website: http://www.wmo.ch

The World Meteorological Organization (WMO) is a 185-member
organization based in Geneva that coordinates global scientific
activity to allow increasingly accurate weather information and
other services for public, private, and commercial use. It is an authoritative scientific voice on the state and behavior of the earth's
atmosphere and climate. The website listed above goes to the
WMO Hydrology and Water Resources Program.

World Resources Institute
10 G St. NE

Suite 800
Washington, DC 20002
Phone: (202) 729-7600
Fax: (202) 729-7610
Website: http://www.wri.org/water/

The World Resources Institute (WRI) is described on its website as "an environmental think tank that goes beyond research to find practical ways to protect the earth and improve people's lives." The website above, "Water Resources and Freshwater Ecosystems," includes information on projects, key issues, and case studies and provides links to related sites.

Glossary

This glossary includes definitions for terms that may not be found in prior chapters. However, it is meant to provide the reader and researcher with a comprehensive list of terms that apply to freshwater issues.[1]

abandoned water right   a water right that has not been put to beneficial use for a certain number of years, determined by legal doctrines established by each state.

absorption   process by which water is assimilated or taken in by other substances, such as soil.

accretion   a gradual increase in the land area adjacent to a river or stream.

acre-foot   the amount of water required to cover one acre, or 43,560 square feet, to a depth of one foot. This equals 43,560 cubic feet, or a bit more than 325,851 gallons, often rounded to 325,900 gallons. An acre-foot generally represents the personal water needs of a family of five for one year.

adjudication   a court proceeding that determines rights to the use of water in a specific region.

alluvium   sediments deposited by the processes of erosion, usually occurring at streams.

aquifer   one or more geologic formations containing sufficient saturated porous and permeable material to transmit water at a rate sufficient to feed a spring or for economic extraction by a well. "Aquifer" is the combination of two Latin words, *aqua,* or "water," and *ferre,* "to bring"; thus, literally, it means something that brings water.

aquifer system   a body of materials that acts as a water-yielding, hydraulic unit.

artesian aquifer   a geologic formation where water is under enough pressure from a permeable stratum of rock overlaid by impermeable rock to rise to the surface without pumping (also called a confined aquifer).

artesian well   a well drilled into an artesian aquifer where enough pressure exists for the water to rise to the surface without pumping. The static water level is above the bottom of the upper confining unit. A flowing artesian well's water level is above the land surface.

average annual recharge   the amount of water that flows back into existing aquifers on an average annual basis. Recharge can come from surface sources, such as streams fed by mountain runoff or the regular flows of a river.

backwashing   technique of reversing the flow of water through a home treatment device filter to clean and remove unwanted or harmful deposits.

barrage   an artificial obstruction placed in water to increase the water level or divert it; used to control peak flow for later release at times of higher demand.

basal groundwater or basal lens   a major body of fresh groundwater that touches underlying saltwater in the lower part of the flow system.

base flow   sustained low flow level of a stream; usually represents groundwater inflow to the stream channel.

beneficial use   the granting of water rights based on when a person applies a quantity of water to a beneficial use, such as farming or mining. Those rights continue as long as the beneficial use is maintained.

bioremediation   a process using living organisms to remove pollutants from contaminated water sources.

biosphere   total of all the ecosystems on the planet, along with their interactions; the sphere of air, water, and land in which all life is found.

blackwater   wastewater from toilet flushing, from sinks used for food preparation, or from the disposal of chemical or chemical-biological substances.

blinds   water samples containing a chemical of known concentration. Such samples are labeled with a fictitious company name and included in the sample flow of a lab in order to test the impartiality of the lab staff.

BMP, best management practices   methods, measures, or practices to prevent or reduce water pollution. BMPs are usually applied as a system of practices rather than as a single practice.

bog   a type of wetland that accumulates significant peat deposits. It depends on precipitation for its primary water source and is usually acidic and rich in plant matter with living green moss.

bolson   an extensive, flat, saucer-shaped, alluvium-floored basin or depression, surrounded by mountains from which drainage has no surface outlet. This is a common term for desert regions of the southwestern United States.

brackish   water containing dissolved solids, ranging from 1,000 to 10,000 milligrams per liter.

brine   water containing more than 35,000 milligrams per liter of dissolved solids.

buoyancy tendency of a substance to float or rise when immersed in a fluid.

casing a watertight, tubular structure installed in an excavated or drilled hole. It is intended to maintain a well opening to confine groundwater to its zone of origin and prevent surface pollutants from entering the water source.

cavern a large underground opening in rock (usually limestone). Caverns occur when some of the rock is dissolved by water. Caverns in igneous rocks may be formed by large gas bubbles.

CERCLA, Comprehensive Environment Response, Compensation, and Liability Act the act that gave the EPA the authority to clean up abandoned, leaking hazardous waste sites (also known as Superfund).

certificate of water right an official document that serves as legal evidence in court to demonstrate a perfected water right (see below).

check dam a dam built in a small watercourse to decrease the velocity of the streamflow, minimize channel erosion, increase deposition of sediment, and divert water from a specific channel.

chlorination adding chlorine to water or sewage to disinfect it or to accomplish other biological or chemical results.

chute spillway a structure that allows water to drop rapidly through an open channel without causing erosion; usually built near the edge of dams.

cistern tank used to collect rainwater that runs off from the roof of a house or building.

climate average weather conditions at a given place over a long period of time, usually thirty years or more; includes extremes in weather behavior during the same period.

cloudburst a torrential downpour of rain. Rainfall in spotty locations and relatively high intensity suggests the discharge of water from a cloud, all at once.

coliform bacteria normally harmless bacteria in the intestinal tract of humans and other animals. Its presence in water is an indicator that the water may be contaminated with other disease-causing organisms found in untreated human and animal waste.

collector well a well located near a surface water supply used to lower the water table and force the infiltration of surface water through the bed of the water body into the well.

combined sewer a sewer system that carries both sanitary sewage and stormwater runoff. Sewers constructed this way require wastewater treatment plants to be sized to deal with stormwater flows. Sometimes a portion of the water receives little or no treatment.

commercial withdrawals   water used for commercial purposes, either from a public supply or self-supplied. Facilities making commercial withdrawals include motels, hotels, restaurants, office buildings, other commercial facilities, and military installations.

condensation   water changing from a gas to a liquid; precedes precipitation.

conduit   a natural or constructed channel to convey water.

cone of depression   a depression in the surface around a well or group of wells from which water is being withdrawn; defines the area of influence of the pumping wells.

confined groundwater   water in an aquifer that is bound by confining rock layers and pressure that is greater than the atmospheric pressure.

conjunctive management   integrated management for the use of two or more water resources, such as an aquifer and a lake (also known as conjunctive use).

connate water   water entrapped in the small spaces of sedimentary rock when it is deposited.

conservation   to protect from loss and waste. Water conservation may mean to save or store water for later use or to prevent water pollution.

consumptive use   the use of withdrawn water in a way that makes it unavailable for reuse in the local region. This can be due to several factors: The water has evaporated, has been contaminated, has seeped into the ground, or is being stored in living matter.

contact recreation   activities involving a significant risk of ingestion of water; includes activities such as wading by children, swimming, water skiing, diving, and surfing.

contamination   the introduction of sewage or other foreign matter into water making it unfit for its intended use.

correlative rights   rights that relate to one another. No owner can take more than his or her share.

creek   a stream of water that it is the natural drainage course for a drainage basin. Some creeks in a humid region would be called rivers if they were located in an arid area.

crest   the top of a dam, dike, or spillway that water must reach before flowing over the structure; the highest elevation reached by flood waters; the highest point of a wave.

dam   a structure of earth, rock, or concrete designed to hold water back to form a pond, lake, or reservoir.

delta   the alluvial deposit dropped by a stream as it enters another body of water.

desalination   the process of salt removal from brackish or seawater.

discharge   the volume of water passing a given point within a given time period; an all-inclusive term describing a variety of flows, such as from a pipe to a stream, or from a stream to a lake or ocean.

discharge area (groundwater)   an area where subsurface water is discharged to the land surface, to surface water, or to the atmosphere.

discharge permit   a permit issued by a state or the federal government allowing the discharge of effluent into water. Many states require both state and federal discharge permits before effluent can be discharged into the water.

dispersion   the movement and spreading of contaminants in an aquifer.

dissolved solids   minerals and organic matter dissolved in water.

diversion   the removal of water from a water body; used to protect land from hillside runoff, divert water away from gullies, or protect buildings from runoff; also means to supply water to areas that need or want it from other regions.

domestic withdrawals   water used for daily household routines; includes water for drinking, food preparation, bathing, flushing toilets, washing clothes and dishes, and watering lawns; may be from a public supply or self-supplied (also called residential water use).

drawdown   the difference between water level in a well before pumping and the water level during pumping; for flowing wells, the reduction of the pressure head because of discharge.

drought   a term generally applied to periods of less than average precipitation over a certain period of time.

effective precipitation   the part of precipitation that produces runoff available to surface or groundwater sources or that is absorbed into the soil.

effluent   any substance, especially liquid, that enters the environment from a point source; usually refers to wastewater from sewage treatment or an industrial plant.

endangered species   a species that has so few individual survivors that it could soon become extinct in all or part of its habitat. When used in conjunction with water, the term usually refers to riparian wildlife or fish populations that are threatened by some circumstance involving the body of water.

erosion   the natural wearing away of a land surface by wind, water, ice, or other agents that result from weather or runoff. Erosion can be intensified by human land-use practices.

estuarine waters   deepwater tidal habitats and tidal wetlands that are usually enclosed by land, such as a bay, the mouth of a river, a salt marsh, or lagoon. These waters have access to the ocean but are occasionally diluted by freshwater runoff from the land.

estuarine zone   a coastline area consisting of estuaries and coastal saltwater wetlands.

estuary   thin zone along a coast where freshwater systems or rivers meet and mix with the salty water of the ocean, includes bays, lagoons, salt marshes, or the mouth of rivers.

evaporation   conversion from a liquid state into a vapor.

evapotranspiration   combination of evaporation and transpiration of water into the atmosphere from living plants, soil, and surface water sources.

external cost   cost of production or consumption that is borne by society and not by the producer.

extinction   complete disappearance of a species.

fen   a wetland that accumulates peat deposits, but not as much as a bog. Fens are also less acidic than bogs because most of their water comes from groundwater rich in calcium and magnesium.

"first in time, first in right"   legal phrase associated with the doctrine of prior appropriation indicating that older water rights have priority over more recent rights; used when there is not enough water to satisfy all claims to rights.

fixed groundwater   water held in saturated material that is unavailable as a source of freshwater for pumping.

flood   an overflow of water from a river or other body of water out of its channel that causes or threatens damage to land, crops, livestock, or property. Floods can happen in urban or rural regions.

floodplain   land next to a river that regularly becomes inundated when the river floods.

flow   the rate of water discharged from a source. Flow is expressed in volume over time.

flow augmentation   the addition of water to meet flow needs, as in the release of water from a reservoir behind a dam.

fog drip   water that is collected on the surface of plants and falls to the ground when warm, moist air moves into the region.

forebay   water behind a dam.

forfeited water right   a water right that is canceled because of several consecutive years of nonuse.

free groundwater   water in interconnected pore spaces in the zone of saturation that is moving under the influence of the water table slope.

freezing   the change of water from a liquid into a solid form (ice) as temperature decreases. The freezing point of freshwater is 0°C, or 32°F.

freshwater   water that contains less than 1,000 milligrams per liter of dissolved solids of any type. Generally, more than 500 milligrams per liter is unacceptable for drinking or industrial use.

frost   a covering of tiny ice crystals on a cold surface, such as grass.

gaging station   the site on a stream, lake, or canal where hydrologic data is collected.

gallon   a common measurement of water. A U.S. gallon of water contains 231 cubic inches, 0.133 cubic feet, or 3.785 liters and weighs 8.3 pounds.

geyser   a thermal spring that emerges periodically and results from the expansive force of superheated steam.

glacial drift   rock material (clay, silt, gravel, sand, rocks, and boulders) that are transported and deposited by the movement of a glacier.

glacier   a huge mass of land ice consisting of recrystallized snow. Glaciers move very slowly downslope or outward.

greywater   wastewater from hand washing, showers, bathtubs, washing machines, lavatories, and sinks that is not used for disposal of chemical or chemical-biological ingredients.

groundwater   water under the surface of the earth that supplies wells and springs; water in the zone of saturation, where all openings in rocks and soil are filled, whose upper surface forms the water table.

groundwater hydrology   branch of hydrology, the study of water on earth and in the atmosphere, that deals with groundwater.

groundwater law   the common law doctrine of riparian rights or the doctrine of prior appropriation as applied to groundwater.

groundwater recharge   the inflow of new water to a groundwater reservoir.

groundwater reservoir   permeable rocks in the zone of saturation (also called an aquifer).

groundwater runoff   runoff that has passed into the ground, become groundwater, and then been discharged into a stream channel, as a spring or seepage water.

groundwater storage   water in groundwater reservoirs.

groundwater system   a groundwater reservoir and its contained water; collective hydrological and chemical processes working together in the system.

gully   a deeply eroded channel created by a concentrated flow of water.

hail precipitation that falls as balls or lumps of ice over 0.2 inch in diameter; formed when precipitation is carried up and down in highly turbulent air currents that alternate between freezing and melting.

hard water water that contains a high level of calcium, magnesium, and other minerals. Hard water reduces the cleansing power of soap and produces a hard scale in hot water lines and appliances.

headgate a gate that controls the flow of water into irrigation canals and ditches; regulated by a watermaster during water distribution.

heat of vaporization the amount of heat necessary to convert water into vapor.

holding pond small basin or pond designed to hold sediment-laden or contaminated water until it can be treated to meet water quality standards or until it can be used in another way.

hydroelectric plant electric power plant where the energy of falling water is used to spin a turbine generator that produces electricity.

hydrologic cycle the natural cycle of water as it changes between liquid, solid, and gaseous states to produce climatic changes (also called the water cycle).

hydrologic unit a geographic area that represents part or all of a surface drainage basin or distinct hydrologic feature.

hydropower electrical energy produced by falling water and captured by a hydroelectric plant to distribute to consumers in a region.

hydrosphere includes all the earth's liquid water, frozen water, floating ice, frozen upper layer of soil, and water vapor in the atmosphere.

ice solid form of water.

impoundment body of water confined by a dam, dike, floodgate, or other barrier; used to collect and store water for the future.

inchoate water right an unperfected water right, which can usually be revoked for various reasons, especially if a competitor for the water can show a senior beneficial use.

indicator organisms microorganisms whose presence indicate pollution or a more harmful microorganism.

indicator tests tests conducted for contaminants or constituents that signal the presence of something else. For example, coliform bacteria indicate the presence of pathogenic bacteria.

industrial withdrawals water withdrawn or used for electric utility generation or other industrial uses; may be from a public supply or self-supplied.

infiltration movement of water into soil or porous rock.

inland freshwater wetlands bogs, swamps, or marshes located inland, beyond coastal saltwater wetlands.

instream use use of water that does not require withdrawal or diversion from its natural watercourse; use of water for navigation, recreation, or the support of fish and wildlife.

interbasin transfer the transfer of water from one watershed to another; usually regulated by the governments involved.

intermittent stream a stream that only flows periodically rather than year-round.

interstate water rivers, lakes, or other waters that flow across or form a part of state or international boundaries; the waters of the Great Lakes.

irrigation efficiency the percentage of water that is applied and can be accounted for in the increase of soil moisture for consumptive use.

irrigation return flow water that is not consumed by plants or evapotranspiration and migrates to a surface or groundwater supply. Water rights litigation may restrict the definition to measurable water returning to the stream from which it was diverted.

irrigation water water applied to crops in arid regions or when rainfall is inadequate.

irrigation withdrawals water used to assist the growth of crops and pastures or to maintain recreational lands.

lagoon a shallow pond where sunlight, bacterial action, and oxygen can work to purify wastewater; often used for the storage of wastewater, sludge, liquid wastes, or spent nuclear fuel.

lake a natural inland body of standing freshwater. Lakes are formed when water from groundwater flow, runoff, or precipitation fills depressions in the earth created by volcanic activity, glaciation, earthquakes, or meteor strikes.

leachate contaminated water that leaks from a disposal site, such as a landfill or dump.

leaching flushing out or extracting dissolved or suspended materials from the soil, solid waste, or another medium, which then percolate down into groundwater.

levee a natural or man-made obstruction along the edge of a stream, lake, river, or wetland; used to restrain the flow of water.

liquid a state of matter, neither gas nor solid, that flows and takes the shape of its container. Water is a liquid in certain temperature ranges.

marsh an area periodically inundated and treeless, often characterized by grasses, cattails, and other monocotyledons (flowering plants, characterized by solitary seed leaves).

MCL, maximum contaminant level   the maximum level allowed by federal law for a contaminant in water; based on health effects and currently available treatment methods.

median streamflow   the rate of stream discharge for which there are equal numbers of greater and lesser flow occurrences in a specified time period.

melting   the change from solid into liquid form; the change from ice into water.

meltwater   water that comes from the melting ice of a glacier or a snowbank.

minimum streamflow   the specific amount of water reserved for various needs, such as recreation, the support of aquatic life, or the minimization of pollution. It does not affect water rights established prior to its institution.

mining of groundwater   groundwater withdrawals that exceed the amount of recharge (also called overdraft).

natural flow   rate of water movement past a specified point on a natural stream where the flow comes from a drainage area with no stream diversion caused by man-made modifications to land use. Natural flow rarely exists in developed countries.

natural resource   any form of matter or energy obtained from the environment that meets human needs. Water is a natural resource.

nonconsumptive use   the use of water in a way that does not reduce the supply. Some examples are fishing, boating, waterskiing, swimming, and some power production.

noncontact recreation   recreational pursuits that do not involve a significant risk of water ingestion, including fishing and recreational boating.

non–point source   a source of pollution that is spread out and difficult to identify and control. Wastes are not released at one specific, identifiable point but from a number of points.

nonpotable water   water unsuitable for drinking.

open system   system that exchanges energy and matter with its environment.

outfall   the location where a wastewater treatment plant discharges treated water into the environment.

peak flow   in a wastewater treatment plant, the highest flow expected under any operational conditions, including prolonged periods of wet weather.

percolating waters   waters passing through the ground beneath the surface without a definite channel.

percolation the slow movement of water through subsurface soil layers, usually continuing downward to groundwater or water table reservoirs.

perennial stream a stream that flows all year round.

perfected water right a right indicating that the uses anticipated by an applicant, made under permit, were for beneficial use; usually irrevocable unless voluntarily canceled or forfeited because of several consecutive years of nonuse.

permafrost frozen soil, subsoil, surface deposit, or bedrock in subarctic or arctic regions that have had below-freezing temperatures continuously for thousands of years.

permeability the capacity of a rock to transmit fluid; a measure of the relative ease of fluid flow in a porous substance.

plume area taken up by contaminants in an aquifer.

pluvial pertaining to precipitation.

point source pollution pollution originating from the discharge of wastes at an identifiable point, such as a smokestack or sewage-treatment plant.

pollution undesirable change in the physical, chemical, or biological characteristics of air, land, or water that can harmfully affect the health or activities of humans or other organisms.

pond a body of water that is usually smaller than a lake and larger than a pool; can be either naturally or artificially confined.

porous substance a substance that allows water to pass through it.

potable water water that is suitable or prepared for drinking.

primary treatment mechanical water treatment in which large solids are screened out and suspended solids settle out as sludge.

prior appropriation a water law doctrine under which the rights of users who demonstrate earlier use of water from a specific source are determined to precede the rights of all later users of water from the same source.

priority date a water right established by application, with the application date as the date of priority.

profundal zone the deep-water region of a lake that is not penetrated by sunlight.

public supply withdrawals water withdrawn by public and private suppliers for use by the general community; water used for a variety of purposes including domestic, commercial, industrial, and public water use.

pump   device that moves, compresses, or alters the pressure of a fluid, such as water, that is being conveyed through a natural or artificial channel.

pumped hydroelectric storage   storage of water for future use in generating electricity. Excess electrical energy produced during a period of low demand is used to pump water up to a reservoir. When demand is high, the water is released to operate a hydroelectric generator.

rain   water drops that fall to earth from the air.

rain gage   any instrument used for recording and measuring the amount, time, and distribution of rainfall.

RCRA, Resource Conservation and Recovery Act   federal legislation that requires hazardous waste to be tracked "from cradle to grave," meaning from the creation point of the waste to its disposal point.

receiving waters   a river, ocean, or other watercourse where wastewater or treated effluent is discharged.

recharge   water entering an underground aquifer through faults, fractures, or direct absorption.

recharge zone   area where a formation allows available water to enter an aquifer.

reclaimed water   domestic wastewater, under the direct control of a treatment plant, that has been treated and raised to a quality suitable for a beneficial use.

reservoir   a natural or man-made pond, lake, tank, or basin where water is collected and used for storage. Large bodies of groundwater are called groundwater reservoirs. Water behind a dam is also called a reservoir.

right of free capture   the concept that the water under a person's land belongs to that person, who is free to capture and use as much as wanted; also called the "law of the biggest pump."

riparian rights   the legal doctrine that bases the right to use water in a stream on the ownership of land adjacent to the stream.

riparian zone   a stream and the ecosystem that encompasses the vegetation and the wildlife that exist on its banks.

river   a natural stream of water of significant volume.

river basin   an area drained by a river and its tributaries.

runoff   the precipitation or snowmelt that reaches streams, rivers, freshwater lakes, or reservoirs.

rural withdrawals   water used in suburban or farm areas for domestic and livestock needs; generally self-supplied; uses include domestic use, drinking water for livestock, replacement of evaporation from stock-watering ponds, dairy sanitation, and the cleaning of waste disposal.

saline water   water that is unsuitable for human consumption or irrigation because of its high content of dissolved solids; generally containing more than 1,000 parts per million of dissolved solids of any type.

salinity   amount of dissolved salts in a given volume of water.

sanitary landfill   a landfill lined with plastic or concrete or located in clay-rich soils in order to prevent hazardous substances from leaking into the environment.

saturated zone   subsurface zone where all the voids are filled with water under pressure greater than that of the atmosphere.

secondary treatment   second step in most waste-treatment systems; usually accomplished by bringing sewage and bacteria together in filters or in the activated sludge process. Bacteria break down the organic parts of sewage wastes.

sediment   particles that have been transported by a fluid that are derived from rocks, soil particles, sand, and minerals.

sedimentation   large-scale water-treatment process in which heavy solids settle to the bottom of the treatment tank.

seep   a location where water contained underground oozes slowly to the surface and often forms a pool; a small spring.

separate sewer   a sewer system that carries only sanitary sewage, not stormwater runoff. With separate sewer systems, wastewater-treatment plants can be sized to treat sanitary wastes only. All the water entering the plant receives complete treatment at all times.

septic tank   underground receptacle for wastewater from a home. Bacteria in the sewage decompose the organic wastes, and the sludge settles to the bottom of the tank; effluent flows out of the tank into the ground through drains.

siltation   the deposition of finely divided soil and rock particles on the bottom of streams, river beds, and reservoirs.

sleet   a precipitation mixture of rain and ice.

sludge   solid matter that settles to the bottom of sedimentation tanks in a sewage treatment plant. Sludge must be disposed of or recycled to the land.

snow   precipitation in the form of crystals, often mixed with simple ice crystals, which fall from a solid cloud sheet. The crystals may fall either separately or in cohesive clusters forming snowflakes.

soil erosion   the processes by which soil is removed from one place and eventually deposited at some new place. Erosion may be caused by such forces as wind, water, waves, glaciers, and construction activity.

spillway   a channel or passageway around or over a dam; used to divert excess water.

spray irrigation use of artificial means to apply finely divided water droplets to crops.

spring a natural fountain that emerges from the ground; the source of a body or reservoir of water.

stormwater discharge precipitation that does not infiltrate into the ground or evaporate because of impervious land surfaces, flowing instead onto adjacent land or water areas from which it is routed into drains or sewer systems.

stream general term for a body of flowing water.

stream segment refers to surface waters of an approved planning area exhibiting common characteristics and processes. Segments normally exhibit common reactions to external stress such as pollutants or discharge.

streamflow discharge that occurs in a natural water channel.

subsidence part of the earth's crust that sinks due to underground excavation, such as the removal of groundwater.

surface irrigation application of water to crops using methods other than spraying so that contact between the edible portion of any food crop and the irrigation water is prevented.

surface water water that flows in streams, rivers, natural lakes, and wetlands as well as in reservoirs constructed by humans.

tertiary treatment the removal of traces or organic chemicals and dissolved solids that remain in wastewater after primary and secondary treatment.

TMDL, total maximum daily load a calculation of the maximum amount of a pollutant that a body of water can receive and still meet water quality standards.

tragedy of the commons the concept, most memorably and succinctly put forth by Garrett Hardin, that no one takes responsibility for the things that everybody owns. For example, if water is not regulated or protected by someone, it will be neglected and eventually become too polluted for use by anyone.

transpiration process by which water passes through plants and into the atmosphere.

tributary a stream that contributes its water to another stream or body of water.

turbid water that is thick or opaque with matter in suspension. Rivers and lakes can become turbid after a rainfall.

vested water right the right granted by a state water agency to use either surface or groundwater.

wastewater used water that goes down the drain in homes and businesses; contains greywater, blackwater, or water contaminated by contact with waste.

water   the liquid that falls from the clouds as rain and forms streams, lakes, and seas. Water is a major constituent of all living matter. It is an odorless, tasteless, colorless, slightly compressible liquid.

water pollution   the degradation of a body of water by a substance or condition to the degree that the water fails to meet specified standards or cannot be used for a specific purpose.

water quality–based toxics control   an integrated strategy used in permitting to assess and control the discharge of toxic pollutants to surface waters.

water quality criteria   scientifically derived ambient limits that are developed and updated by the EPA under section 304(a)(1) of the Clean Water Act. The criteria are recommended concentrations or levels that should not be exceeded in a water body, in order to protect aquatic life or human health.

water quality standards   laws or regulations that fall under section 303 of the Clean Water Act. These standards consist of the designated use or uses of a body of water and the water quality criteria that are necessary to protect those uses.

water table   the level at which the ground becomes saturated with water; the surface of an unconfined aquifer that fluctuates because of seasonal precipitation.

water-table aquifer   an aquifer confined only by atmospheric pressure. Water levels will not rise in the well above the confining bed.

water well   any artificial excavation for the purpose of exploring for or pumping groundwater.

waterlogging   the saturation of soil with irrigation water so that the water table rises very close to the surface.

watershed   the land area from which water drains toward a common watercourse in a natural basin.

weather   the day-to-day variation in atmospheric conditions.

wetland   an area that is regularly wet or flooded and has a water table that stands at or above the land surface for at least part of the year; includes bogs, ponds, fens, estuaries, or marshes.

withdrawal   water that is taken from a surface or groundwater source and then moved to the place where it will be used.

xeriscape   method of landscaping for water and energy efficiency and lower maintenance.

yield   the quantity of water expressed either as a continuous rate of flow or as a volume per unit of time; may be collected for a given use, or uses, from surface or groundwater sources in a watershed.

zone of aeration   a region in the ground above the water table. Water in the zone of aeration is under atmospheric pressure and will not flow into a well.

zone of saturation   the space below the water table in which all the pore spaces are filled with water. The water in the zone of saturation is groundwater.

Notes

1. Sources especially valuable in the compilation of this glossary were Peter E. Black's *Watershed Hydrology* (Chelsea, MI: Ann Arbor Press, 1996), G. Tyler Miller Jr.'s *Living in the Environment*, 5th ed. (Belmont, CA: Wadsworth Publishing Co., 1988), Jeffrey S. Ashley and Zachary A. Smith's *Groundwater Management in the West* (Lincoln: University of Nebraska Press, 1999), the University of Arizona Water Resources Research Center glossary (online; available: http://ag.arizona.edu/AZWATER/reference/gloss.html), and the Edwards Aquifer glossary (online; available: http://www.edwardsaquifer.net/glossary.html.

Index

About the Authors

Zachary Smith is a Regents' Professor of Political Science at Northern Arizona University in Flagstaff.

Grenetta Thomassey is a Ph.D. candidate in the Department of Political Science at Northern Arizona University in Flagstaff.